British Red Data Books:
3. Invertebrates other than insects

Edited by J. H. Bratton

1991

Artwork and film by Apple Pie. Printed by W. Lake 1M

Contents

Habitat photographs

Foreword

Three years after the publication of *British Red Data Books: 2. Insects* it gives me great pleasure to welcome a companion volume treating the diverse invertebrate groups other than insects. Many fascinating and even bizarre species are included here, with their biology, status and conservation needs reviewed for wildlife conservationists, specialist zoologists and general naturalists. As among the insects, many of these other invertebrates have very specialised life histories, and in consequence they are sensitive indicators of environmental conditions and changes. Indeed, some species are thought to be relicts from shortly after the retreat of the ice sheets, when the landscape of Britain had been recently remoulded by glaciers. We believe that the sites where they remain have experienced a long continuity of special conditions, whose fragile nature must not now be altered through human interference or neglect. Many invertebrates are vulnerable to even small changes in land-use or management, and their remaining localities need careful treatment if these populations are to survive in future

Until now, little attention has been given to conserving these animals because of the lack of readily available summaries of their occurrence and needs. This Red Data Book represents an important first step in bringing them to wider notice and in promoting awareness of the problems they face in surviving here in Britain. It should also be a stimulus to those naturalists who study invertebrates to fill gaps in our knowledge, so that a future edition can treat more fully such crucial aspects as the management necessary to satisfy their habitat requirements. Furthermore, it is a challenge to conservationists to broaden their horizons and take practical steps to monitor and safeguard these somewhat neglected species.

The places where threatened invertebrates occur are often important for other kinds of wildlife too, and it is essential to bring about approaches to land-use and management which achieve a harmonious balance between their sometimes differing needs. The presence of these invertebrates should strengthen the case for effective habitat protection and management, as well as giving new insights into those environmental features which are of greatest conservation significance. There has been a long tradition of studying invertebrates in Britain, and this volume is based on the contributions of many amateur and professional naturalists. We must now take the opportunity to build on the foundation they have given us and thereby enrich wildlife conservation as a whole.

William Wilkinson.

Sir William Wilkinson
Chairman, Nature Conservancy Council, May 1983 – March 1991.

Introduction

Interest in the conservation of invertebrates is rapidly attaining parity with that in more popular groups of plants and animals. There is undoubtedly a growing awareness of the need to make provision for this most diverse constituent of British wildlife. Invertebrates are no longer always treated as an afterthought when producing nature reserve management plans. The excuse, long adhered to, has been that invertebrates are too numerous and most of them too poorly understood to be catered for. However, in recent years this inadequacy of available information has provided the stimulus for several studies of the ecological requirements of invertebrates and of the impacts upon invertebrates of established management practices. Even without detailed autecological knowledge, invertebrate conservation is possible by applying general principles and ensuring the maintenance of the range of niches likely to support the invertebrate interest of a site. There is now a strong desire among managers and wardens of conservation sites to improve their understanding of the techniques of invertebrate conservation. An important factor in changing attitudes has been the availability of a Red Data Book dealing with British insects (Shirt 1987), which highlighted the number of threatened species in Britain and the causes of their decline. It is now the turn of the other non-marine invertebrates to have their statuses assessed and the plight of the threatened species made more widely known.

As was the case with the insects, it has not been possible to review all groups of invertebrates falling within the potential scope of this book. Knowledge of the British invertebrate fauna exceeds that for any other comparable area in the world, but that knowledge is still patchy, and groups of invertebrates have had to be excluded where expert advice could not be found. No attempt was made to assess the Protozoa, for instance. In other cases, phyla have been discussed in part only, the Crustacea and Arachnida for example. However, imperfect as it may be, this book is the result of wide consultation among expert naturalists, both amateur and professional, and it is hoped that no major sources of relevant information have remained untapped.

This is the third Red Data Book to concentrate on British wildlife. The first, now in its second edition, dealt with vascular plants (Perring & Farrell 1977, 1983). This was followed by Shirt (1987), mentioned above. Great Britain is not the only European country drawing attention to its invertebrates through Red Data Books. The bibliography in Collins & Wells (1987) lists a number of Red Data Books and Red Lists dealing wholly or in part with European invertebrates, some of which have summaries in English, as does the recent Finnish Red Data Book (Rassi & Vaisanen 1987). Wells, Pyle & Collins (1983) covered the invertebrates of the world but only gave token representatives in the cases of some phyla with the aim of raising the profile of invertebrate conservation.

The bulk of the book in hand consists of data sheets, each dealing with one species, in the standard format of Red Data Books pioneered by IUCN. Each species dealt with is placed in a threat category reflecting how serious is the risk of its disappearing from the British fauna. The threat categories are based on those used by Wells, Pyle & Collins (1983), including a category not used by Shirt (1987). This is category K, Insufficiently Known, which includes species suspected of qualifying for inclusion in categories 1, 2 or 3 but lacking sufficient evidence for them to be placed with certainty. (The use of the letter K is a result of category I having been used for Indeterminate, yet another IUCN threat category but one which is not used in the current work.) All the categories are defined elsewhere (p. 19).

Selection of the species

The invertebrates included in this Red Data Book constitute that portion of our fauna whose survival in Great Britain is considered to be under threat. Two main procedures for species selection have been followed. Where levels of biological recording are sufficient for the status of a species to be assessed directly, the rare and declining species can be selected by examination of recent and historical records. This has been possible for leeches, molluscs and isopods, and to some extent for other crustaceans, myriapods and spiders. An alternative approach has been employed for groups of invertebrates lacking a recording scheme or where the recording scheme is the province of a very small number of recorders and lacks a thorough coverage of the country. Here, more reliance has been placed on using habitat fidelity and the scarcity of potential habitat when selecting species for inclusion. For example, Figure 1 shows the distribution of records of the centipede *Brachyschendyla dentata* Brolemann & Ribaut and the pseudoscorpion *Dendrochernes cyrneus* (C.L. Koch). *B. dentata* appears to be the rarer. However, it is a small soil-dwelling species and most records are from urban or suburban sites. The most successful method of finding *B. dentata* is to use Tullgren funnels to extract the fauna from soil samples, a technique not often used in myriapod survey. This suggests that the paucity of records of this centipede is due to difficulty of collecting rather than genuine rarity and that persistent effort is likely to reveal this species eventually in many places in southern England. It is not

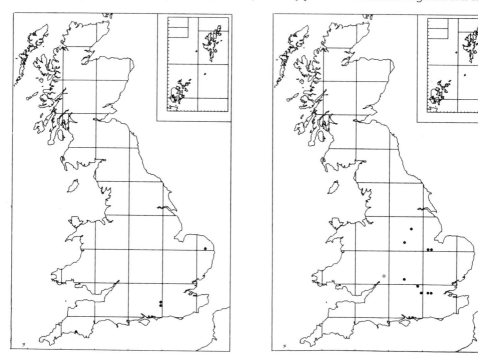

Figure 1. The distribution of records of the centipede *Brachyschendyla dentata* (left) and the pseudoscorpion *Dendrochernes cyrneus* (right).

given threatened status in this book. *D. cyrneus* is also difficult to collect, living within dead wood. However, all but one of its records are from ancient woodland or parkland sites where the dead wood habitat is both of great importance and vulnerable to loss. There has been no increase in its known range for many years and it appears to be genuinely rare and restricted to a scarce habitat, justifying its being placed in the Rare category.

It needs to be stressed that a species with few records is not necessarily rare, and a rare species is not necessarily threatened. However, extreme rarity, even in the absence of identifiable threats, has been regarded as a justification for the inclusion of a species in this book, since unforeseen threats to British wildlife appear with dismaying frequency and often with a rapidity which defies response.

Numerous foreign species of invertebrates are accidentally imported into Britain each year and occasionally one will establish breeding colonies. Species introduced by such artificial means are not a priority for conservation effort and it has been the intention to exclude alien species from this book. If such recently introduced exotic species were considered to qualify as part of Britain's threatened wildlife, it would lead to warehouses, markets and patches of wasteland around docks and airports taking on an importance to conservation far beyond what is justified by the scarcity and age of the habitat. However, the means by which invertebrates colonise Britain is not always known, and it is possible that some species with Red Data Book status do not occur naturally here. The colonisation of Britain by molluscs in the period since the last glaciation has been studied by examining accumulations of shells in dated geological deposits, but even this group of invertebrates contains species whose origins are unclear (see Kerney 1966). It is illegal under the Wildlife and Countryside Act 1981 to introduce species of animal into the wild which are "not ordinarily resident" or "not a regular visitor to Great Britain in a wild state". Since one purpose of a Red Data Book is to draw up priorities for conservation measures, it would be perverse if a high conservation priority were accorded to species introduced illegally or before the law was passed, and it would be inappropriate for non-native species to dilute the effects of the limited resources available for invertebrate conservation in Great Britain. The place of non-natives in Red Data Books was discussed by Rassi & Vaisanen (1987) in relation to selection of threatened species in Finland. For example, they included long-established plant introductions which are found only in natural or ancient man-made habitats such as land under low-intensity agriculture, but excluded recent accidental introductions such as decorative or ballast plants. A similar attitude has been taken in this book to the invertebrates. It is reasonable to view ancient introductions, dating from prehistoric or early historic periods of human colonisation or trading, as part of our national heritage. Two such, the snails *Lacinaria biplicata* (Montagu) and *Monacha cartusiana* (Muller), have been given a place in this Red Data Book. The need to define a precise date separating such ancient introductions from non-qualifying aliens has not arisen.

The justification for producing Red Data Books lies largely in setting priorities in conservation. It is reasonable to give high priority to conserving the elements of our wildlife which are least secure. One possible response would be to establish captive breeding populations of threatened species. For some species this could probably be achieved and the future of the species thus assured. However, it would be a misuse of this book if the species in it were seen as objects to be preserved in isolation. Most are rare because they occur in shrinking and increasingly fragmented and degraded habitats or require unusual aspects of a habitat such as a traditional but now uneconomical form of management. Such sites supporting Red Data Book invertebrates frequently support rich and unusual communities of wildlife, incorporating scarce plants, vertebrates and other invertebrates. This is demonstrated by the number of Red Data Book species reported from SSSIs and nature reserves, most of these protected areas having been established for reasons other than the presence of rare invertebrates. Red Data Book invertebrates should thus be seen as indicative of a site and habitat worthy of conservation effort and not as the only important constituent of the site. This book will only have been a success if it helps to prompt people with influence over the future of our countryside to take into account the needs of invertebrate wildlife.

Two further points are relevant here. First, the identification of invertebrates frequently necessitates the collection and dissection of specimens. The intensity of collecting required by survey work is unlikely to affect the viability of the wild populations in question; thus the banning of collecting of rare invertebrates can be a hindrance rather than an aid to their conservation. (The amassing of large series of rare species, a popular pastime in earlier decades, has no place in survey work or conservation.) Secondly, invertebrates can be a very sensitive tool for monitoring habitat quality. They may respond rapidly to slight changes in conditions, such as shading or water level, before the effects on vegetation are noticeable. Invertebrates can thus act as an early warning system to chronic deterioration in the habitat, facilitating prompt remedial action.

Legislative protection of British non-insect invertebrates

Thirteen species of non-insect invertebrate are specially protected under Section 9 of the Wildlife and Countryside Act 1981. For twelve of these species, it is illegal to kill, take or sell specimens, except under licence. Possession of a specimen of any of these twelve species, whether dead or alive, is also an offence unless it was obtained legally (for example, before the Act came into force). The thirteenth species is the Atlantic Stream Crayfish *Austropotamobius pallipes* (Lereboullet), for which the offence relates to taking and sale only. Licences for killing, taking or possessing for scientific or educational purposes, marking and recapture, conservation, protection of zoological collections, or photography are issued by the NCC (Section 16(3), a-e). Licences for killing or taking for the preservation of public health or safety, the prevention of the spread of disease, or the prevention of serious damage are issued by the relevant agriculture Minister (the Minister of Agriculture, Fisheries and Food in England or the Secretary of State in Scotland or Wales) (Section 16(3), f-h). Licences to sell specimens or to offer or advertise them for sale are issued by the Department of the Environment (Section 16(4), b). Eggs and immature stages of protected species are covered by the law as well as adults (Section 27(3)).

The species listed in Schedule 5 of the Act, including those added as a result of the first Quinquennial Review, are as follows:

Ivell's Sea Anemone	*Edwardsia ivelli*
Starlet Sea Anemone	*Nematostella vectensis*
Trembling Sea-mat	*Victorella pavida*
Glutinous Snail	*Myxas glutinosa*
Sandbowl Snail	*Catinella arenaria*
Lagoon Sandworm	*Armandia cirrhosa*
Medicinal Leech	*Hirudo medicinalis*
Fairy Shrimp	*Chirocephalus diaphanus*
Apus	*Triops cancriformis*
Atlantic Stream Crayfish	*Austropotamobius pallipes*
Lagoon Sand Shrimp	*Gammarus insensibilis*
Fen Raft Spider	*Dolomedes plantarius*
Ladybird Spider	*Eresus niger*

With the exception of *A. pallipes*, the above species all have Red Data Book status.

It should be noted that Section 14 of the Wildlife and Countryside Act 1981 makes it an offence to release or allow to escape into the wild any species of animal which "is of a kind which is not ordinarily resident in and is not a regular visitor to Great Britain in a wild state". The NCC interprets this as applying to any stock of foreign origin, whether obviously genetically different or not, and a licence from the Department of the Environment is required for any such release.

11

The United Kingdom has ratified three international agreements concerning species protection: the Convention on the Conservation of European Wildlife and Natural Habitats (the Bern Convention), the Convention on International Trade in Endangered Species (CITES), and the Convention on the Conservation of Migratory Species of Wild Animals (the Bonn Convention). The four extant British species of non-insect invertebrate included on Appendix III of the Bern Convention are:

Atlantic Stream Crayfish	*Austropotamobius pallipes*
Roman Snail	*Helix pomatia*
Freshwater Pearl Mussel	*Margaritifera margaritifera*
Medicinal Leech	*Hirudo medicinalis*

Anon (1979) explained the Bern Convention. No British species of non-insect invertebrate is listed on CITES or the Bonn Convention.

Note added in proof:
The government announced in January 1991 that it intended to give special protection to the Freshwater Pearl Mussel *Margaritifera margaritifera* by adding it to Schedule 5 of the Wildlife and Countryside Act 1981.

Acknowledgements

This Red Data Book is the result of co-operation between concerned naturalists, biologists and conservationists from a variety of backgrounds. It has drawn on the expertise of amateurs and full-time professionals alike, many of whom have given readily of their time and knowledge. The contributions to the book are as diverse as the contributors. Most of the data sheets were originally compiled by specialists, though in a few instances the first draft was undertaken by the editor. Where possible, the texts were then circulated to other experts for comment. Many naturalists were contacted for further information concerning the locations, dates and circumstances of their discoveries of rare invertebrates, and the formation of the threats and conservation sections involved enquiries to County Trusts, reserve wardens, the NCC's scientific and regional staff, etc. It is intended that all who contributed to a data sheet should be acknowledged therein. If anyone has been unjustly omitted, an oversight on the part of the editor is the cause. There are other contributors who, by the nature of their contribution, are not credited on a data sheet but who offered information equally vital, information which allowed some candidate species to be dropped from the final Red Data Book. The editor and the NCC are grateful to all the above.

The authors of data sheets are as follows: A.D. Barber (Plymouth College of Further Education), J.H. Bratton (Nature Conservancy Council), Dr J.M. Elliott (Freshwater Biological Association), Dr R. Gibson (Liverpool Polytechnic), C. Hambler, Dr P.J. Hayward, Dr M.P. Kerney (British Museum (Natural History)), Dr G. Legg (Booth Museum of Natural History, Brighton), R.L. Manuel (Oxford University), Dr P. Merrett (Institute of Terrestrial Ecology), D.R. Seaward and Dr R.B. Williams.

Other advice and information was supplied by Dr K.N.A. Alexander (National Trust), Dr R.B. Angus (Royal Holloway & Bedford New College), Dr N.P. Ashmole (Edinburgh University), M. Askins, M.P. Bailey (NCC), Dr R. Bamber (Central Electricity Generating Board), B. Banks (NCC), Dr R.S.K. Barnes (Cambridge University), M. Beeson, Dr L.S. Bellamy (Gloucestershire College of Arts & Technology), T.J. Bennett (National Trust), Dr G. Beven, A.D. Blest, D.C. Boyce (Welsh Peatland Invertebrate Survey, NCC), Dr S.J. Brierley (National Rivers Authority), Dr J. Biggs, Dr E.H. Bignal (NCC), A.D. Blest, J.G. Blower (Manchester University), A. Bolton, E. Bradford, J.M. Breeds (NCC), D. Brewster (Broads Authority), A.C. Cade (NCC), Dr R. Capaccioni-Azzati (Universitat de Valencia), M. Carrie, D.N. Carstairs (NCC), H. Carter (Reading Museum), K.M. Catley, S. Chambers (Royal Museum of Scotland), A.O. Chater (BM(NH)), Dr J. Chatfield, C. Chatters (Hampshire & Isle of Wight Trust), D.J. Clark, R.B. Coleman, Dr B. Colville, J.A.L. Cooke, Dr M.J. Costello (Department of Agriculture and Fisheries for Scotland), M. Coventry (Isle of Wight County Council), J. Crocker, E.A. Crowson, Dr J.G.M. Cuppen (Landbouwhogeschool Wageningen), M. Curry (Lincolnshire & South Humberside Trust), Dr D.J. Curtis, G.J. Dalglish (NCC), M. Davies (NCC), S. Dobson, Dr J.P. Doody (NCC), Dr C.M. Drake (NCC), R.J. Driscoll (Castle Museum, Norwich), Dr E. Duffey, Dr A. Duncan (Royal Holloway & Bedford New College), Dr E.H. Eason, E.G. Easton (BM(NH)), C.S. Elton (Oxford University), Dr A.A. Fincham (BM(NH)), R.A. Findon (NCC), Dr W.J. Fojt (NCC), A.P. Fowles (NCC), Dr G. Fryer, M.J. Fulton, Dr P.D. Gabbutt (Manchester University), Dr P. Garwood (Newcastle University), R.S. George, T. Gledhill (FBA), M. Goodchild, J. Gray, D.W. Guntrip, S. Halsey (BM(NH)), K. Halstead, C. Hambler, J.W. Hancock, P.T. Harding (ITE), P.R. Harvey, J. Hearn, Dr G.A. Hendry (Sheffield University),

13

P.D. Hillyard (BM(NH)), Dr P.R. Holmes (WPIS, NCC), Dr D.T. Holyoak, J. Hoosan (NCC), Dr S.P. Hopkin (Reading University), D. Horsfield (NCC), C.A. Howes (Doncaster Museum), M.R. Hughes (NCC), Dr R.G. Hughes (Queen Mary College), N. Jackson, E. Jones, Dr H.D. Jones (Manchester University), P.E. Jones, R. Jones, Dr R.E. Jones (Lynn Museum, Kings Lynn), Dr L.A. Jones-Walters (NCC), A.N. Keay, Dr R.S. Key (NCC), Dr P. Kirby (NCC), D.J. Kite (NCC), S.J.J. Lambert (NCC), Dr G. Legg (Booth Museum of Natural History, Brighton), R. Leighton, Dr J.G.E. Lewis, R.A. Lindsay (NCC), Dr C. Little (Bristol University), G.H. Locket, Dr E.J. Lovesay, R.M. McGibbon (NCC), A.S.Y. Mackie (National Museum of Wales), D.W. Mackie, R.L. Manuel (Oxford University), D. Martin (Severn-Trent Water Authority), M.E. Massey (NCC), Dr G.C. Matthews, N. McMillan, C.M. Merrett (National Museum of Wales), Dr C.J. Mettam (University of Wales College of Cardiff), J.E.D. Milner, Dr R. Mitchell (NCC), Dr P.G. Moore (University Marine Biological Station, Millport), I.K. Morgan (NCC), M.J. Morgan (University College of North Wales, Bangor), R.K. Morris (NCC), F.M. Murphy, J.A. Murphy, D.R. Nellist, A. Norris (Leeds City Museum), M.A. Palmer (NCC), J.R. Parker, M.S. Parsons (NCC), E.G. Philp (Maidstone Museum), Pond Action (Oxford Polytechnic), D. Powell (Agricultural Development Advisory Service), C.D. Preston (ITE), D.A. Procter (NCC), J.B. Ratcliffe (NCC), D.K. Reed (WPIS, NCC), K. Regini (Gloucestershire Trust), D.T. Richardson, A. Rivett (Suffolk Trust), Dr M.J. Roberts, Dr A.J. Rundle, Dr S.P. Rushton (Newcastle University), A. Russell-Smith, J.H.P. Sankey, C.F. Sartory, Dr R.T. Sawyer, D.R. Seaward, M.B. Seddon, Dr M.R. Shaw (Royal Museum of Scotland), C.J. Smith, Dr S. Smith, Dr R.G. Snazell (ITE), Dr R.A. Stevens (Plymouth Polytechnic), Prof. J.H. Stock (Instituut voor Taxonomische Zoologie, Amsterdam), A.E. Stubbs (NCC), R. Surry (Dorset Environmental Records Centre), Dr D.W. Sutcliffe, Dr S.L. Sutton (Leeds University), I. Thomas (Welsh Water Authority), Dr R. Thomas (Berkshire, Buckinghamshire & Oxfordshire Naturalists' Trust), T.J. Thomas, W.A. Thornhill, C.R. Tubbs (NCC), M. Tuck (NCC), S.M. Turk (Cornish Biological Records Unit), J.W. Turner, N.M.C. Twyman-Musgrave (NCC), Dr R.D. Ward (University of Technology, Loughborough), Dr S.D. Webster (NCC), J.R. White (NCC), Dr R.B. Williams, S.A. Williams, Dr M.J. Willing, P. Withers, Dr R.J. Wolton (NCC), P.A. Wright (NCC), R.M. Wright (NCC) and Dr A.B. Yule (UCNW). The habitat photographs were taken by J.H. Bratton (NCC), Dr I.F.G. McLean (NCC), Dr D.A. Ratcliffe (formerly NCC), P. Wakely (NCC), Prof. J. and Mrs M.E. Webster and Dr S.D. Webster (NCC). The distribution maps in Figure 1 were supplied by the Biological Records Centre, ITE, Monks Wood. The text was read and helpfully criticised by Dr I.F.G. McLean (NCC), P.T. Harding (ITE) and P.H. Oswald (NCC). Dr S.G. Ball (NCC) gave essential help by adapting word-processing software to the editor's requirements for this book.

Request for further information

The JNCC is collating data on all British Red Data Book species and would be pleased to receive records and biological information on any of the species dealt with here, as well as views on the inclusion, exclusion or grading of any species. The biology and habitat requirements of many Red Data Book species are poorly known. This information is urgently needed to allow the correct management to be assessed and where possible implemented for the conservation of these species. Please address all correspondence to Invertebrate Site Register, Joint Nature Conservation Committee, Monkstone House, City Road, Peterborough PE1 1JY

Abbreviations

BBONT	Berkshire, Buckinghamshire & Oxfordshire Naturalists' Trust
CITES	Convention on International Trade in Endangered Species
FBA	Freshwater Biological Association
FNR	Forest Nature Reserve
ITE	Institute of Terrestrial Ecology
IUCN	International Union for Conservation of Nature and Natural Resources
JNCC	Joint Nature Conservation Committee
LNR	Local Nature Reserve
NCC	Nature Conservancy Council
NNR	National Nature Reserve
RSNC	Royal Society for Nature Conservation
RSPB	Royal Society for the Protection of Birds
SSSI	Site of Special Scientific Interest

The data sheets

The data sheets are divided into eight sections. Below the sheet heading are given the scientific name with the authority, major synonyms and occasionally other details needed to establish which taxon is being described. There then follow six paragraphs: Identification, Distribution, Habitat and ecology, Status, Threats, and Conservation.

Under Identification are given references to publications which allow the biologist to identify the species in question, this being a topic outside the scope of Red Data Books.

The paragraph headed Distribution reviews the localities in which the species has been recorded in Great Britain, sometimes with a brief description of European and world range and with reference to a published distribution map for Great Britain if this exists. Precise details of current sites are omitted in a few cases where the sites are sensitive to disturbance. Where possible, locality names are followed by a Watsonian vice-county as delineated by Dandy (1969).

Habitat and ecology are given in as much detail as possible because knowledge in this category is the key to successful conservation. In the main, only information gathered in Great Britain and Ireland is presented. The habitat of many of these species has been recorded in mainland Europe, but there it often differs markedly from the British experience and could be misleading if used as a basis for habitat management in this country. Species on the edge of their range in Britain are often acutely restricted in habitat, whereas in the core of their range they may show little habitat fidelity. Thus ecological information drawn from elsewhere in Europe is used sparingly and is always qualified by a reference to the region of origin.

The paragraph covering Status is generally used to give a brief explanation of the choice of RDB category, including any comments on the taxonomic or native status of the species.

Threats listed include generalised statements on loss of habitat in Britain and conjecture about activities likely to damage the habitat. This section also documents instances where damage to the habitat or other threats to the species have materialised.

Unfortunately, the Conservation paragraph is frequently much briefer than the preceding one. Sites with a protected status, such as SSSIs or nature reserves, are mentioned, with the names of conservation organisations whose responsibility they are. The full titles of the various County Trusts are not given as name changes are currently in vogue, with many of them switching to being called Wildlife Trusts. Suggestions or guidelines for management of the habitat are given wherever possible, but there are very few instances where these can be based on sound scientific studies of the species in question. There is the risk of data sheets becoming repetitive where the same threats and the same conservation recommendations are listed for a series of species having similar habitat requirements. The aim has nevertheless been to make each data sheet self-contained, rather than to cross-refer between the data sheets, but to quote readily available texts which discuss habitat management rather than include lengthy discussions of habitat management in the data sheets. Useful management guidelines can be found in Stubbs (1972, 1983), Butterflies Under Threat Team (1986) and Rowell (1988), dealing with dead wood, lowland heath, chalk grassland and peatlands (including fens) respectively.

The final section of each data sheet gives the name of its author(s) and any sources of information which have been used but not referred to in the previous text.

Preparation of the data sheets has taken into account all relevant information made available to the editor up to October 1990. Some more recent information is given in an addendum.

Threat category definitions and criteria for non-insect invertebrates

Extinct
Taxa which formerly had wild breeding populations in Great Britain but which are now believed to have died out.

Endangered (RDB 1)
Taxa in danger of extinction and whose survival is unlikely if the causal factors continue operating. Included are taxa which are known only as a single population in only one 10 km square, taxa which only occur in habitats known to be especially vulnerable, and taxa which have shown a continuous decline over the last twenty years and now exist in five or fewer 10 km squares.

Vulnerable (RDB 2)
Taxa believed likely to move into the Endangered category in the near future. Included are taxa of which most or all of the populations are decreasing because of over-exploitation, extensive destruction of habitat or other environmental disturbance; taxa with populations that have been seriously depleted and whose ultimate security is not yet assured; and taxa with populations that may still be abundant but are under threat from serious adverse factors throughout their range.

Rare (RDB 3)
Taxa with small populations which are not at present Endangered or Vulnerable, but are at risk. These taxa are usually localised within restricted geographical areas or habitats, or they are thinly scattered over a more extensive range. Usually, such taxa are not likely to exist in more than fifteen 10 km squares of the National Grid. This criterion may be relaxed where populations are likely to exist in more than fifteen 10 km squares but occupy small areas of especially vulnerable habitat.

Insufficiently Known (RDB K)
Taxa suspected of falling within categories 1-3, but about which there is insufficient information to be certain. For example, such taxa may be recently discovered or recognised; belong to under-recorded groups of organisms; be difficult to identify; or live in habitats where they are likely to be overlooked. There may be doubts about whether a recently discovered species is native or has been recently introduced by man, and this uncertainty could result in the species being placed in category K.

Out of Danger (RDB 4)
Taxa formerly meeting the criteria of one of the above categories but which are now considered relatively secure owing to effective conservation measures or the removal of the previous threat to their existence. (No species in this book fall within this category, but it is nevertheless available for future use.)

Endemic (RDB 5) Taxa which are thought not to occur naturally outside the British Isles. Taxa within this category may also be in any other threat category or not be seriously threatened at all.

Summary table

Below is a table summarising the placings of non-insect invertebrate species within the Red Data Book threat categories. Unlike the summary table presented in the Red Data Book for insects (Shirt 1987), no attempt has been made here to give a total number of British species in each taxonomic group or to express the number of threatened species as a percentage of each taxonomic group. It was decided that, for groups including brackish-water species, the total number of British non-marine species could not be precisely defined and that, for Chilopoda and Diplopoda, the difficulty of excluding alien species from the totals would leave the figures open to dispute. Many of the groupings used in the table have so few British species that the use of percentages would be inappropriate.

Taxonomic group	Threat category						
	Ext	RDB 1	RDB 2	RDB 3	RDB K	RDB 5	Total
Coelenterata	0	1	0	1	0	0	2
Nemertea	0	0	0	0	1	0	1
Bryozoa	0	0	0	1	1	0	2
Mollusca	0	10	7	13	3	0	33
Annelida: Polychaeta	0	0	0	0	1	0	1
Annelida: Hirudinea	0	0	0	1	1	0	2
Myriapoda: Diplopoda	0	0	0	0	2	0	2
Myriapoda: Chilopoda	0	0	0	0	3	0	3
Crustacea: Anostraca	1	0	1	0	0	0	2
Crustacea: Notostraca	0	1	0	0	0	0	1
Crustacea: Mysidacea	0	1	0	0	0	0	1
Crustacea: Isopoda	0	0	0	1	1	0	2
Crustacea: Amphipoda	0	0	0	2	2	1	4 *
Arachnida: Pseudoscorpiones	0	0	0	1	1	0	2
Arachnida: Araneae	0	22	31	26	7	0	86
Total	1	35	39	46	23	1	144

Niphargellus glenniei is in both categories RDB K and RDB 5.

Taxonomic list of the species judged to be under threat

COELENTERATA

RDB 1, Endangered

Edwardsiidae
Edwardsia ivelli Manuel

RDB 3, Rare

Edwardsiidae
Nematostella vectensis Stephenson

NEMERTEA

RDB K, Insufficiently Known

Tetrastemmidae
Prostoma jenningsi Gibson & Young

BRYOZOA

RDB 3, Rare

Lophopidae
Lophopus crystallinus (Pallas)

RDB K, Insufficiently Known

Victorellidae
Victorella pavida Saville Kent

MOLLUSCA

RDB 1, Endangered

Hydrobiidae
Pseudamnicola confusa (Frauenfeld)

Lymnaeidae
Myxas glutinosa (Muller)

Planorbidae
Segmentina nitida (Muller)

Succineidae
Catinella arenaria (Bouchard-Chantereaux)

Vertiginidae
Vertigo modesta (Say)
Vertigo genesii (Gredler)
Vertigo geyeri Lindholm
Vertigo angustior Jeffreys

Pupillidae
Lauria sempronii (Charpentier)

Sphaeriidae
Sphaerium solidum (Normand)

RDB 2, Vulnerable

Valvatidae
Valvata macrostoma Morch

Lymnaeidae
Lymnaea glabra (Muller)

Planorbidae
Anisus vorticulus (Troschel)
Gyraulus acronicus (Ferussac)

Succineidae
Oxyloma sarsi (Esmark)

Vertiginidae
Truncatellina cylindrica (Ferussac)

Helicidae
Perforatella rubiginosa (Schmidt)

RDB 3, Rare

Hydrobiidae
Marstoniopsis scholtzi (Schmidt)

Truncatellidae
Truncatella subcylindrica (Linnaeus)

Assimineidae
Paludinella littorina (Chiaje)

Succineidae
Succinea oblonga Draparnaud

Vertiginidae
Truncatellina callicratis (Scacchi)
Vertigo moulinsiana (Dupuy)
Vertigo lilljeborgi (Westerlund)

Enidae
Ena montana (Draparnaud)

Clausiliidae
Laciniaria biplicata (Montagu)

Helicidae
Monacha cartusiana (Muller)
Helicodonta obvoluta (Muller)

Sphaeriidae
Pisidium pseudosphaerium Schlesch
Pisidium tenuilineatum Stelfox

RDB K, Insufficiently Known

Caecidae
Caecum armoricum De Folin

Tergipedidae
Tenellia adspersa (Nordmann)

Milacidae
Tandonia rustica (Millet)

ANNELIDA:
Polychaeta

RDB K, Insufficiently Known

Opheliidae
Armandia cirrhosa Filippi

ANNELIDA:
Hirudinea

RDB 3, Rare

Hirudinidae
Hirudo medicinalis Linnaeus

RDB K, Insufficiently Known

Glossiphoniidae
Placobdella costata (Fr. Muller)

MYRIAPODA:
Diplopoda

RDB K, Insufficiently Known

Trachysphaeridae
Trachysphaera lobata (Ribaut)

Chordeumatidae
Chordeuma sylvestre C.L. Koch

MYRIAPODA: Chilopoda	**RDB K, Insufficiently Known**

Geophilidae
Geophilus proximus C.L. Koch

Lithobiidae
Lithobius lapidicola Meinert
Lithobius tenebrosus Meinert

CRUSTACEA: Anostraca	**Extinct**

Artemiidae
Artemia salina (Linnaeus)

RDB 2, Vulnerable

Chirocephalidae
Chirocephalus diaphanus Prevost

CRUSTACEA: Notostraca	**RDB 1, Endangered**

Triopsidae
Triops cancriformis (Bosc)

CRUSTACEA: Mysidacea	**RDB 1, Endangered**

Mysidae
Mysis relicta Loven

CRUSTACEA: Isopoda	**RDB 3, Rare**

Armadillidiidae
Armadillidium pictum Brandt

RDB K, Insufficiently Known

Trichoniscidae
Metatrichoniscoides celticus Oliver & Trew

CRUSTACEA: Amphipoda	**RDB 3, Rare**

Corophiidae
Corophium lacustre Vanhoffen

Gammaridae
Gammarus insensibilis Stock

RDB K, Insufficiently Known

Niphargidae
Niphargellus glenniei (Spooner)

Melitidae
Allomelita pellucida (Sars)

RDB 5, Endemic

Niphargidae
Niphargellus glenniei (Spooner)

ARACHNIDA:
Pseudoscorpiones

RDB 3, Rare

Chernetidae
Dendrochernes cyrneus (C.L. Koch)

RDB K, Insufficiently Known

Neobisiidae
Neobisium carpenteri agg.

ARACHNIDA:
Araneae

RDB 1, Endangered

Eresidae
Eresus niger (Petagna)

Dictynidae
Altella lucida (Simon)

Gnaphosidae
Gnaphosa occidentalis Simon
Callilepis nocturna (Linnaeus)

Clubionidae
Clubiona rosserae Locket

Liocranidae
Agroeca lusatica (L. Koch)
Apostenus fuscus Westring

Thomisidae
Pistius truncatus (Pallas)

Salticidae
Pellenes tripunctatus (Walckenaer)

Lycosidae
Alopecosa fabrilis (Clerck)
Aulonia albimana (Walckenaer)

Pisauridae
Dolomedes plantarius (Clerck)

Theridiidae
Dipoena coracina (C.L. Koch)
Enoplognatha tecta (Keyserling)
Robertus scoticus Jackson
Robertus insignis O. P.-Cambridge

Araneidae
Gibbaranea bituberculata (Walckenaer)
Hypsosinga heri (Hahn)

Linyphiidae
Walckenaeria mitrata (Menge)
Walckenaeria stylifrons (O. P.-Cambridge)
Carorita limnaea (Crosby & Bishop)
Lepthyphantes antroniensis Schenkel

RDB 2, Vulnerable

Dictynidae
Dictyna major Menge

Gnaphosidae
Haplodrassus soerenseni (Strand)

Clubionidae
Clubiona subsultans Thorell
Clubiona juvenis Simon
Cheiracanthium pennyi O. P.-Cambridge

Zoridae
Zora silvestris Kulczynski

Thomisidae
Xysticus luctator L. Koch

Philodromidae
Thanatus formicinus (Clerck)

Salticidae
Heliophanus auratus C.L. Koch
Neon valentulus Falconer

Oxyopidae
Oxyopes heterophthalmus Latreille

Agelenidae
Tuberta arietina (Thorell)

Hahniidae
Hahnia candida Simon

Mimetidae
Ero aphana (Walckenaer)

Theridiidae
Dipoena erythropus (Simon)
Dipoena melanogaster (C.L. Koch)
Dipoena torva (Thorell)

Linyphiidae
Gonatium paradoxum (L. Koch)
Trichopterna cito (O. P.-Cambridge)
Pelecopsis elongata (Wider)
Trichoncus hackmani Millidge
Trichoncus affinis Kulczynski
Diplocephalus connatus Bertkau
Typhochrestus simoni de Lessert
Rhaebothorax paetulus (O. P.-Cambridge)
Carorita paludosa Duffey
Porrhomma rosenhaueri (L. Koch)
Centromerus levitarsis (Simon)
Centromerus incultus Falconer
Centromerus albidus Simon
Lepthyphantes midas Simon

RDB 3, Rare

Dictynidae
Lathys stigmatisata (Menge)

Uloboridae
Uloborus walckenaerius Latreille
Hyptiotes paradoxus (C.L. Koch)

Gnaphosidae
Haplodrassus umbratilis (L. Koch)
Haplodrassus minor (O. P.-Cambridge)
Micaria alpina L. Koch

Clubionidae
Clubiona similis L. Koch
Clubiona genevensis L. Koch

Zoridae
Zora armillata Simon

Salticidae
Euophrys browningi Millidge & Locket
Sitticus floricola (C.L. Koch)
Phlegra fasciata (Hahn)

Lycosidae
Pardosa paludicola (Clerck)
Arctosa fulvolineata (Lucas)
Tricca alpigena (Doleschall)

Agelenidae
Tuberta maerens (O. P.-Cambridge)
Tuberta macrophthalma Kulczynski

Theridiidae
Episinus maculipes Cavanna
Enoploqnatha oelandica (Thorell)

Araneidae
Araniella alpica (L. Koch)

Linyphiidae
Baryphyma duffcyi (Millidge)
Pelecopsis radicicola (L. Koch)
Tapinocyboides pygmaeus (Menge)
Maro lepidus Casemir
Centromerus aequalis (Westring)
Centromerus cavernarum (L. Koch)

RDB K, Insufficiently Known

Agelenidae
Tegenaria picta Simon

Hahniidae
Hahnia microphthalma Snazell & Duffey

Theridiidae
Theridion pinastri L. Koch

Linyphiidae
Baryphyma gowerense (Locket)
Glyphesis servulus (Simon)
Pseudomaro aenigmaticus Denis
Centromerus persimilis (O. P.-Cambridge)

COELENTERATA

The phylum Coelenterata is represented mainly by marine species, including the jellyfish (Scyphozoa), corals and sea anemones (Anthozoa) and hydroids and sea-firs (Hydrozoa). Also included in the last class are the freshwater hydras. Though these are familiar to most naturalists, the identification to species of all but *Hydra viridissima* (Pallas) is a matter for specialists and little information exists on their distribution or frequency of occurrence (the studies of Heath (1969) being an exception). It was thus decided that insufficient evidence exists to assess them for Red Data Book status. Those wishing to attempt the identification of British hydras should consult Grayson & Hayes (1968) and Grayson (1971).

The coelenterates described in this Red Data Book are members of the fauna of coastal brackish water. An extensive survey of coastal lagoons organised by the NCC in the mid 1980s has provided the necessary basis for selecting threatened species in this habitat; thus, despite the paucity of coelenterate recorders, there is good justification for including these species in the Red Data Book. Coastal lagoons suffer from a variety of threats such as reclamation during industrial development or agricultural expansion, casual infilling with rubbish, and isolation and drainage during sea defence work. A few receive protection as bird reserves, but, where the levels of disturbance prevent their having ornithological interest, their conservation value is not readily apparent since they support few of the flowering plants or the more attractive insects. However, the rigours of the brackish lagoon environment, with its fluctuating salinity and water levels and often considerable heat stress in the summer, have led to a specialised fauna, of which many species cannot tolerate or compete in fully marine or freshwater conditions.

Two further British coelenterates deserve mention. The freshwater jellyfish *Craspedacusta sowerbyi* Lankester is rare in Britain, but, as an alien species native to Brazil (Hancock 1983), it lies outside the remit of this Red Data Book. The hydroid *Cordylophora caspia* (Pallas) (= *C. lacustris* Allman) (not mentioned by Grayson & Hayes (1968)) was considered for inclusion. This inhabitant of weakly brackish pools and rivers may be in decline owing to the destruction of lagoons as mentioned above and to the increased industrial discharge into our rivers in recent decades. However, enough extant colonies are known to exclude this species from the Red Data Book categories.

EDWARDSIA IVELLI

ENDANGERED

Ivell's Sea Anemone, Burrowing Sea Anemone

Phylum COELENTERATA
Class ANTHOZOA

Order ACTINIARIA
Family EDWARDSIIDAE

Edwardsia ivelli Manuel, 1975.

Identification

Manuel (1975, 1981, 1983). A highly contractile animal not readily recognised as a sea anemone. Distinguished from another burrowing edwardsiid, *Nematostella vectensis* Stephenson, by its coloration and its fewer, relatively shorter tentacles.

Distribution

Known only from Widewater Lagoon, near Lancing, West Sussex, where it was discovered by R. Ivell in 1973.

Habitat and ecology

The single known site is a large, shallow, mixopolyhaline (= 18-30 ppt total salts) lagoon of about 7.5 ha, averaging about 1 metre in depth. Most of the bottom substratum consists of deep soft mud, presumably overlying shingle, with an oxidised surface layer varying from 1 to 50 mm thick. Further details of the site and its history are given by Ismay (1982). Specimens have been caught in the top 2 to 5 cm of mud. In the laboratory they feed readily on nauplii of the brine shrimp *Artemia* and presumably other organisms from within the mud, such as nematodes. Some specimens have been kept alive for a year in this manner.

Status

Several collections in 1973 yielded about twenty specimens but since then the species has shown a marked decline. A single specimen collected in December 1983 (Sheader & Sheader 1984) is the only record of *E. ivelli* this decade. (A strong rumour that *E. ivelli* was seen in 1985 or 1986 has not been confirmed.)

Threats

In warm summers, oxygen levels in the lagoon are very low and this may have eliminated *E. ivelli* along with two other important lagoon invertebrates, *Littorina saxatilis tenebrosa* (Olivi) and *Gammarus insensibilis* Stock (Sheader & Sheader undated).

Conservation

Adur District Council is aware of the importance of Widewater Lagoon and is sympathetic to its conservation. A paper outlining conservation proposals has been produced (Ismay 1982). The site is also the only known British locality for the marine hydroid *Clavopsella navis* Millard (C.F. Sartory pers. comm.) and the area has ornithological and botanical interest. It is highly desirable that the site should receive recognition at national level, perhaps by notification as an SSSI. Further study of the ecological requirements of *E. ivelli* is also necessary. In 1988 this species was given protection by its addition to Schedule 5 of the Wildlife and Countryside Act 1981.

Author

R.L. Manuel.

31

NEMATOSTELLA VECTENSIS

RARE

Starlet Sea Anemone

Phylum COELENTERATA

Order ACTINIARIA

Class ANTHOZOA

Family EDWARDSIIDAE

Nematostella vectensis Stephenson, 1935, synonymous with *N. pellucida* Crowell, 1946.

Identification

Williams (1975, 1987); Manuel (1981).

Distribution

Occurs in England, Canada and the U.S.A. In England it is found on the east coast in Norfolk and Suffolk (Williams 1976, 1987, 1988) and on the south coast in South Hampshire, the Isle of Wight and Dorset (Sheader in Herbert 1988; Williams 1976, 1987). There were fears that this species had become extinct on the Isle of Wight (Williams 1976), but its recent rediscovery there includes the type locality in Bembridge Harbour (Sheader in Herbert 1988). A population at Pagham, West Sussex, is now thought by M. Sheader to be extinct (Williams 1987). In Canada, only known from the Atlantic coast (Nova Scotia); in the U.S.A., from Washington, Oregon and California on the Pacific coast, and ranging between Massachusetts and Florida on the Atlantic coast (Williams in Wells, Pyle & Collins 1983).

Habitat and ecology

Usually buried upright in fine soft muds at the edges of creeks on saltmarshes and in brackish pools but never on the shoreline proper. Sometimes found attached to sea-grasses (e.g. *Ruppia* or *Zostera*) or algae (e.g. *Cladophora* or *Chaetomorpha*). It cannot burrow in sand. No known predators in England, but the grass shrimp *Palaemonetes pugio* Holthuis is a predator in Georgia, U.S.A. (Kneib 1985). Markedly euryhaline (recorded in England at salinities from 8.96 to 51.54 ppt) and eurythermous (recorded at -1 to 28°C in England). Limiting factors are probably heavy wave action, extreme hypoxia and desiccation. Unselective in feeding, the recorded prey including copepods, midge larvae, corixids and small gastropods. The original habitats of this species were probably shallow saltmarsh pools and the edges of saltmarsh creeks as currently seen in America. This distribution pattern allows dispersal by tidal action. In England, most populations are isolated in pools bounded by sea walls or shingle banks. Williams (in Wells, Pyle & Collins 1983) gives further references.

Status

During the decade from 1970, the known English populations were declining, but since 1980 a number of new localities have been discovered (Sheader in Herbert 1988; Sheader & Sheader 1984; Williams 1987, 1988). However, in England this species is still under threat since the localities known are in so few restricted areas and its habitat is especially vulnerable. Although individuals may be very numerous (over 5 million in a single pool) (Williams in

Wells, Pyle & Collins 1983), it should be emphasised that the number of sites is more significant than the number of individuals. If a marsh should become polluted or a pool dry up, the whole population, regardless of its size, would be exterminated. This has already occurred on occasion in England (Williams 1976).

Threats   Populations in small lagoons, especially those bounded by sea walls or shingle banks, are very vulnerable to pollution or desiccation (Williams 1976). Four recently discovered sites in a lagoon system in South Hampshire may be adversely influenced by the proposed rebuilding of a sea wall (M. Sheader *in litt.*). At Gilkicker Point, South Hampshire, several lagoons have been infilled. Cockle Pond, Gosport, another South Hampshire site for *Nematostella*, is used for model boating tournaments and algicides are regularly used to check the growth of large algae (M. Sheader *in litt.*). It is not clear whether this is harmful to the anemone. There are proposals for the building of a marina in Bembridge Harbour. Even if this does not destroy the pools, changes to their salinity regime would be likely to occur which would make them unsuitable for *N. vectensis* (M. Sheader & A.L. Sheader *in litt.*).

Conservation   Although some populations are within established nature reserves or SSSIs, this does not necessarily lessen the threat. It has been proposed to translocate (as defined by the Joint Committee for the Conservation of British Insects) populations either to stable, protected lagoons or to open marshes unbounded by sea walls and free from other human influence, so that natural spreading can occur (Williams 1976; Williams in Wells, Pyle & Collins 1983). In 1988 this species was given protection by its addition to Schedule 5 of the Wildlife & Countryside Act 1981, and any such scheme would require a licence.

Author   R.B. Williams.

PLATYHELMINTHES

This is a large phylum in which most species are parasitic. There are free-living British species within the class Turbellaria, of which about fifty are within the orders Acoela and Rhabdocoela, these constituting the microturbellaria. There are insufficient distribution records for microturbellaria to be included in this Red Data Book. A third order, the Polycladida, has only marine representatives in Britain. However, the fourth order, Tricladida, includes the freshwater flatworms which are familiar to most British naturalists. There are twelve species of freshwater flatworm to be found in Great Britain (three of which are aliens) as well as a small number of coastal species with varying tolerances of salinity. The rarest of the native species is *Bdellocephala punctata* (Pallas), but there are sufficient records from a wide area and diversity of habitats to disqualify it from a place in this Red Data Book. Less well known are the terrestrial triclads, of which seven species are recorded from Great Britain, most of which are aliens. Two were initially seen as contenders for a place in the Red Data Book but eventually eliminated. *Microplana scharffi* (von Graff) has few British records but these are widely scattered from Scotland to Cornwall and it was felt that there was insufficient evidence of any threat to this species. *Rhynchodemus sylvaticus* (Leidy) is known from only four counties, but again these are widely spread. Also, this species was first described from North America and thus may not be native to Britain.

The triclads are delicate animals but compensate for this by well-developed powers of regeneration. They are predators on other invertebrates, and the roles of the aquatic species in the food web have been well studied. An extensive bibliography is given in each of the two identification works covering British triclads, Reynoldson (1978) (freshwater species only) and Ball & Reynoldson (1981).

There are separate national recording schemes for the aquatic and terrestrial triclads run under the auspices of the Biological Records Centre at Monks Wood. Dr H.D. Jones of Manchester University, who organises the recording scheme for terrestrial species, kindly supplied the information which allowed the assessment of *R. sylvaticus* and *M. scharffi*.

NEMERTEA

The phylum Nemertea has few students in Britain, and the freshwater and terrestrial components of the group are among the least studied. Nemerteans or ribbon worms are primitive invertebrates usually placed between the Platyhelminthes and the Nematoda in phylogenetic classifications. They are elongate, soft-bodied and mostly very fragile. Many are brightly and intricately patterned. Most species are marine. Many are carnivores and scavengers and may ingest intact prey organisms as large as or larger than themselves. The only terrestrial species found in Britain is *Argonemertes dendyi* (Dakin), a native of southwestern Australia which has been found in a number of localities on the south and west coasts of England and Wales. Britain's two freshwater species are considered native. *Prostoma graecense* (Bohmig) has a worldwide distribution and has been recorded from a few sites in southern England. *P. jenningsi* Gibson & Young is given Red Data Book status as it has only been recorded from the type locality in South Lancashire.

Gibson (1982) is the standard identification work for British nemerteans but it stresses that reliable identification to species is often only possible by using histology and thus requires expertise in laboratory techniques. R. Gibson (Faculty of Science, Liverpool Polytechnic, Byrom Street, Liverpool L3 3AF) would welcome specimens which cannot be satisfactorily identified by using his book.

PROSTOMA JENNINGSI

A freshwater ribbon worm

INSUFFICIENTLY KNOWN

Phylum NEMERTEA
Class ENOPLA

Order HOPLONEMERTINI
Family TETRASTEMMIDAE

Prostoma jenningsi Gibson & Young, 1971.

Identification

Gibson (1982). Can be separated from the other British freshwater nemertean, *P. graecense* (Bohmig), only by histological techniques.

Distribution

Known only from the type locality, a pond at Croston, South Lancashire.

Habitat and ecology

The pond has its origins in old small-scale quarry workings.

Status

A survey of over two hundred ponds in the Lancashire, Merseyside and Wirral region failed to reveal further sites for this species. However, freshwater nemerteans are probably more widespread in the British Isles than is realised and it would be wrong to place *P. jenningsi* in a higher threat category on the basis of current knowledge.

Threats

Some years ago the pond was contaminated by a spillage of agricultural fertiliser and the nemertean has not been found since 1978, before the spillage.

Conservation

The pond has been used by a local angling society and this may provide some protection against infilling and intentional pollution. It is unlikely that the pond would warrant notification as an SSSI on current evidence.

Author

R. Gibson.

BRYOZOA

The Bryozoa (previously Polyzoa) constitute a phylum with about 270 British species, the majority of which are marine. Some species are tolerant of a wide range of salinities and their range extends into estuaries and coastal lagoons. Estuaries and lagoons also support a specialist bryozoan fauna consisting of species never found in fully marine conditions. In addition, the class Phylactolaemata and a few species of the Gymnolaemata are restricted to fresh waters. The freshwater fauna and the brackish-water specialists constitute the portion of the Bryozoa considered in this Red Data Book.

Despite the great beauty of living bryozoans, well demonstrated by Allman (1856), they are not a popular field of study for freshwater naturalists. They are fairly common animals, colonial, but easily overlooked by the pond-netter, as they retract their tentacles when disturbed and an inactive colony can resemble plant roots or a snail egg-mass, depending on the growth form. Most British freshwater species form a mass of branching tubes. From these, the individual animals (zooids) extend their ciliated tentacles to feed on fine particles (bacteria, algae, Protozoa, etc) in suspension in the water. A few species form a gelatinous colony, and heavily calcified forms are to be found among the marine and brackish species. The resting stages (statoblasts) of bryozoans are more commonly encountered in fresh water than the fully developed colonies. Statoblasts are produced asexually and are the means of dispersal. Resembling small seeds, they are easily transported by other animals passing from one water body to another. They survive periods of desiccation and indeed may require a dry or cold period before hatching into a new colony. Under particularly auspicious conditions, bryozoan colonies can form a high proportion of the biomass and there are instances of their becoming a nuisance by blocking water pipes.

Mundy (1980) provides a key to all the species covered by this Red Data Book, but for identification of all the brackish and marine forms it is necessary to consult the *Synopses of the British fauna* (Ryland & Hayward 1977; Hayward & Ryland 1979, 1985; Hayward 1985). Illustrations and photographs of several species and an alternative key to genera are included for the freshwater species in Fitter & Manuel (1986). Unfortunately there is no national recording scheme for the freshwater species. This lack of a core body of distribution data has made the selection of species for the Red Data Book rather more speculative than is desirable.

A few taxa deserve mention in addition to those represented by data sheets. *Aspidelectra melolontha* (Landsborough) and *Conopeum seurati* (Canu) are species found in brackish water which have few confirmed British records at present, but sufficient to suggest that, if all suitable habitat were searched, enough populations would be found to place them outside the scope of this book. *Bowerbankia gracilis* Leidy encompasses at least two species, one of which may prove to be limited to low-salinity habitats, but it is obviously impossible to attempt to give a threat category to a species which cannot yet be reliably recognised. Two further species, *Victorella muelleri* (Kraepelin) and *Bulbella abscondita* Braem, are currently on the British list owing to the work of Braem (1951), who stated that they were included in early material of *V. pavida* Saville Kent collected from the Surrey

Canal and Victoria Docks, London. However, specimens do not exist to support these records and neither species has been recorded from British localities since. Two freshwater species, *Hyalinella punctata* (Hancock) and *Plumatella emarginata* Allman, have few British records but both were found most recently in the vicinity of the home of the author of the FBA key (Mundy 1980), a strong sign that a species is under-recorded. Neither species has a history of decline, strong habitat fidelity or a small geographical range, and taxonomic difficulties in the genus *Plumatella* give an extra reason for excluding the latter species from this Red Data Book.

Bryozoa were not treated in detail in *The IUCN Invertebrate Red Data Book* (Wells, Pyle & Collins 1983) but a number of species were mentioned as possibly in decline. Bushnell (1974) is equally (and justifiably) hesitant about declaring species to be endangered. He points out that zooids of most species are unable to tolerate more than mild water pollution in whatever form but that some statoblasts have been shown to remain viable after sustained exposure to high concentrations of heavy metals, pesticides, raw sewage and bacterial attack. This may allow the survival of bryozoans in waters subject to sporadic pollution. Non-toxic silt loading may be one of the major threats to Bryozoa, as few species can raise their zooids above the substratum, and even species with this ability are prone to being grazed back to the base by fish.

LOPHOPUS CRYSTALLINUS   RARE

Phylum BRYOZOA   Order PLUMATELLIDA
Class PHYLACTOLAEMATA   Family LOPHOPODIDAE

Lophopus crystallinus (Pallas, 1768), synonymous with *L. bakeri* van Beneden.

Identification   Mundy (1980).

Distribution   Allman (1856) gives records from the millpond near Little Baddow, South Essex, and Willow Walk, Chelsea, Middlesex. There are also undated records from Port Meadow, Oxfordshire (pre-1960, possibly pre-war) (R.L. Manuel pers. comm.), the River Ravensbourne, Kent, and Wheatfen Broad, East Norfolk (Mundy 1980). In East Suffolk, it has been recorded from ponds at Burgh Castle in 1910, Fritton Lake in 1933, and near Ipswich (undated) (Anon 1937). In the first half of this century *Lophopus* was found in Rockland Broad, Surlingham Broad and nearby dykes, the River Yare at Surlingham and Brundall, a dyke flanking the North Denes at Great Yarmouth (Hurrell 1904, 1911, 1943) and, in 1943, a dyke connected to the River Yare at Surlingham (Ellis 1944), all in East Norfolk, but there have been no subsequent records from the Broads (Driscoll 1982). Holloway (1947) found colonies at Hartwell, Buckinghamshire, in 1944. Gurney (1924) describes rearing colonies from mud collected from Lang Mere, West Norfolk, and R.A. Watson (unpublished) recorded it from Bagmore Pit, another of the Breckland meres of West Norfolk, in the early 1970s. The only other recent records known are from Chil Brook, Eynsham, Oxfordshire, where it was seen in March and November 1977 but has not been recorded on numerous visits since, and an artesian spring at Barton-upon-Humber, North Lincolnshire, where it was found from 1982 to 1984. It is also known from Ireland, central Europe, southwestern Russia, Iran and America.

Habitat and ecology Found in lakes, ponds, ditches and slow rivers. The rather small gelatinous colonies are usually attached to waterplants, usually the stems or undersides of leaves. It can occur in great abundance. Hurrell (1911) mentions a dyke near Surlingham Broad in which *Lophopus* was so plentiful that "a single haul would have filled an ordinary-sized pail". Water-lilies and duckweed are often mentioned as the substrata, but it has also been found on irises, reeds and rushes and less often on dead wood and fallen leaves. It rarely occurs on hard substrata. Low water temperatures may benefit this species. At Hartwell it was recorded through the winter, including a period under ice, but disappeared in the spring; on the occasion of its discovery in Chil Brook, the water temperature was 4°C; and at Barton the output of the artesian spring is at a constant 10°C. Colonies are reportedly eaten by snails, trichopteran larvae and oligochaetes (Marcus 1934, cited in Bushnell 1974).

Status	One of the rarer British bryozoans. Formerly considered not uncommon in the Broads, and often abundant where it does occur. It is also considered a rarity in America and is mentioned as a possible candidate for international Red Data Book listing (Wells, Pyle & Collins 1983).

Threats   Habitat loss, water pollution and perhaps increased water turbidity. The compounded effects of sewage and agricultural eutrophication and increased pleasure boat traffic have caused the loss of submerged aquatic plants from most of the Norfolk Broads, and this loss of substrate may be a major factor in the decline of *L. crystallinus* in this area (R.J. Driscoll pers. comm.).

Conservation   Surlingham, Rockland and Wheatfen Broads lie within the Yare Broads and Marshes SSSI. Lang Mere is within the East Wretham Heath SSSI, which is a Norfolk Trust reserve. The artesian spring at Barton is within an SSSI. This spring ceases to flow after periods of low rainfall and the pools inhabited by *Lophopus* can shrink in size. It is possible that this exposure of the marginal mud could be of value in stimulating the hatching of the bryozoan's resting eggs.

Authors   P.J. Hayward and J.H. Bratton, with additional information from Hurrell (1927), Bushnell (1974) and R.L. Manuel (pers. comm.).

VICTORELLA PAVIDA   INSUFFICIENTLY KNOWN
Trembling Sea-mat

Phylum BRYOZOA   Order CTENOSTOMATA
Class GYMNOLAEMATA   Family VICTORELLIDAE

Victorella pavida Saville Kent, 1870.

Identification   Mundy (1980); Hayward (1985).

Distribution   First described from the Surrey Canal and Victoria Docks, London, in 1870. Rediscovered at Swanpool, West Cornwall, in 1968 (Barnes, Dorey & Little 1971) and still present in 1985 (Little 1985). There are no other British records.

Habitat and ecology   Grows on submerged stones, wood and waterplants in fresh and brackish water, stones being the main substrate in Swanpool. Its ecology has been described by Italian and Indian biologists, who suggest that its life cycle and reproductive pattern are partly governed by seasonal variation in salinity and temperature. At Swanpool in the late 1960s, there was a permanent colony in the outlet tunnel which spread into the pool proper in summers when the salinity and temperature rose (Dorey, Little & Barnes 1973). 1983 saw the culvert replaced with one of a larger diameter and at a different level. Also, freshwater run-off from a nearby housing estate was diverted to the pool at this time. The predicted consequences of this were that summer salinities would rise but that salt would be more easily washed out than previously, leading to more erratic changes in the salinity of Swanpool (Little 1985). In September 1985, *V. pavida* was abundant at both ends of the pool, and possibly the higher salinity regime since the installation of the 1983 culvert has been to the benefit of this species. At that time the salinity varied from 3.1 ppt at the surface to 26 ppt at 3 metres depth, which was the highest salinity ever recorded at that site (C. Little unpublished). It is possible that *Plumatella repens* (L.), another bryozoan found in Swanpool, could compete for space with *V. pavida* (C. Little pers. comm.), though the species have their peaks of abundance at different times of year (Little 1986) so neither is likely to eliminate the other.

Status   Swanpool is the only site from which it has been recorded this century, despite an extensive NCC survey of coastal lagoons in the 1980s. However, bryozoans are easily overlooked by the non-specialist and the possibility of *V. pavida* having escaped notice at other sites justifies caution in assigning a threat category to this species.

Threats   It has disappeared from the type locality, possibly owing to dockland developments which led to a permanent reduction in salinity of the water.

Conservation   Maintenance of brackish conditions and prevention of pollution at Swanpool are obvious recommendations. In 1988, this species was protected by its addition to Schedule 5 of the Wildlife and Countryside Act 1981.

Author   P.J. Hayward.

MOLLUSCA

There are seven classes of Mollusca, six of which occur in Britain. This Red Data Book contains examples of only two, the Gastropoda and Bivalvia, the other classes being represented in Britain only by marine species. While this Red Data Book does not seek to cover the marine fauna, it is difficult to make a precise distinction between marine and freshwater molluscs, there being gastropods to be found, often in great abundance, in coastal waters of all salinities. Recording of British molluscs is shared between two national recording schemes, one covering marine species, the other freshwater and terrestrial, but there is a slight overlap among the brackish species, and four of the species included in this Red Data Book fall solely within the remit of the marine scheme.

The basis for assessing the status of British molluscs is stronger than for any other group of invertebrates covered by this book. There are two reasons for this. Molluscs have long been a popular group with British natural historians, so that documentation of the British species, particularly the non-marine component, stretches back well into the 19th century and county distribution maps were produced as early as 1921. Secondly, the calcareous shells of molluscs survive well in sediment, so that the modern conchologist can trace the distribution of the shell-bearing species in former times.

The need for calcium for the production of the shell is a major constraint on the distribution of molluscs, calcium-rich soils and waters generally having a far richer fauna than calcium-poor areas. Though an active mollusc will become desiccated fairly rapidly under arid conditions, this has been less of an influence on mollusc distribution, as a number of species are able to aestivate during dry summer periods. Thus open chalk downland supports a rich assemblage of species and some aquatic snails are typically found in seasonal pools. The richest habitat, however, is ancient woodland on base-rich soil, as it fulfils the requirements for calcium and water, with the added advantage that it was once the most widespread habitat in Britain and hence most British molluscs originally occupied woodland.

The damage caused to garden plants by a few species of gastropod has led to the popular belief that all slugs and snails are herbivores. This is not the case, a variety of food sources being utilised, and gastropods play a role in the breakdown of dung and carcases. A few species are active predators on other invertebrates. The bivalves follow an entirely different strategy, drawing a current of water through the body and filtering out the plankton and organic sediment held in suspension.

A few molluscs have efficient dispersal mechanisms, rapidly appearing in, for example, newly created ponds. The means by which this is achieved is not well understood, but the apocryphal waterfowl's feet take much of the credit. However, many molluscs show poor powers of dispersal. This accounts in part for the rarity of many species and allows molluscs to be used as indicators of sites where there has been a long continuity of stable ecological conditions. The origins of our terrestrial and freshwater mollusc fauna and the factors responsible for the current distribution patterns are discussed by Kerney (1966).

There are three species of mollusc considered by Wells, Pyle & Collins (1983) to be threatened internationally which have been recorded in Great Britain but have not been given Red Data Book status in this country. The bivalve *Margaritifera auricularia* (Spengler) is listed as Indeterminate by Wells, Pyle & Collins (1983), its European status is given as Vulnerable by Collins & Wells (1987) and it is included in Appendix II of the Bern Convention. In Great Britain, numerous shells have been dredged from the River Thames near London, where they were associated with Neolithic implements. However, there have been no British records from recent centuries (Ellis 1978), and this species may now be verging on total extinction (Altaba 1990). The closely related species *Margaritifera margaritifera* (L.) is listed as Vulnerable by both Wells, Pyle & Collins (1983) and Collins & Wells (1987) and is in Appendix III of the Bern Convention. Its status in Europe has recently been investigated by Bauer (1986, 1988). River pollution, including high silt-loading due to dredging, and over-exploitation by pearl collectors are the main threats to this species. Its status in Britain is being closely monitored (e.g. Young & Williams 1983a, 1983b; Wood & Pearce 1988). Although *M. margaritifera* does not currently fall within the Red Data Book categories for this country, it is a scarce species whose conservation is giving rise to some concern here and its increasing rarity in mainland Europe gives extra significance to the British population. See note on p. 12. The third species is the large gastropod *Helix pomatia* L., listed as Rare by Wells, Pyle & Collins (1983) and Vulnerable by Collins & Wells (1987). It too is included in Appendix III of the Bern Convention. Welch & Pollard (1975), considering this species throughout its range, thought collecting to be the main threat. Wild specimens are collected for teaching and research but the largest proportion are taken for human consumption. This has led to legislative protection in some European countries with close seasons, regulation of the size of snails collected, or total bans on collecting. Welch & Pollard (1975) reported that there was little commercial collecting in Britain and this is thought still to be the case. Here the major threat comes from loss of the chalk grassland habitat. However, the decline is not severe enough to warrant Red Data Book status for *H. pomatia* in Great Britain. There are doubts whether *H. pomatia* is native to Britain, but it has certainly been resident for many centuries and would not be precluded from the Red Data Book on these grounds.

No molluscs are endemic to the British Isles, though two species almost fall into this category. *Ashfordia granulata* (Alder) is widespread though not common in Great Britain, rather uncommon in Ireland, and otherwise known only from the Channel Islands and Finistere, France. *Leiostyla anglica* (Wood) has numerous widely scattered records in northern and western Great Britain and a small number of colonies in south-east England. It is more common in Ireland, but otherwise is found only in the Channel Islands and Ile de Re, France. Neither species is currently under threat in Britain, though the future of *L. anglica* is not secure in south-east England.

There are two British societies devoted to the study of molluscs, the Conchological Society of Great Britain and Ireland and the Malacological Society of London. These each produce a periodical, the *Journal of Conchology* and the *Journal of Molluscan Studies* (formerly *Proceedings of the Malacological Society*) respectively. In addition, both societies produce a newsletter. Distribution atlases have been produced for the marine (Seaward 1982) and non-marine (e.g. Roebuck 1921; Kerney 1976) molluscs, but such tasks are never complete and further survey work is always welcomed by both schemes. For ecological information, the two classic papers by Boycott (1934, 1936) have yet to be superseded, though additional information appears regularly in the two journals mentioned above. A booklet dealing with the conservation of Britain's non-marine molluscs has been produced by the NCC (Kerney & Stubbs 1980). Conservation of the marine species is one of the concerns of the Marine Conservation Society.

VALVATA MACROSTOMA

VULNERABLE

Phylum MOLLUSCA
Class GASTROPODA

Order MESOGASTROPODA
Family VALVATIDAE

Valvata macrostoma Morch, 1864, also known as *Valvata pulchella* (Studer).

Identification

Ellis (1969); Adam (1960). Care is needed in identifying this species; juveniles of depressed forms of the common and highly variable *Valvata piscinalis* (Muller) are often mistaken for it, and some literature records are consequently unreliable.

Distribution

This is a central and north European species, though its exact range is somewhat unclear owing to confusion with other taxa. In Britain, scattered populations are known from eight vice-counties (15-20 sites in South Hampshire, East Sussex, Oxfordshire, East Suffolk, East and West Norfolk, Cambridgeshire and South Lincolnshire). A map of the distribution in Britain is given in Kerney (1976).

Habitat and ecology

V. macrostoma is restricted to still or slowly-moving water in well-vegetated lowland habitats with a high species diversity, primarily drainage ditches in marshland levels. It is a calcicole. Other threatened molluscs may be associated with it, notably *Anisus vorticulus* (Troschel), *Segmentina nitida* (Muller) and *Pisidium pseudosphaerium* Schlesch (Ellis 1931). Colonies tend to be sharply defined, limited to short lengths of drainage ditches (D.T. Holyoak pers. comm.).

Status

This rare mollusc is still abundant at a few sites in the Pevensey Levels, East Sussex, and in the Fenland basin, but it is losing ground. Around Ely and Wicken in Cambridgeshire it has not been recorded since about 1930, and in the Avon valley, South Hampshire, not since 1956.

Threats

The exact cause of the decline of this species is unclear. Habitat damage and destruction by excessive disturbance (e.g. dredging) and by eutrophication are obvious dangers (Hingley 1979). The region of the Lewes Brooks, East Sussex, from which *V. macrostoma* had been recorded, now lies under the A27 Lewes by-pass (Hicklin 1986).

Conservation

Some sites are within the Pevensey Levels NNR. It occurs at five other SSSIs, which include Baston Fen, a Lincolnshire and South Humberside Trust reserve; the Nene Washes RSPB reserve, Cambridgeshire; and Wheatfen Broad, East Norfolk, a reserve bought as a memorial to E.A. Ellis. The ditch systems in which it occurs require periodic removal of the vegetation to prevent their becoming choked by emergent plants. Such clearance should avoid the colonies of *V. macrostoma* if possible. As a more general rule, only short stretches of ditch, say 50 metres, should be cleared at any one time, and the whole system cleared in rotation. This allows all stages of the ditch colonisation to be represented at all times. The clearance should remove only the weed and organic matter which have accumulated and not dig down into the bed of the ditch, as this would be likely to damage the wildlife by the formation of ochre deposits.

Author   M.P. Kerney.

PSEUDAMNICOLA CONFUSA .   ENDANGERED

Phylum MOLLUSCA   Order MESOGASTROPODA
Class GASTROPODA   Family HYDROBIIDAE

Pseudamnicola confusa (Frauenfeld, 1863), formerly known as *Amnicola confusa* (Frauenfeld), *Paludestrina confusa* (Frauenfeld) or *Hydrobia similis* (Draparnaud). Some continental authors now use the name *Mercuria confusa* (Frauenfeld).

Identification   Ellis (1969); Macan (1949).

Distribution   This is mainly a western Mediterranean species, with scattered outposts on the Atlantic coasts of Europe, north to the British Isles and the Netherlands. In England it has been confirmed in recent years only at a very few sites, in the River Arun, West Sussex; the River Roding, South Essex; and the River Alde, at Herringfleet Marshes and Oulton Broad, East Suffolk. The largest surviving populations are probably those in Oulton Broad. There are older records from the Thames estuary; the East Kent marshes; Thornham, West Norfolk (in 1960); and Saltfleet, North Lincolnshire (in 1913). The distribution in Britain is given in Kerney (1976).

Habitat and ecology   *P. confusa*, though nominally a brackish-water snail, lives in barely saline water (1-5 ppt NaCl) in river estuaries and tidal ditches and pools. It prefers soft muddy substrates, in quiet sheltered situations at the base of emergent vegetation (*Phragmites*, *Carex*, etc.), and frequents places that are covered by water only at high tide. It is usually associated with freshwater species only, not with brackish-water molluscs such as *Ovatella* and *Hydrobia* (Oldham 1922).

Status   This is a declining species, at risk because of its narrow ecological requirements and by being at the edge of its geographical range in Europe. Though abundant in the lower Thames in the mid nineteenth century, it was considered extinct there by 1896 owing to industrial pollution (Castell 1962). However, in 1984 a small colony was found living in Barking Creek at the mouth of the River Roding, South Essex (Harris 1985).

45

River Yare, Cantley, East Norfolk. The small snail *Pseudamnicola confusa* was recorded from the fringing reed–beds of this stretch of river in the 1940s, but recent searches have failed to refind it. Although the habitat appears to be intact, it is likely that river pollution has been the cause of the snail's demise. (Photo by I.F.G. McLean.)

Threats	All populations are potentially at risk, especially from barrages or other river control schemes affecting the narrow salinity range which the species requires. A ditch in Strumpshaw Marsh, East Norfolk, which supported this species in 1977 became unsuitable when a dam was installed which isolated the ditch from the saline influence of the River Yare (R.J. Driscoll pers. comm.). In April 1985 a road accident involving a chemical tanker carrying pesticide caused serious pollution of the River Roding and killed much of its wildlife, but the *P. confusa* population has survived that incident.
Conservation	It occurs within a Suffolk Trust reserve, Carlton Marshes, which is also an SSSI, on the south side of Oulton Broad.
Author	M.P. Kerney.

MARSTONIOPSIS SCHOLTZI   RARE

Phylum MOLLUSCA   Order MESOGASTROPODA
Class GASTROPODA   Family HYDROBIIDAE

Marstoniopsis scholtzi (Schmidt, 1856), formerly known as *Bythinella scholtzi* (Schmidt), *B. steinii* (Martens), *Paludestrina taylori* (E.A. Smith) or *Amnicola taylori* (E.A. Smith).

Identification	Ellis (1969); Macan (1949); Adam (1960).
Distribution	This is a north European species, extending from France and Britain eastwards to north Germany, Poland and south Scandinavia. In England it lives in a few canals in the Manchester area (South Lancashire and Cheshire, five 10 km squares) and in two localities in East Anglia (Great Ouse, West Norfolk, River Deben, East Suffolk). It formerly occurred near Stirling, Stirlingshire. A distribution map for Britain is given in Kerney (1976) but this predates the discovery of the East Anglian populations.
Habitat and ecology	*M. scholtzi* lives in still or slowly moving water in canals and in lowland rivers. It appears to prefer quiet weedy conditions over a muddy substrate (Preece & Wilmot 1979).
Status	This species may be native in southeast England (as a fossil shell of Roman date is known from the Thames) but elsewhere it has probably been introduced. Near Manchester it was first noted in 1900 (canals at Droylsden, South Lancashire, and Dukinfield, Cheshire) and in Stirling in 1931 (canal pond at Grangemouth (Waterston 1934)). Apart from the disappearance of the Grangemouth colony in the 1950s, there is no evidence that the populations are declining, and at least in the Manchester canals this species is seemingly resistant to some degree of pollution. However, these Manchester populations of unknown provenance

should not be allowed to detract from the importance of the possibly native populations in East Anglia.

Threats   As with all riverine species, acute pollution is a threat. Long-term deterioration in water quality, such as eutrophication leading to loss of aquatic plants, is another danger. River management work such as dredging and bank reinforcement could also be damaging. In the Manchester area canals are largely redundant and there may be the risk of their destruction by infilling. Conversely, increased boat traffic along rivers and canals can eliminate waterplants by erosion of the banks and by causing the perpetual suspension of silt in the water.

Author   M.P. Kerney.

TRUNCATELLA SUBCYLINDRICA   RARE
Looping Snail

Phylum MOLLUSCA   Order MESOGASTROPODA
Class GASTROPODA   Family TRUNCATELLIDAE

Truncatella subcylindrica (Linnaeus, 1767), formerly known as *T. truncatula* (Draparnaud) and including *T. montagui* Lowe (see Fretter & Graham 1978a).

Identification   Fretter & Graham (1978a).

Distribution   The Atlantic islands of the Canaries and Madeira, and European coasts from the Black Sea and Mediterranean to southern England. It has been reported from twelve places along the English south coast, from Fowey, East Cornwall, to Newhaven, East Sussex, and one site in East Anglia, near Felixstowe, East Suffolk.

Habitat and ecology Found deep in moist rotting sea-grass or saltmarsh vegetation at high water mark in sheltered tidal lagoons and estuaries where salinity remains fairly high for most of the time. Often buried within shingle or under stones or plants on mud. Out of water, the animal moves rather like a looper caterpillar, using alternately the snout and the short foot to grip the substrate. Adult females attach their eggs singly to particles or stones and the young hatch as small snails with no waterborne dispersal phase. At maturity, the shell becomes truncated by loss of its apex.

Status   At the northern extremity of its range in Britain. Most of the records from its thirteen sites date from the nineteenth century and few clearly refer to living animals. There are currently only five known colonies: the largest at the Fleet, Dorset, where it has been recorded for over 130 years (Seaward 1980, 1986; Little *et al.* 1989); Southampton Water, South Hampshire, 1986 (D.W. Guntrip

48

pers. comm.); Langstone Harbour, South Hampshire, 1990 (J. Light pers. comm.); Yar estuary, Freshwater, Isle of Wight, 1990 (J. Light pers. comm.); and Pagham Harbour, West Sussex, 1985 (M.B. Seddon pers. comm.). Although obviously rare, the animal is small and easily overlooked, so it may be found living in a few more sites.

Threats

There are no known major threats to its existing colonies; however, the specialised habitat and small number of colonies render it vulnerable. Plans for a power station on the shore of the Fleet at Herbury are now in abeyance. The Fleet receives its sea water from Portland Harbour, which is under considerable recreational and developmental pressure and suffers occasional pollution. The lack of any developmental dispersal phase in *T. subcylindrica* renders it very vulnerable to loss of habitat, since its powers of recolonisation are presumably poor, and fragmentation of a population would be particularly detrimental. However, the Pagham Harbour colony is of special interest in that the Harbour was reclaimed for agricultural use from 1873 until 1910, when the sea breached the shingle barrier. The open coast in either direction would seem inhospitable to *Truncatella*.

Conservation

The Fleet is an SSSI, a Ramsar site and a private nature reserve. Pagham Harbour is an SSSI and LNR. Langstone Harbour and the Yar estuary are SSSIs.

Author

D.R. Seaward, using information from Fretter & Graham (1978a) and personal observations.

PALUDINELLA LITTORINA   RARE

Phylum MOLLUSCA   Order MESOGASTROPODA
Class GASTROPODA   Family ASSIMINEIDAE

Paludinella littorina (Chiaje, 1828), formerly known as *Assiminea littorina* (Chiaje) and including *P. littorea* (Forbes & Hanley) (see Fretter & Graham 1978a).

Identification

Fretter & Graham (1978a).

Distribution

"This is primarily a Mediterranean species (absent from the Black Sea) which extends along Eastern Atlantic coasts from Madeira north to a limit on the S. coast of England" (Fretter & Graham 1978a). There are records from nine places in southern England and two in south Wales, but most of these are between 70 and 130 years old.

Habitat and ecology

At high water mark, among moist rotting sea-grass or saltmarsh vegetation or under stones, or in crevices high on the shore. In the

49

former it may associate with *Truncatella subcylindrica* (L.) and the pulmonate snail *Ovatella myosotis* (Draparnaud), and in the latter with the pulmonates *Otina ovata* (Brown) and *Leucophytia bidentata* (Montagu). Nothing is known of the food, breeding or growth cycle.

Status   Of the eleven recorded occurrences, only two are clearly of living specimens rather than shells. These are from rock crevices at high water mark at Whitecliff Bay, Isle of Wight, in 1852 (Forbes & Hanley 1853, Vol. 4, as *Rissoa littorea*) but not subsequently, and from the Fleet, Dorset, in the 1850s, in 1888 and since 1985 (Forbes & Hanley 1853; Sykes 1890; Light 1986; Little *et al.* 1989; pers. obs.). Thus the only currently known colony is at the Fleet, where it is occasional in suitable high water mark deposits at several points along the Chesil shore. A single fresh but empty shell was found in 1987 in Chichester Harbour, West Sussex (M. Goodchild pers. comm.), so this tiny species may exist at further sites.

Threats   No immediate threats are known, but the specialised habitat and small number of colonies render it vulnerable. There are potential threats to the Fleet. Plans for a power station there are now in abeyance, but Portland Harbour, from which the Fleet receives its sea water, is under increasing recreational and developmental pressure and suffers occasional pollution.

Conservation   The Fleet is an SSSI, a Ramsar site and a private nature reserve. Chichester Harbour and Whitecliff Bay are also SSSIs.

Author   D.R. Seaward, using information from Forbes & Hanley (1853), Fretter & Graham (1978a) and personal observations.

CAECUM ARMORICUM   INSUFFICIENTLY KNOWN

Phylum MOLLUSCA   Order MESOGASTROPODA
Class GASTROPODA   Family CAECIDAE

Caecum armoricum De Folin, 1869.

Identification   Van Aartsen & Hoenselaar (1984).

Distribution   The Atlantic coast from Portugal to the Bay of St Malo, Channel (van Aartsen & Hoenselaar 1984), and the Fleet, Dorset (Seaward 1989).

Habitat and ecology   There is little information since this species was apparently only known from shells until discovered living in the Fleet in 1987. Here it is locally abundant in a very specialised and restricted micro-habitat occupied by a mollusc community dominated by *Lasaea rubra* (Montagu) var. *pallida* and with *Onoba aculeus* (Gould) frequent and *Leucophytia bidentata* (Montagu) occasional. This community occupies the spaces between the small pebbles of Chesil Beach, around 5 cm or more deep, along parts of the Fleet shore where sea water issues from the Beach, keeping the interstices clear of clay (Seaward 1989). *C. armoricum* is probably closely related to *C. glabrum* (Montagu), which feeds upon diatoms and lays eggs from which free-swimming veliger larvae hatch; after settlement, the tiny spiral protoconch is lost and the shell grows as a short arc, the upper end of which is sealed by a callus. *C. glabrum* occurs on "sandy and sandy-muddy bottoms to about 250 metres; not intertidal" (Fretter & Graham 1978b). All stages of *C. armoricum* are present at the Fleet from post-larval to adult.

Status

This species was originally described from the shell (De Folin 1869). Subsequent records were of shells washed up on beaches from the Algarve, Portugal, to the Bay of St Malo, Channel (seven sites). The only recorded occurrence of the live animal is from the Fleet in Dorset, where it is locally abundant as described above. The adult shell is up to 2 mm long by about 0.1 mm in diameter, so it is easily overlooked and perhaps there are other undiscovered colonies living close to the places where shells have been found. This species is certainly internationally rare on present evidence.

Threats

None known, but, unless other colonies are found, it is obviously highly vulnerable to disturbance and pollution of the Fleet and its specialised habitat. The marine life of the Fleet depends on a free flow of good quality sea water from Portland Harbour, which is under considerable recreational and developmental pressure and suffers occasional pollution.

Conservation

The Fleet is an SSSI, a Ramsar site and a private nature reserve. Part of Portland Harbour is an SSSI.

Author

D.R. Seaward, using personal observations and information from the references cited and from J.J. van Aartsen and H.J. Hoenselaar (pers. comms). Data for *C. glabrum* are from Fretter & Graham (1978b).

TENELLIA ADSPERSA — INSUFFICIENTLY KNOWN

A sea slug

Phylum MOLLUSCA
Class GASTROPODA

Order NUDIBRANCHIA
Family TERGIPEDIDAE

Tenellia adspersa (Nordmann, 1845), formerly known as *Embletonia pallida* Alder & Hancock.

Identification

Thompson & Brown (1984).

Distribution

This species is found worldwide. British records are from Aberlady

Bay, East Lothian, in the Firth of Forth; Northumberland; the north Norfolk, southeast and south coasts; the Bristol Channel; and Liverpool Bay.

Habitat and ecology   Current knowledge is summarised by Thompson & Brown (1984). It can live in waters subject to wide variations in temperature and salinity, on the lower shore or in shallow water, in saline lagoons, or in canals with little contact with the sea. The food is mainly hydroids of various species. In the Fleet, the prey is usually *Obelia dichotoma* (L.). The hermaphrodite parent produces eggs which may develop either as planktonic larvae or directly as creeping juveniles.

Status   Five of the eleven British records date from before 1900. In the present century it has been reported from saltmarsh pools in the Firth of Forth (Nicol 1935); New England Creek, a saline lagoon in South Essex, where it was "fairly common" (Howes 1939); a creek in north Norfolk (five animals) (Hamond 1972); a lagoon near Dersingham, West Norfolk (a single individual) (Bishop 1976 & pers. comm.); the beach at Portishead, North Somerset (a single individual) (Boyden *et al.* 1977; C. Little pers. comm.); and the Fleet, Dorset, where it was frequent from 1975 to 1982, then not found again until 1987 when it was present in small numbers (pers. obs.). The decline at the last site may be related to a reduction in hydroid abundance. Although easily overlooked, it is certainly rare and there is at present only one definite British site.

Threats   Brackish lagoons are a very vulnerable habitat, many having been lost through saltmarsh reclamation, isolation from the sea during construction of sea defences, infilling or pollution through being used for rubbish disposal, or natural hydroseral succession. The considerable recreational and developmental pressure on Portland Harbour and occasional pollution there pose a threat to the Fleet, as Portland Harbour is the source of sea water to the Fleet. Plans for a power station at Herbury on the shore of the Fleet are now in abeyance.

Conservation   Portishead Beach forms part of an SSSI. The Fleet is an SSSI, Ramsar site and private nature reserve. New England Creek lies within the Foulness SSSI. The lagoon near Dersingham probably lies within the Snettisham RSPB reserve. Aberlady Bay is an SSSI and LNR.

Author   D.R. Seaward, using information from Thompson & Brown (1984) and personal observations.

LYMNAEA GLABRA

VULNERABLE

Phylum MOLLUSCA
Class GASTROPODA

Order BASOMMATOPHORA
Family LYMNAEIDAE

Lymnaea glabra (Muller, 1774).

Identification   Ellis (1969); Macan (1949).

Distribution   This is a west European species, reaching 61°N in Scandinavia, but everywhere local. In Britain, it was formerly fairly widely distributed in acidic lowland areas of England, Wales and south Scotland, north to Perth. There are records from 38 vice-counties. It is now rare, with the largest concentration of records in the southern part of the Vale of York. Kerney (1976) gives the distribution in Britain.

Habitat and ecology   *L. glabra* lives in soft water in small muddy pools and ditches, especially in places which dry out periodically and where the aquatic flora is poor. Usually it lives either alone or with a very few other molluscs equally tolerant of desiccation (notably *Aplexa hypnorum* (L.), *Anisus leucostoma* (Millet) and *Pisidium personatum* Malm). Conversely, it is never found in rich aquatic habitats with a high molluscan diversity. Many sites are on ancient uncultivated land on acid sandy or gravelly soils, such as heaths and commons. In south Yorkshire it is found in swampy land drains and ephemeral ponds. Boycott (1936) includes a detailed description of the habitat requirements of this species.

Status   This species has become extinct over large parts of lowland England and shows a continuing decline. It may be noted that the only known surviving Irish population was recently destroyed by farm drainage; see Hurley (1981).

Threats   Drainage of boggy areas and the elimination of small ponds and field drains. Also ploughing or direct chemical enrichment causing eutrophication of water bodies through leaching. It occurs in the New Forest, South Hampshire, and even here there have been recent instances of drainage with the aim of improving the grazing. Equally damaging would be the deepening of seasonal pools, converting them to permanent ponds, such as is frequently carried out on nature reserves for the benefit of Odonata.

Conservation   There are recent records from eight SSSIs, including Red Moor, a County Trust reserve in East Cornwall.

Author   M.P. Kerney.

MYXAS GLUTINOSA   ENDANGERED
Glutinous Snail

Phylum MOLLUSCA   Order BASOMMATOPHORA
Class GASTROPODA   Family LYMNAEIDAE

Myxas glutinosa (Muller, 1774), formerly known as *Amphipeplea glutinosa* (Muller) or *Lymnaea glutinosa* (Muller).

Identification   Ellis (1969); Macan (1949).

Distribution   This species is north European, occurring between the Alps and the Arctic Circle. It is very local throughout its range. In Britain, it has been recorded in the past century from about 35 sites (in 15 vice-counties) in southern and eastern England north to Yorkshire and with outposts in Bala Lake, Merionethshire, and Lake Windermere, Westmorland. Kerney (1976) shows the distribution of records of this species in Britain.

Habitat and ecology *Myxas* lives in spacious bodies of quiet, very clean water in slow rivers, canals, drainage ditches and lakes. Most occurrences are in hard water, notable exceptions being Windermere (calcium 6-8 ppm) and Bala Lake (calcium 2 ppm). It avoids turbid or weed-choked places and shows a preference for firm substrates (in canals in Ireland it is typically found crawling on stones or on the masonry of locks and bridges rather than on the vegetation). In Lake Windermere it is recorded living on stones lying in firm mud in about a metre of water.

Status   This species has declined dramatically over the past century. It is now of the greatest rarity in Britain. Most records date from before 1914. The only reports in the last sixty years are as follows: Deal, East Kent, *ca* 1930; Chislet Marshes, East Kent, 1930; River Yare near Norwich, East Norfolk, 1940; Bala Lake, Merionethshire, 1952-54 (not refound by searches in 1964 and 1989); Lake Windermere, Westmorland, 1957 (not refound in the 1970s or 1980s). In 1988-1990 it was discovered in a lake in Berkshire in the vicinity of Oxford, an area from which it was last reported in 1916. Collins & Wells (1987) categorise this species as Vulnerable in Europe.

Threats   The reasons for the decline of *Myxas* are unknown, but it may be a species unusually sensitive to physical disturbance (e.g. turbidity) and to chemical pollution (including phosphate and nitrate enrichment from arable land).

Conservation   Bala Lake (Llyn Tegid) and Lake Windermere are in National Parks. The former is an SSSI. *Myxas* is protected by inclusion in Schedule 5 of the Wildlife and Countryside Act 1981.

Author   M.P. Kerney.

ANISUS VORTICULUS

VULNERABLE

Phylum MOLLUSCA
Class GASTROPODA

Order BASOMMATOPHORA
Family PLANORBIDAE

Anisus vorticulus (Troschel, 1834), formerly known as *Planorbis vorticulus* Troschel.

Identification   Ellis (1969); Adam (1960).

Distribution   This is a mainly central and south European species, local throughout its range. In Britain, it has been reported from about fifteen sites in six vice-counties (East and West Sussex, Middlesex, East Suffolk, East and West Norfolk). The chief surviving populations lie in a compact area in the marshlands east of Norwich, East Norfolk. Scattered colonies also occur at Cley, West Norfolk; Staines, Middlesex (Kerney & May 1960); Amberley, West Sussex; and Lewes and Pevensey, East Sussex. The distribution in Britain is mapped in Kerney (1976).

Habitat and ecology   *A. vorticulus* is a calciphile snail which lives chiefly in marsh drains in levels, in clean, still water with a rich aquatic flora (*Lemna trisulca*, *Hydrocharis*, *Ceratophyllum*, etc.). It often floats on the surface among *Lemna*. A diverse mollusc fauna is usually present and this may include other threatened species such as *Valvata macrostoma* Morch, *Segmentina nitida* (Muller) and *Pisidium pseudosphaerium* Schlesch (Ellis 1928, 1931, 1932; Long 1968).

Status   This species is still fairly numerous at a few sites in the Broads, in East Sussex (Pevensey and Lewes Levels), and in a pond at Staines. Records for Amberley Wild Brooks and Cley date from the 1960s, and its survival at these sites requires confirmation. There are old records and Postglacial fossils from the fenland basin, where the species has apparently become extinct.

Threats   All surviving populations are potentially or actually threatened by drainage, overfrequent dredging and eutrophication. The former pasture in the Lewes Levels has now been largely converted to arable land and the use of fertilisers on this and the remaining pasture is threatening to degrade the water quality in the ditches. Share Marsh, an area of grazing levels west of Lowestoft, East Suffolk, formerly supported this and other rare aquatic molluscs but deep drainage associated with conversion to arable agriculture in the early 1980s has destroyed the habitat over all of this marsh (I.F.G. McLean pers. comm.).

Conservation   Part of Amberley Wild Brooks is a Sussex Trust reserve and part of the Pevensey Levels is an NNR. *Anisus vorticulus* also occurs on the Norfolk Trust's reserve at Burgh Common. These and three other of its sites are SSSIs. The designation of the South Downs as an

Environmentally Sensitive Area has helped to preserve small areas of the Lewes Levels, now an SSSI, from agricultural 'improvement' and it is hoped that some arable land can be converted back to low-input pasture (B. Banks pers. comm.). The management of ditches in grazing levels for this and other scarce aquatic molluscs (see above) requires regular clearance of the aquatic vegetation, since, without management, such ditches are rapidly dominated by *Phragmites*, *Sparganium* or other emergent plants. To ensure the continuous presence within the site of the desired waterweed communities, it is necessary to clear part of the ditch system each year, in rotation. It is better to clear several small lengths of ditch than one long length, as this gives better opportunities for recolonisation from the uncleared stretches. The length of the rotation depends on the speed with which the ditches become choked with emergent vegetation. Minor channels on the Pevensey Levels may not be cleared for over twenty years (Hingley 1979).

Author   M.P. Kerney.

GYRAULUS ACRONICUS   VULNERABLE

Phylum MOLLUSCA   Order BASOMMATOPHORA
Class GASTROPODA   Family PLANORBIDAE

Gyraulus acronicus (Ferussac, 1807), formerly known as *Planorbis acronicus* Ferussac. It should be noted that the taxonomy of the genus *Gyraulus* is confused, and the identity of the British form with the species known as *acronicus* in Scandinavia and in the Alps is not firmly established.

Identification   Ellis (1969); Adam (1960).

Distribution   The distribution in Europe is unclear (see note above). In Britain, the species is restricted to the upper Thames (and a few tributaries such as the River Lodden) between about Marlow and Oxford. There are recent records from eleven 10 km squares. Its British distribution is given in Kerney (1976).

Habitat and ecology   In the River Thames, *G. acronicus* has been noted as living in quiet stretches and backwaters, among weeds and on stones (Cooper 1924). In recent years it has rarely been found alive, though not infrequently collected as fresh empty shells in flood debris.

Status   In the earlier part of the Postglacial period fossils show that *G. acronicus* had a wider range than today, living additionally in the lower Thames and in the River Lea in South Essex, Hertfordshire and Middlesex. There is no clear evidence that this decline continues, but more needs to be known about this species, which is rarely collected alive.

Threats	Water pollution or gross habitat disturbance are likely to be adverse factors. A serious pollution accident in the upper Thames would probably destroy most populations.
Author	M.P. Kerney.

SEGMENTINA NITIDA   ENDANGERED

<table>
<tr><td>Phylum MOLLUSCA
Class GASTROPODA</td><td style="text-align:right">Order BASOMMATOPHORA
Family PLANORBIDAE</td></tr>
</table>

Segmentina nitida (Muller, 1774).

Identification	Ellis (1969); Adam (1960).
Distribution	On the Continent, *S. nitida* is found locally throughout lowland Europe, north to southernmost Scandinavia (to 62°N in Finland). In Britain in the nineteenth and early twentieth centuries it was locally but widely distributed, northwards to Yorkshire (about 90 sites in 27 vice counties). Since 1965 it has been found in only a handful of places (seven 10 km squares) in the Norfolk and Suffolk Broads east of Norwich; in Monkton and Westbere Marshes, East Kent; and in the Pevensey and Lewes Levels, East Sussex. Its distribution is shown in Kerney (1976).
Habitat and ecology	*S. nitida* occurs in drainage ditches in levels, where it lives in clean, hard water with dense vegetation, among thick growths of *Glyceria, Lemna trisulca*, etc. The associated mollusc fauna is generally rich and may include other threatened rarities such as *Valvata macrostoma* Morch, *Anisus vorticulus* (Troschel) and *Pisidium pseudosphaerium* Schlesch. *S. nitida* has in the past also been recorded from lakes and ponds, situated usually on former floodplains or in areas of reclaimed marshland.
Status	This species has declined dramatically over the past century, and this decline continues. *S. nitida* seems now to be extinct over most of England, even in areas where it was once common, most notably around London (last recorded at Walton-on-Thames, Surrey, 1952). Collins & Wells (1987), assessing the status of invertebrates in Europe, placed this species in the Vulnerable category.
Threats	The reasons for the decline are not understood, but overfrequent dredging of marsh drains, the lowering of water levels and eutrophication have presumably all played their part. It may be significant that surviving populations are in areas of traditional marshland grazing, where phosphate and nitrate enrichment from fertilisers consequently remains low. In the Pevensey Levels, Hingley (1979) found that the rarer molluscs, including *S. nitida*, thrived in drains which had not been cleared recently and

Pevensey Levels SSSI, East Sussex. Weedy freshwater ditches through unimproved pasture support a suite of threatened molluscs. The spider *Dolomedes plantarius* was also discovered here recently. Even with careful ditch management, the invertebrate fauna can still be lost if fertiliser-enriched water enters from nearby arable land. (Photo by P. Wakely.)

considered pump drainage, the use of herbicides and frequent ditch clearance would cause the loss of the rarer species. Only fragments of 'unimproved' pasture remain in the Lewes Levels, much of the area having been converted to arable land or the pasture reseeded and fertilised, and thus the long-term survival of this and other rare aquatic molluscs at this site is in doubt. Share Marsh, near Lowestoft, East Suffolk, formerly supported *S. nitida*, but in the early 1980s much of the grazing was converted to arable agriculture and the deeper, more efficient drainage ditches no longer support the necessary rich aquatic flora (I.F.G. McLean pers. comm.).

Conservation It occurs within five SSSIs, including the Pevensey Levels NNR and Burgh Common Norfolk Trust reserve. Parts of the Lewes Levels have recently been notified as an SSSI and it is hoped that some arable land can be converted back to low-input pasture, which should ameliorate the eutrophication of the ditches (B. Banks pers. comm.). Clearance of grazing marsh drains is necessary for the conservation of this species but should be carried out on only short stretches of drain in any one year to facilitate recolonisation of the cleared stretches. The frequency of clearance should be controlled by the rate at which emergent vegetation over-runs the ditch rather than being on a fixed and regular timetable.

Author M.P. Kerney.

CATINELLA ARENARIA   ENDANGERED
Sandbowl Snail

Phylum MOLLUSCA   Order STYLOMMATOPHORA
Class GASTROPODA   Family SUCCINEIDAE

Catinella arenaria (Bouchard-Chantereaux, 1837), formerly known as *Succinea arenaria* Bouchard-Chantereaux.

Identification Quick (1933); Kerney & Cameron (1979). Note that *C. arenaria* may require dissection for certain separation from *Succinea oblonga* Draparnaud (*q.v.* below).

Distribution This is a rare western European species, found at isolated sites from the Alps to the Arctic Circle. It is mainly coastal and montane. In Britain, it is known from two places only: Braunton Burrows, North Devon, and near Sunbiggin Tarn, Orton Fell, Westmorland. In the nineteenth century it was present at Britton Ferry, near Swansea, Glamorgan, but it is now extinct there. A distribution map is given in Kerney (1976) but lacks the Westmorland record.

Habitat and ecology *C. arenaria* lives in a base-rich fen fed by springs (Orton Fell) and in the damp, sparsely vegetated hollows of a stabilised dune system (Braunton Burrows). It requires bare ground and lives mostly on the bare mud or sand at the base of the low vegetation (Boycott 1921; Quick 1933; Coles & Colville 1979). At Orton Fell, it is associated with the endangered species *Vertigo geyeri* Lindholm (*q.v.* below).

Status This is a glacial relict species, largely eliminated during the early Postglacial period by forest growth. The two surviving colonies appear stable. The population at Braunton Burrows is extensive, but that at Orton Fell very limited. This species is categorised as Vulnerable in Europe (Collins & Wells 1987).

Threats Drainage or habitat disturbance. The Orton Fell site is potentially the more fragile owing to its small size, and excessive trampling should be avoided. At Braunton Burrows, the decline in the rabbit population has allowed some dune slacks, which may have been suitable for *C. arenaria*, to develop a thick vegetation of *Salix repens* and moss with no bare ground remaining. There is also the danger of further water abstraction or drainage adjacent to the Burrows, which could affect the reserve.

Conservation Braunton Burrows is an NNR. A sheep-grazing regime has been initiated there to compensate for the lower rabbit population. In the seaward section of the dunes there is still plenty of bare ground within dune slacks and *C. arenaria* occurs in most apparently suitable locations there. Disturbance of the vegetation by people and rabbits maintains these bare patches. In three dune slacks, the vegetation and top layer of soil have been removed in order to conserve the botanical interest, and such areas may also benefit *C. arenaria*. Brind (1978) mapped the distribution of *C. arenaria* at Braunton Burrows and described the occupied habitats, providing a sound basis for future monitoring and other ecological studies. The Orton Fell site lies within the Sunbiggin Tarn SSSI. *C. arenaria* is protected by inclusion in Schedule 5 of the Wildlife and Countryside Act 1981.

Author M.P. Kerney, with additional information from J.M. Breeds.

SUCCINEA OBLONGA   RARE

Phylum MOLLUSCA   Order STYLOMMATOPHORA
Class GASTROPODA   Family SUCCINEIDAE

Succinea oblonga Draparnaud, 1801.

Identification Quick (1933); Kerney & Cameron (1979).

Distribution This is a European and western Asiatic species. In Europe, it reaches about 61°N in Scandinavia. In Britain, there are only a few recent records (in ten 10 km squares), from Hawkhurst and Appledore, Kent; Ripon, Midwest Yorkshire; near Goole, Southwest Yorkshire; Meathop, Westmorland; and a number of small populations in Ayrshire, Stirlingshire and Perthshire. Older records, mainly from the nineteenth century, exist from a few other counties. This species remains relatively common in parts of Ireland. A distribution map for Britain is given in Kerney (1976).

Habitat and ecology *S. oblonga* lives in damp, unshaded, sparsely vegetated places such as the floodplains of rivers and the margins of lakes, marshes and ditches. It likes bare muddy or stony surfaces (Kevan 1931).

Status This is a relict species, found commonly as a fossil in cold-climate deposits dating from the glacial periods. In Kent and Sussex, it temporarily returned in the wake of prehistoric and Roman deforestation, but has now largely receded once more from this area. There is little evidence of significant further recent decline in Britain, but the species must be considered at risk because of its rarity and rather specialised requirements.

Threats Most of the Scottish sites are on floodplains, especially in the Forth valley, which might be affected by embankment or flood control schemes.

Conservation It occurs within Meathop Woods and Quarry SSSI, Westmorland, and Ripon Parks SSSI, Midwest Yorkshire, the latter being Ministry of Defence land managed sympathetically for conservation.

Author M.P. Kerney.

OXYLOMA SARSI   VULNERABLE

Phylum MOLLUSCA   Order STYLOMMATOPHORA
Class GASTROPODA   Family SUCCINEIDAE

Oxyloma sarsi (Esmark, 1886), formerly known in Britain as *Succinea elegans*, but this name has been applied to more than one species and is therefore ambiguous.

Identification Quick (1933); Kerney & Cameron (1979). Note that dissection may be necessary to distinguish this species from certain forms of the common succineid *Oxyloma pfeifferi* (Rossmassler).

Distribution This is a north European species, known from several disjunct areas between the Alps and southern Scandinavia. In Britain, it has been recorded in recent years only from a few places in the Norfolk and Suffolk Broads (notably Oulton Broad, East Suffolk) and in the Lea valley on the North Essex/Hertfordshire border. There are old records from Kent, Middlesex, Cambridgeshire and

Bedfordshire. Its distribution is shown in Kerney (1976).

Habitat and ecology *O. sarsi* inhabits richly vegetated fens of lowland type at the margins of rivers and lakes and in drainage dykes in levels. It is more aquatic than the common *Oxyloma pfeifferi*, never straying far from standing water and usually found either on emergent vegetation, such as *Phragmites* or *Glyceria maxima*, or actually crawling on floating waterplants. Other molluscan rarities, notably *Vertigo moulinsiana* (Dupuy)(*q.v.* below), may occur in association. Unlike *O. pfeifferi*, this species appears to be a calcicole.

Status This is a relict species, more widely distributed in the earlier part of the Postglacial period (fossils have been found in, for example, Lincolnshire and North Wales). The decline continues. In Europe this species is categorised as Vulnerable (Collins & Wells 1987).

Threats Most surviving populations are at risk from pollution, dredging or river management schemes. Share Marsh, near Lowestoft, East Suffolk, formerly supported this species, but it is unlikely to have survived the deep drainage carried out in the early 1980s when the area was converted from grazing marsh to arable agriculture (I.F.G. McLean pers. comm.).

Conservation It occurs within Surlingham Broad, East Norfolk, and Carlton Marshes, East Suffolk, both County Trust reserves and SSSIs. In 1954, two old shells were found at Wicken Fen, Cambridgeshire, an SSSI and nature reserve owned by the National Trust.

Author M.P. Kerney.

TRUNCATELLINA CYLINDRICA   VULNERABLE

Phylum MOLLUSCA   Order STYLOMMATOPHORA
Class GASTROPODA   Family VERTIGINIDAE

Truncatellina cylindrica (Ferussac, 1807), formerly known as *Vertigo cylindrica* (Ferussac).

Identification Ellis (1969); Kerney & Cameron (1979).

Distribution This is a species of southern and western Europe, reaching about 61°N in Scandinavia. It is very local throughout its range. In Britain, it is at present known from only two sites: Potton church, Bedfordshire, and Went Vale, near Kirk Smeaton, Southwest Yorkshire. Both colonies are very small. It has been reported in the past from about sixteen further sites, from Somerset to Fife. The distribution in Britain is mapped in Kerney (1976).

Habitat and ecology *T. cylindrica* lives in short, dry calcareous grassland in sandy or stony ground, typically among such plants as *Sedum*, *Thymus* or *Artemisia*. It has been found at the base of natural rocks or the foot of old stone walls. In Lincolnshire and east Yorkshire it has been recorded also from sand dunes (last seen 1894).

Status   *T. cylindrica* is probably under-recorded owing to its minute size, and may not be as rare as the records suggest. However, it is undoubtedly uncommon, and furthermore it exhibits a history of long-term decline. The subfossil record indicates that in the Neolithic and Bronze Age periods it possessed a wider distribution in southern Britain. Its subsequent retreat may be connected with increasingly effective arable farming, coupled with climatic deterioration. In the past fifty years it has been found living only at Thetford, West Norfolk (Davis 1952); Potton, Bedfordshire; and Went Vale, Southwest Yorkshire (Norris 1976). The Thetford population has now disappeared and attempts to refind it at several older sites have also failed, for example at Easby Abbey, Northeast Yorkshire (recorded 1883), Burgh Castle, East Suffolk (1909), and Edinburgh Castle rock, Midlothian (several records, 1836-1930).

Threats   Habitat destruction. Trampling by visitors may be to blame for the loss of the Edinburgh population, and at Burgh Castle the cause is almost certainly the scraping and tidying up of the Roman walls, which began in 1929. There is very little suitable habitat at Went Vale, the surrounding area being wooded.

Conservation   At Went Vale it occurs within Brockadale SSSI, a Yorkshire Trust reserve.

Author   M.P. Kerney.

TRUNCATELLINA CALLICRATIS   RARE

Phylum MOLLUSCA   Order STYLOMMATOPHORA
Class GASTROPODA   Family VERTIGINIDAE

Truncatellina callicratis (Scacchi, 1833), formerly known as *T. britannica* Pilsbry or *Vertigo britannica* (Pilsbry).

Identification   Ellis (1969); Kerney & Cameron (1979). Note that most British specimens differ considerably from typical *T. callicratis* from southern Europe and may be hard to distinguish by the inexpert from *T. cylindrica* (Ferussac) (*q.v.* above), of which they were once considered a variety.

Distribution   *T. callicratis* is mainly Mediterranean, Pyrenean and Alpine. Scattered colonies are known along the south coast of England from Torquay, South Devon, to Ventnor, Isle of Wight. The best

Church Ope Cove, Isle of Portland SSSI, Dorset. Such sparsely vegetated rocky calcareous cliffs on the south coast are the habitat of the snail *Truncatellina callicratis*. (Photo by P. Wakely.)

known locality is Church Ope Cove, Isle of Portland, Dorset, where it is very numerous. The distribution of the British populations is mapped in Kerney (1976).

Habitat and ecology *T. callicratis* lives in short, dry calcareous grassland in exposed places, among rocks and screes on cliffs by the sea (Davis 1955).

Status Though very local, *T. callicratis* appears to be reasonably secure within its range, especially at suitable sites on the Jurassic limestone cliffs between the Isle of Portland and Durlston Head, Dorset. There is no geological or historical evidence of overall decline.

Threats Habitat loss. Quarrying of the Isle of Portland has reduced the amount of semi-natural grassland there. However, old quarry debris can produce suitable habitat for this species, as at Church Ope Cove.

Conservation Church Ope Cove is within the Isle of Portland SSSI. *T. callicratis* also occurs within the Sidmouth to Beer Coast SSSI, South Devon, and at several places within the South Dorset Coast SSSI, some populations being within National Trust property in both cases.

Author M.P. Kerney.

VERTIGO MOULINSIANA   RARE

Phylum MOLLUSCA   Order STYLOMMATOPHORA
Class GASTROPODA   Family VERTIGINIDAE

Vertigo moulinsiana (Dupuy, 1849).

Identification Ellis (1969); Kerney & Cameron (1979).

Distribution On the Continent, this species is widely distributed north to Denmark and southernmost Sweden, but is regarded as rare in all countries. In England, scattered colonies occur in a band from Dorset to Norfolk, with isolated sites in Northamptonshire (Sutton Bog), Shropshire (Sweat Mere Fen) and North Devon (Braunton Burrows; last seen 1933). The largest surviving populations are in the Norfolk Broads. A distribution map for Britain is given in Kerney (1976).

Habitat and ecology This snail is restricted to old long-established calcareous wetlands, usually bordering rivers or lakes. Normally it lives in grasses and sedges (e.g. *Glyceria maxima* or *Carex*) close to the ground, but in autumn it may ascend taller vegetation such as *Phragmites*.

Status	This is now a rare and declining species. In the earlier part of the Postglacial period it was much more widely distributed, reaching as far north as Yorkshire. Its retreat is probably partly due to lower temperatures (the species is near the northern limit of its European range) but habitat loss is undoubtedly the main cause. Although still known from about 25 sites, nearly all must be considered vulnerable and several others are known to have been lost in recent years. It is considered Endangered in Europe (Collins & Wells 1987).

Threats Fen drainage and river management schemes. The species appears to be more sensitive than some marsh *Vertigo* (e.g. *V. antivertigo* (Draparnaud)) to habitat disturbance and is scarcely known to colonise secondary man-made sites. This species is in decline throughout Europe, in part due to falling temperatures since the climatic optimum. A population at Share Marsh, near Lowestoft, East Suffolk, was lost when the grazing levels were drained and converted to arable agriculture in the early 1980s (I.F.G. McLean pers. comm.).

Conservation Currently known from eleven SSSIs in England, including six nature reserves: Bure Marshes NNR in Norfolk, Surlingham Broad (Norfolk Trust), Market Weston Fen, Carlton Marshes (both Suffolk Trust), Sawbridgeworth Marsh (held jointly by the Essex Trust and the Herts and Middlesex Trust) and Wicken Fen, Cambridgeshire (National Trust).

Author M.P. Kerney.

VERTIGO MODESTA   ENDANGERED

Phylum MOLLUSCA   Order STYLOMMATOPHORA
Class GASTROPODA   Family VERTIGINIDAE

Vertigo modesta (Say, 1824), formerly known as *V. arctica* Wallenberg.

Identification Kerney & Cameron (1979).

Distribution This is a circumpolar Holarctic species. In Europe, it is almost entirely northern montane and high Alpine. In Britain, it is known from only a single locality, discovered in 1987, at 980 metres on Geal Charn in the Ben Alder range southwest of Dalwhinnie in south Inverness-shire (Marriott & Marriott 1988). *V. modesta* was found living at two spots, about 50 metres apart.

Habitat and ecology The site lies in a north-facing corrie. The vegetation is low heath/scrub, including *Salix lanata*, *S. reticulata* and *Dryas octopetala*. The substrate is limestone. The habitat is broadly similar to those where *V. modesta* lives in the Scandinavian mountains.

Status The species is clearly a glacial relict in Britain. Though further colonies may perhaps be discovered by diligent search elsewhere at high elevations, this type of base-rich habitat is uncommon in the Scottish mountains and the species is likely to be extremely rare in the British Isles.

Threats Any disturbance of the site, as by trampling or by change in land-use.

Author M.P. Kerney.

VERTIGO LILLJEBORGI   RARE

Phylum MOLLUSCA   Order STYLOMMATOPHORA
Class GASTROPODA   Family VERTIGINIDAE

Vertigo lilljeborgi (Westerlund, 1871).

Identification Ellis (1969); Kerney & Cameron (1979).

Distribution On the Continent, this species is restricted to Scandinavia, where it is relatively common. In Britain, it lives in widely scattered places in the highland zone: in Wales, the English Lake District and southern and central Scotland. Records exist for 25 vice-counties. A British distribution map is given in Kerney (1976).

Habitat and ecology *V. lilljeborgi* lives in saturated, decaying vegetation in *Carex* and *Juncus* swamps, sometimes shaded by alders. Most sites are at the margins of lakes and on river floodplains, always in places subject to periodic deep natural flooding (an unusual necessity for this species). Occasionally it is found in small enclosed bogs. It tolerates acidic conditions, and is only rarely associated with other species of *Vertigo* (occasionally with *V. antivertigo* (Draparnaud)) (Kevan & Waterston 1933; Dance 1972; Long 1974; Chater 1985; D.T. Holyoak pers. comm.).

Status This is a boreo-alpine relict, formerly more widely distributed in the British Isles. Though still fairly widespread, it is declining and some populations have disappeared in the last fifty years.

Threats The principal threat comes from the raising or stabilisation of water levels in lakes and rivers for the creation of reservoirs or hydro-electric schemes. Agricultural drainage may also be damaging, and the very isolated Welsh sites in Carmarthenshire and Cardiganshire are particularly vulnerable. Afforestation is continuing in the British uplands, and the acidification of water caused by extensive conifer plantations is possibly a threat to this mollusc.

Conservation   Seven of its sites have a degree of protection: Cors Erddreiniog, Anglesey, is an NNR; Blelham Bog, Westmorland, is an NNR and National Trust property; Loweswater, Cumberland, and Loughrigg Tarn, Westmorland, are National Trust properties; and Sunbiggin Tarn, Westmorland, Loch Moraig, East Perthshire, and Loch Cill Chriosd, North Ebudes, are SSSIs.

Author   M.P. Kerney.

VERTIGO GENESII   ENDANGERED

Phylum MOLLUSCA   Order STYLOMMATOPHORA
Class GASTROPODA   Family VERTIGINIDAE

Vertigo genesii (Gredler, 1853).

Identification   Kerney & Cameron (1979).

Distribution   On the Continent, this species is virtually restricted to the Alps and to the mountains of central Scandinavia. It is very local throughout its range. In Britain, it is known living at a single site only: Widdybank Fell, Teesdale, Co. Durham. The population is apparently very small.

Habitat and ecology   In Teesdale, *V. genesii* lives among mosses and low-growing sedges (mainly *Carex demissa*) in an alkaline flush fed by springs within a gentle hillside depression at 495 metres altitude. In winter, the hollow may fill with up to 10 metres of drifted snow. Relict Arctic-Alpine plants, most notably bog sandwort *Minuartia stricta*, occur close by, though apparently not in direct association with *V. genesii* (Coles & Colville 1980). The Teesdale habitat is typical of those where *V. genesii* occurs in the Swedish mountains.

Status   Like *V. geyeri* Lindholm (*q.v.* below), this is a glacial relict species, once abundant in lowland England. It rapidly became extinct in the lowlands in the early Postglacial period as the result of climatic change. In Europe, this species is considered Vulnerable (Collins & Wells 1987).

Threats   Habitat change of any kind, including hydrological change. There is no obvious immediate threat to the colony, though its small size renders it vulnerable to accidental damage, for example by human or animal trampling. The Teesdale Way, a new long-distance footpath, may be routed through Widdybank Fell and there are fears that this could lead to major erosion as has occurred along the Pennine Way. A large acreage of the adjacent valley, which

Widdybank Fell, Upper Teesdale NNR, Co. Durham. This area of sugar limestone with base-rich flushes, famous for its relict arctic-alpine flora, also supports the only known British colony of the mollusc *Vertigo genesii*, another relict species which was abundant in lowland England in the glacial period. (Photo by I.F.G. McLean.)

may have supported further populations of this species, was inundated in 1970 with the construction of Cow Green Reservoir (Clapham 1978).

Conservation	The site lies within the Upper Teesdale NNR.
Author	M.P. Kerney.

VERTIGO GEYERI   ENDANGERED

Phylum MOLLUSCA   Order STYLOMMATOPHORA
Class GASTROPODA   Family VERTIGINIDAE

Vertigo geyeri Lindholm, 1925, formerly sometimes erroneously known as *Vertigo genesii*.

Identification Ellis (1969); Kerney & Cameron (1979).

Distribution This species occurs in Europe mainly in the mountains of Scandinavia and in the Swiss and Austrian Alps. It also lives in a few places in central Ireland. In Britain, it is known at one site only: near Sunbiggin Tarn, Orton Fell, Westmorland. This population was discovered too recently for inclusion in the distribution map in Kerney (1976), which shows only fossil records for Great Britain.

Habitat and ecology The English site is an open calcareous fen in a hillside depression fed by springs, although in Ireland and on the Continent *V. geyeri* also occurs in flat lowland fens. At Orton Fell, it is restricted to places relatively free from *Sphagnum* and other mosses and where there is a prolific growth of *Eleocharis quinqueflora*, *Schoenus nigricans* and the smaller *Carex* species (Coles & Colville 1979). It is associated with the Endangered species *Catinella arenaria* (Bouchard-Chantereaux) (*q.v.* above).

Status This is a glacial relict species in Britain. Fossils show that it was once common in lowland England but was exterminated in the lowlands during the Postglacial period by climatic change and drainage by man. The population at Orton Fell is probably small. The European status of this species is given as Vulnerable by Collins & Wells (1987).

Threats The unique population at Orton Fell appears to be under no particular threat, but habitat change, especially any affecting the hydrological balance of the site, must be guarded against. Excessive trampling should also be avoided.

Conservation The site is within the Sunbiggin Tarn SSSI.

Author M.P. Kerney.

VERTIGO ANGUSTIOR   ENDANGERED

Phylum MOLLUSCA   Order STYLOMMATOPHORA
Class GASTROPODA   Family VERTIGINIDAE

Vertigo angustior Jeffreys, 1830.

Identification   Ellis (1969); Kerney & Cameron (1979).

Distribution   This species occurs throughout Europe (except Scandinavia) but is very local throughout its range. In Britain, it is known to survive only at Martlesham Creek and Fritton Marshes, East Suffolk; Market Weston Fen, West Suffolk; Flordon Common, East Norfolk; Whiteford Burrows and Oxwich Burrows, Glamorgan; and Gait Barrows, West Lancashire. Other sites have been lost. Several of the extant populations are too recently discovered to be included in the distribution map in Kerney (1976).

Habitat and ecology   *V. angustior* lives in marshy ground of high, even humidity, subject neither to periodic desiccation nor to deep or prolonged flooding. It requires unshaded conditions and inhabits short vegetation composed of grasses, mosses or low herbs quickly warmed by the sun. The vegetation may be grazed. It has been found in boggy grassland (e.g. Flordon Common), in coastal marshes (e.g. Whiteford Burrows) and in the depressions of a limestone pavement (Gait Barrows) (Norris & Colville 1974; Marriott & Marriott 1982; Killeen 1983; Preece & Willing 1984).

Status   *V. angustior* is a species in serious decline. Fossils show that it was abundant in the open landscapes of lowland Britain at the beginning of the Postglacial period, its habitats later being largely suppressed by mid-Postglacial forest growth. Existing sites probably represent chance survivals in places which escaped a dense tree cover and where hydrological conditions remain unaltered. In Europe this species is considered to be Vulnerable (Collins & Wells 1987).

Threats   All habitats are fragile and may be easily destroyed by drainage, afforestation or other changes in land-use. The main danger lies in any disturbance of the very delicate hydrological conditions essential to this species. At Oxwich, natural erosion of the dunes has altered the tidal pattern, leading to increased deposition of sediment, which is gradually raising the land surface at the dune— saltmarsh transition zone. This is slowly leading to drier conditions, and the vegetation is now becoming rather rank with some scrub encroachment. Seepage from the dunes keeps the transition zone damp, but this could fail in a drought year.

Conservation   Gait Barrows, Whiteford Burrows and Oxwich Burrows are NNRs. Flordon Common and Market Weston Fen are SSSIs, the latter also

Whiteford NNR, Glamorgan. The upper saltmarsh supports the spider *Baryphyma gowerense* and the largest British population of the snail *Vertigo angustior*. The latter occurs where fresh water seeps onto the saltmarsh from the dunes, an unusual feature of this site. Horse-grazing maintains the open vegetation. (Photo by J.H. Bratton.)

being a Suffolk Trust reserve. At Oxwich, it may be necessary to implement some scrub clearance and mowing, or preferably light grazing, in order to reinstate the short turf.

Author   M.P. Kerney, using information from M.R. Hughes and M.J. Willing (pers. comms).

LAURIA SEMPRONII   ENDANGERED

Phylum MOLLUSCA   Order STYLOMMATOPHORA
Class GASTROPODA   Family PUPILLIDAE

Lauria sempronii (Charpentier, 1837).

Identification   Kerney & Cameron (1979).

Distribution   This is a south European species, mainly Pyrenean and Alpine. In Britain, it is known living only at one place between Cirencester and Stroud, East Gloucestershire. The colony is of limited extent. It was formerly also present at another East Gloucestershire site, Haresfield Beacon. The map in Kerney (1976) shows only the latter colony and the sites of Flandrian (Postglacial) fossils.

Habitat and ecology   At its single surviving site, *L. sempronii* inhabits a massive old limestone boundary wall, occurring among *Sedum*, *Hedera* and *Geranium robertianum* (Long 1986). Though unshaded by trees, the wall is in a relatively moist, sheltered situation on a valley side. On the Continent, this species is found also in woods and among natural rocks.

Status   In spite of its present biogeographical isolation, the British population is probably native. There are late Postglacial fossils known from southeast England. *L. sempronii* was first discovered living in this country at Haresfield Beacon in 1894, though the specimens were not recognised until 1971 (Kerney & Norris 1972). Recent searches of the area around Haresfield Beacon, a mixture of deciduous woodland, calcareous grassland, and limestone rocks and walls, have been fruitless.

Threats   Removal of the wall or damage to it, for example by over-vigorous stripping of ivy and other vegetation.

Conservation   The owner of the wall is aware of the site's importance and is sympathetic towards the snail's conservation. Part of Haresfield Beacon is National Trust property. It is also a geological SSSI, which gives a degree of protection against gross alteration of the site.

Author   M.P. Kerney.

73

ENA MONTANA

RARE

Phylum MOLLUSCA
Class GASTROPODA

Order STYLOMMATOPHORA
Family ENIDAE

Ena montana (Draparnaud, 1801).

Identification Ellis (1969); Kerney & Cameron (1979).

Distribution This species is mainly central European and Alpine. Scattered populations occur in England in Somerset, Gloucestershire, Wiltshire, Hampshire, Hertfordshire, Oxfordshire and West Suffolk. There are old records from West Sussex, Berkshire and Buckinghamshire, but no specimens have been found at these sites in recent years. A distribution map for Britain is given in Kerney (1976).

Habitat and ecology *E. montana* is principally a species of old deciduous woods on well-drained calcareous soils. It lives among ground litter and fallen timber, but in wet weather will climb a few feet up smooth tree trunks, especially of beech and ash. It also lives in ancient hedgerows, and in the Mendips it can be found in hazel or ash scrub among limestone rocks (Boycott 1939). At one site in Suffolk it survives in an old grassy ditch, unshaded by hedges (D.T. Holyoak pers. comm.). Populations are rarely large, though at one anomalous site at Buntingford, Hertfordshire, it abounds in a roadside ditch among rubbish and nettles.

Status This species had a considerably wider distribution in southern Britain during the Neolithic and Bronze Age periods, probably helped by the higher summer temperatures then prevailing. Since then it has progressively declined. Populations are now very scattered, with the greatest concentration in the Cotswolds. Some sites are relatively secure, but many, especially in hedgerows, are at risk from modern agricultural practices.

Threats Clear-felling or large-scale replanting of deciduous woodland, including its conversion to conifer plantation; removal of dead timber; and removal of hedgerows. Felling of timber as part of the normal woodland cropping cycle need not be damaging provided that it does not involve extensive areas at one time, heavy machinery is not allowed to devastate the woodland floor, and refuges are left from which recolonisation can occur.

Conservation Occurs at sixteen sites which are SSSIs, nature reserves and/or National Trust properties, including at least three woods within Cotswold Commons and Beechwoods NNR.

Author M.P. Kerney.

TANDONIA RUSTICA

Phylum MOLLUSCA
Class GASTROPODA

INSUFFICIENTLY KNOWN

Order STYLOMMATOPHORA
Family MILACIDAE

Tandonia rustica (Millet, 1843), formerly known as *Milax rusticus* (Millet) or *Milax marginatus* (Draparnaud).

Identification

Kerney & Cameron (1979).

Distribution

This species is widely distributed in central and eastern Europe. In Britain, it is known from one site only: One Tree Hill, near Sevenoaks, West Kent, where it was discovered in 1986 (Philp 1987). Only two specimens have been found, despite careful searching on three or more occasions.

Habitat and ecology

On the Continent, *T. rustica* frequents woods and uncultivated places, mainly on calcareous soils. Unlike its close relations, the common *T. sowerbyi* (Ferussac) and *T. budapestensis* (Hazay), it shows no obvious association with man. At One Tree Hill it was found under fallen timber in old deciduous woodland on Cretaceous limestone (Kentish Ragstone).

Status

This is a slug of distinctive appearance and is therefore likely to be genuinely rare in Britain, rather than merely overlooked. Its restriction to 'wild' habitats makes it unlikely to be a casual introduction into Britain, though this cannot be ruled out at present.

Threats

The destruction of its woodland habitat and the removal of dead timber and ground litter. The traditional woodland cycle of selective felling and replanting is unlikely to be damaging to the population of *T. rustica* provided that only small blocks of trees are felled within the larger total stand and natural regeneration is allowed or replanting is with trees native to the site. Clear-felling of a whole wood and the churning of the litter layer by heavy machinery would present a serious threat. Replanting with conifers would probably eliminate *T. rustica*. Colonisation or recolonisation over open ground between woodlands is unlikely to occur.

Conservation

The second British specimen was found within the National Trust's property at One Tree Hill and both were within the One Tree Hill and Bitchet Common SSSI. The scarp here supports much woodland, most of which is probably ancient, so there is a large area which may support *T. rustica*. During felling operations, a small proportion of trunks left to pass through the decay cycle on the woodland floor would probably be beneficial to this and many other woodland invertebrates. The plateau woodland at One Tree Hill suffered extensive damage in the hurricane of October 1987 but the scarp woodland was less seriously affected.

Author	M.P. Kerney, with additional information from K.N.A. Alexander and E.G. Philp (pers. comms).

LACINIARIA BIPLICATA   RARE

Phylum MOLLUSCA	Order STYLOMMATOPHORA
Class GASTROPODA	Family CLAUSILIIDAE

Laciniaria biplicata (Montagu, 1803), formerly known as *Clausilia biplicata* (Montagu).

Identification	Ellis (1969); Kerney & Cameron (1979).
Distribution	The species is mainly central European, with outposts extending westwards to Holland, Belgium and northeast France. In Britain, it lives in a few places on the banks of the River Thames in or near London (Kew, Richmond, Isleworth, Chiswick, Purfleet). There are old records, mostly nineteenth century, from a much wider area of southern England, from Somerset to Cambridgeshire. A distribution map appears in Kerney (1976).
Habitat and ecology	*L. biplicata* inhabits ground litter, usually under willow trees or in nettle beds. Most sites are near water though not in marshy places (Boycott 1929). At Purfleet, South Essex, it lives on a dry overgrown chalk bank. It is commonly associated with human rubbish and with synanthropic molluscs such as *Tandonia budapestensis* (Hazay) and *Oxychilus draparnaudi* (Beck). It has been successfully established in gardens on a number of occasions.
Status	The history of *L. biplicata* in Britain is not clear, though its synanthropic habit suggests that it may be an old accidental introduction. It has been found in deposits of Roman age in London. It is now declining. In London many nineteenth century localities have been obliterated by riverside development (Castell 1962). Elsewhere in England attempts to refind it at several old localities have failed, including the type locality for the species, Easton Grey, North Wiltshire. The most recent record outside London is from Bickenhall, South Somerset, in 1945 (Turner 1950).
Threats	The few known surviving sites are all within the built-up area of London and vulnerable to destruction by riverside development. For instance, housing development has destroyed its habitat at Nazareth House, Isleworth, where it was found in 1985 (A.C. Cade pers. comm.).
Conservation	Isleworth Ait, Middlesex, which supports *L. biplicata*, is covered by a voluntary conservation agreement with the London Wildlife Trust.
Author	M.P. Kerney.

76

MONACHA CARTUSIANA

RARE

Phylum MOLLUSCA
Class GASTROPODA

Order STYLOMMATOPHORA
Family HELICIDAE

Monacha cartusiana (Muller, 1774), formerly known as *Helix cartusiana* Muller or *Theba cartusiana* (Muller).

Identification   Ellis (1969); Kerney & Cameron (1979).

Distribution   This is principally a Mediterranean and southeast European species. It lives in a few places in East and West Sussex, East Kent and East Suffolk. There are older records from South Hampshire, Surrey, West Suffolk and East Norfolk. Populations are usually sharply defined. Kerney (1976) gives a distribution map.

Habitat and ecology   *M. cartusiana* lives in open, unshaded places on calcareous soils. Most colonies are in dry short-turfed chalk grassland, but it has also been found in rather moister places, among grass, nettles and weeds of waste ground on road banks, by ploughed fields and in alluvial pastures by the sea. It tends, however, to avoid stands of tall 'hay meadow' character. At Deal, East Kent, it is locally abundant in grassy vegetation on sandhills.

Status   This species was almost certainly accidentally introduced to Britain from southern Europe by prehistoric (Neolithic) farmers. Fossils show that it was once more widely distributed in southeast England, being frequent on the chalk of the North Downs and on calcareous soils in East Anglia. Its retreat may perhaps be linked with the decline in summer temperatures since the Postglacial thermal optimum. During the past century the species has disappeared from some further areas, notably Surrey (last record Banstead Downs, 1910). Changes in farming practices are probably responsible. Essentially an opportunist 'weed species' at the edge of its European range, *M. cartusiana* is not at serious risk of disappearing altogether from Britain, though individual populations may be ephemeral, responding to short-term climatic changes and human pressures.

Threats   Habitat disturbance or destruction, especially loss of short-turfed chalk grassland. Much downland in the south of England has been ploughed for arable agriculture in recent decades, and many of the surviving fragments are being lost to hawthorn scrub owing to the decline in sheep-farming.

Conservation   Known from Sandwich Bay and Hacklinge Marshes SSSI, East Kent, including the reserves of the Kent Trust and RSPB; Lydden and Temple Ewell Downs SSSI and LNR, also East Kent; Wilmington Downs SSSI and Lewes Brooks SSSI, East Sussex; and Amberley Mount to Sullington Hill SSSI, West Sussex. In 1959, it occurred at

Mount Caburn NNR, East Sussex, part of the South Downs, whose mollusc fauna includes several threatened species. Large areas of herb-rich downland turf have been lost to arable agriculture (like the freshly sown field on former downland in the middle distance) and to scrub invasion where grazing ceases (seen inside the fence-line around the quarry). (Photo by P. Wakely.)

Farlington Marshes, now an LNR within the Langstone Harbour SSSI, South Hampshire. Three of its sites are National Trust properties. This species appears to thrive on very closely grazed downland (M.J. Willing pers. comm.) and thus should benefit from the management regimes used for downland butterflies.

Author   M.P. Kerney.

PERFORATELLA RUBIGINOSA   VULNERABLE

Phylum MOLLUSCA   Order STYLOMMATOPHORA
Class GASTROPODA   Family HELICIDAE

Perforatella rubiginosa (Schmidt, 1853)

Identification   Adam (1960); Kerney & Cameron (1979). Note that the shell of this species closely resembles that of *Trichia plebeia* (Draparnaud), with which it may be confused in the absence of anatomical confirmation. The habitat is nevertheless different and the ranges of the two species in Britain are not known to overlap.

Distribution   This is principally an east European and Siberian species, in Europe mainly restricted to the valleys of the Danube and the Rhine. In England, it is known from six places (in three 10 km squares). Five sites are on the floodplain of the River Thames between South Stoke, Oxfordshire, and Brentford, Middlesex. The sixth is on the River Medway floodplain at Aylesford, West Kent. It was recognised in Britain only in 1981, at Syon Marsh, Brentford, Middlesex (Verdcourt 1982; Naggs 1983). Three of the colonies are on islands in the Thames in west London (Brentford Ait West; Isleworth Ait; Corporation Island, Twickenham).

Habitat and ecology *P. rubiginosa* lives on wet river floodplains and is apparently restricted to places subject to periodic inundation. Typically, it occurs among flood rubbish in muddy, poorly vegetated ground shaded by willows; typical associates are the semi-aquatic species *Lymnaea truncatula* (Muller), *Oxyloma pfeifferi* (Rossmassler), *Zonitoides nitidus* (Muller) and *Deroceras laeve* (Muller). The colony at South Stoke is in an unshaded floodplain marsh with *Carex* tussocks.

Status   Though it is certainly under-recorded, careful searches at other appropriate sites suggest that this species is not common. It must be considered vulnerable because of the specialised nature of its habitat, which is easily altered or destroyed. A population at Pangbourne, Berkshire, from which specimens were collected in 1955, has now disappeared.

79

Threats	Habitat change, especially by flood control schemes or riverside developments.
Conservation	Syon Marsh is part of Syon Park SSSI. There has been concern that increased water abstraction from the Thames would affect the tidal range at Syon Park and increase salinity levels, but, on the basis of an environmental impact study, adverse changes at Syon Park are no longer expected (D.J. Kite pers. comm.).
Author	M.P. Kerney.

HELICODONTA OBVOLUTA   RARE

Phylum MOLLUSCA   Order STYLOMMATOPHORA
Class GASTROPODA   Family HELICIDAE

Helicodonta obvoluta (Muller, 1774), formerly known as *Helix obvoluta* Muller.

Identification	Ellis (1969); Kerney & Cameron (1979).
Distribution	This is principally a central European species and is common in much of France and Germany. In England, disjunct colonies occur in a narrow band along the escarpment face of the South Downs from Amberley, West Sussex, to Petersfield, South Hampshire (map in Cameron (1972)). There is also an isolated population at Crab Wood, near Winchester, South Hampshire, recently rediscovered. Kerney (1976) also gives a distribution map.
Habitat and ecology	*H. obvoluta* lives in beech or ash woods on chalk, in leaf litter and under logs and fallen branches. Occasionally it climbs a little way up smooth tree trunks. It is also found in ash/hazel scrub. Nearly all the remaining sites are on steep slopes (Beeston 1919; Cameron 1972).
Status	Fossils dating from the Neolithic period onwards (mainly in archaeological contexts) show that *H. obvoluta* was once more widely distributed in southern England. Its former range extended north to the Cotswolds (Chedworth, East Gloucestershire; Roman period) and west to Dorset. On the North Downs in Surrey its disappearance may be fairly recent, judging from the presence of dead shells lying on the surface in beech woods at Mickleham, near Dorking (Castell 1962). Within its main narrow range along the South Downs it remains common at a number of places and its future is reasonably secure provided that gross habitat disturbance and clear-felling are avoided. It may be noted that at least some of these Sussex woods are plantations of Georgian date.

Threats	Excessive habitat disturbance such as by clear-felling or the over-zealous removal of fallen timber.
Conservation	It is recorded from several SSSIs along the South Downs. Crab Wood is in part an SSSI and in part an LNR managed by the Hampshire and Isle of Wight Trust. *H. obvoluta* also occurs on the National Trust's property at Bignor Hill, West Sussex; and in the Hundry, a Forestry Commission plantation in the Queen Elizabeth Country Park, South Hampshire, where its conservation is written into the management plan.
Author	M.P. Kerney.

SPHAERIUM SOLIDUM   ENDANGERED

Phylum MOLLUSCA   Order VENEROIDA
Class BIVALVIA   Family SPHAERIIDAE

Sphaerium solidum (Normand, 1844).

Identification	Ellis (1978).
Distribution	This is mainly a central and eastern European species. In all countries where it occurs it is reported to be local. In England, it has been found at several places along about 15 km of the River Witham in Lincolnshire, between Brothertoft and Kirkstead. It was discovered in the Witham only in 1968. The distribution is mapped in Kerney (1976).
Habitat and ecology	*S. solidum* has been found along the River Witham both in the main channel and immediately adjacent to it in deep drains opening into the river via sluices. The river itself is canalised, artificially deepened and straightened. In spite of its turbidity, it has a molluscan fauna of the richest kind. Most of the specimens of *S. solidum* so far recovered have been of dead (though perfectly fresh) shells, probably moved by currents from their position of life (Redshaw & Norris 1974). On one occasion it was collected alive in a deep drain, on silty mud bare of vegetation (D.T. Holyoak pers. comm.).
Status	Though no Postglacial fossils of *S. solidum* are yet known from Britain, it is unlikely to be a recent introduction. The populations in the Witham appear well-established and stable.
Threats	No immediate threat is apparent. Nevertheless, the restriction of this species to one stretch of a single river places the entire British population at risk from pollution upstream.
Author	M.P. Kerney.

81

PISIDIUM PSEUDOSPHAERIUM   RARE

Phylum MOLLUSCA   Order VENEROIDA
Class BIVALVIA   Family SPHAERIIDAE

Pisidium pseudosphaerium Schlesch, 1947.

Identification   Ellis, 1978.

Distribution   Abroad, this species occurs mainly in the lowlands between the Alps and south Scandinavia. It is very local throughout its range. In Britain, a few widely separated populations are known from the Pevensey and Lewes Levels, East Sussex; Staines, Middlesex; Minsmere River marsh, East Suffolk; the Caldicot Levels, Monmouthshire; Moccas Park, Herefordshire; the Wirral, Cheshire; and Croft-on-Tees, Northwest Yorkshire. There is also an old (1906) record from the Somerset Levels at Glastonbury. These are mapped in Kerney (1976).

Habitat and ecology   *P. pseudosphaerium* lives in marsh drains and ponds. Its habitat is specialised and essentially of transient character: clear clean water in stagnant places choked with aquatic plants, often over a richly organic, even anaerobic, bottom. It frequently occurs with *P. obtusale* (Lamarck) and *P. milium* Held, but rarely with other species of *Pisidium* (Kuiper 1949; Dance 1956, 1957). In southern England, it frequents places containing rare, relict molluscs, notably in the Pevensey and Lewes Levels (with *Valvata macrostoma* Morch, *Anisus vorticulus* (Troschel) and *Segmentina nitida* (Muller)) and at Staines (with *A. vorticulus*) (*q.v.* above for these species).

Status   *P. pseudosphaerium* is under-recorded. Nevertheless, it shows signs of having a relict distribution and it is likely that passive dispersal does not occur easily outside limited areas in which refuges exist. It must be considered at potential risk.

Threats   Drainage of levels; elimination or 'improvement' of stagnant ponds and ditches; eutrophication. Shortwood Pond, Staines, is used by anglers and has botanical interest, and the needs of both may conflict with maintaining the habitat of *P. pseudosphaerium*. The Lewes Levels have suffered from conversion of unimproved pasture to arable land or reseeding and application of fertilisers, with a consequent loss of water quality in the ditches (B. Banks pers. comm.).

Conservation   Moccas Park is an NNR and sites at Pevensey lie partly within an NNR. Parts of the Lewes Levels are an SSSI. This species requires waters choked with aquatic plants. The succession of the ditch flora (the hydrosere) needs to be allowed to progress further than would be the usual practice if ditch management was geared to the needs of land drainage, and indeed further than may be considered usual even on nature reserves. However, it is vital that ditch management does not lapse completely, as the preferred habitat is only a temporary stage in the hydrosere and will be lost in the absence of any management. Short stretches of ditch should be cleared of vegetation on a long rotation, as this ensures that all stages of the hydrosere are always represented. The same principle can be applied to pond management, with only a segment of the pond being cleared in any one year.

Author	M.P. Kerney.

PISIDIUM TENUILINEATUM   RARE

Phylum MOLLUSCA   Order VENEROIDA
Class DIVALVIA   Family SPHAERIIDAE

Pisidium tenuilineatum Stelfox, 1918.

Identification	Ellis (1978).
Distribution	On the Continent, this is considered a rare species, occurring in the area between the Mediterranean and southernmost Sweden. In Britain, *P. tenuilineatum* has been found in scattered localities mainly in central southern England and the Welsh borders (fifteen vice-counties). It is extinct in many places. A distribution map for Britain appears in Kerney (1976).
Habitat and ecology	*P. tenuilineatum* lives mainly in canals and lowland rivers. It has twice also been found in large ponds (South Harting, West Sussex (Kerney 1970) and Aymestrey, Herefordshire). Numbers of individuals are usually low at any site. On the Continent it is reported also from limestone springs, a type of habitat in which it has not yet been found living in Britain though it occurs as a fossil in early Postglacial spring deposits in Kent and in the Isle of Wight.
Status	This species shows evident signs of a decline and must be considered at risk. North of London, in Buckinghamshire, Bedfordshire and Northamptonshire, only dead shells have been recovered in recent years in spite of deliberate searching, although associated species of *Pisidium* remain unaffected. This area includes the type locality of the species (Grand Union Canal, Marsworth, Buckinghamshire (Stelfox 1918)).
Threats	The reason for the disappearance of this species from some sites, especially in canals, is not clear.
Conservation	Occurs within the Itchen Valley (Winchester Meadows) SSSI, South Hampshire.
Author	M.P. Kerney.

ANNELIDA

The four classes of the phylum Annelida are Archiannelida, Polychaeta, Oligochaeta and Hirudinea. Only the Hirudinea (leeches) are considered fully in this book. One species of polychaete annelid is also included.

The sixteen species of leeches occurring in Britain are moderately well recorded largely owing to the availability of illustrated identification keys (Mann 1954; Elliott & Mann 1979). There is no national recording scheme for leeches, but records have been collated by Dr J.M. Elliott of the Freshwater Biological Association and deposited at the Biological Records Centre, Monks Wood. A provisional atlas has been produced (Elliott & Tullett 1982). Two species are considered at risk in Britain and have been included in this Red Data Book, though there is an element of doubt about one and it has been placed in category K.

It is widely believed that leeches are blood-sucking parasites, but only six British species feed on the blood of vertebrates, the rest being predators on other invertebrates. The Medicinal Leech *Hirudo medicinalis* L. (RDB 3) and *Placobdella costata* (Fr. Muller) (RDB K) are the only species likely to draw blood from humans.

Most species of leech complete their life cycle in one year, though *Hirudo medicinalis* probably takes at least two years to reach the breeding stage. Leeches produce gelatinous or hard cocoons around their eggs. There may be one or many eggs per cocoon, depending on the species. These cocoons may be attached to the substratum, or a few species carry them on the ventral surface of the body until the eggs hatch. The period to hatching is usually one or a few weeks. Elliott & Mann (1979) summarise the ecology of the British species, citing Mann (1962) and numerous autecological papers as sources of further details. Sawyer (1986) provides a detailed account of leech biology and behaviour.

The Polychaeta are a predominantly marine class of annelids with no freshwater representatives in Britain but a number of brackish-water species. A comprehensive survey of brackish lagoons organised by the NCC in the mid-1980s has suggested that a small number of the polychaetes of this habitat are scarce, but only one, *Armandia cirrhosa* Filippi, has been included in this Red Data Book. Among marine biologists, polychaetes are a moderately popular group for study, warranting the production of the Polychaete Research Newsletter (available from Dr C.J. Mettam, School of Pure and Applied Biology, University of Wales College of Cardiff). A well-illustrated identification guide to three orders has recently been published (George & Hartmann-Schroder 1985), but for the remainder it is necessary to consult less readily available works such as Fauvel (1923, 1927).

Further studies may reveal Red Data Book candidates in the other groups within the Annelida. Earthworms (suborder Lumbricina within the class Oligochaeta) include a number of species with very few British records, but in such a poorly recorded group this is considered insufficient evidence that they are under threat. The production of a new identification work, Sims & Gerard (1985), may encourage more naturalists to study earthworms. There is the possibility that earthworms could be useful tools to the conservationist if some species are indicators of undisturbed soils, thereby pointing to areas with habitat continuity.

The aquatic Oligochaeta are covered by an FBA key (Brinkhurst 1971), but few freshwater biologists attempt identifications of this group and there are insufficient data on which to select species for this Red Data Book.

ARMANDIA CIRRHOSA

Lagoon Sandworm

INSUFFICIENTLY KNOWN

Phylum ANNELIDA
Class POLYCHAETA

Order OPHELIIDA
Family OPHELIIDAE

Armandia cirrhosa Filippi, 1861, formerly known as *A. cirrosa*.

Identification

Fauvel (1927) gives a brief description. Amoureux (1983) provides a summary of the species in the genus.

Distribution

In Britain, known only from Eight Acre Pond, Lymington, South Hampshire. It is also recorded from the Mediterranean (e.g. in the Alfaques inlet of the R. Ebro delta, Spain (Capaccioni-Azzati pers. comm.)), the Adriatic at Trieste, and Madeira.

Habitat and ecology

In Britain it occurs in brackish water of a salinity close to full-strength sea water, in shingle and sand sediments. The proportion of shingle in the sediments of Eight Acre Pond is unusually high, which may explain why it is restricted to this pond when shingle is not uncommon in south coast lagoons. There is no freshwater inflow to Eight Acre Pond. The two outflows are controlled by sluices with a tidal flap, which reduce tidal fluctuation to 10-20 cm, with the result that virtually no bottom sediment is exposed at low tide. However, in some winters the pond has been drained for several months in order to reduce wave erosion of the banks and to provide feeding areas for wading birds. In summer 1985 *A. cirrhosa* occurred at a mean abundance of 443 per square metre, with a maximum of 2,250 per square metre. The total population was estimated to be fifteen to sixteen million individuals. This species appears to have an annual life cycle; thus large seasonal and annual fluctuations in the population size are to be expected. In the Alfaques inlet, it was found in sand at a salinity of 36.6 parts per thousand.

Status

Although a large population may be less vulnerable than a small one, the fact that the known population is confined to one water body makes this species very susceptible to habitat modification. In view of its possibly being restricted to one pond, it may qualify for the Endangered category. Fauvel (1927) suggested that *A. cirrhosa* may be merely immature *A. polyophthalma* Kukenthal, but *A. cirrhosa* has now been confirmed as a species in its own right.

Threats

Rebuilding of the sea wall between Keyhaven and Lymington may affect Eight Acre Pond. Any attempts to isolate the pond from seawater incursion or lower the salinity by other means would be detrimental. There is a belief that, because brackish pools have a less diverse fauna than freshwater pools, conversion to fresh water improves their conservation value. This is a misconception in many cases, as the brackish fauna is often much more threatened than the freshwater fauna which could be expected to colonise. During the summer Eight Acre Pond is used as a boating lake, and this may carry the risk of pollution if motorboats are used.

Conservation   In 1988 *A. cirrhosa* was protected by its addition to Schedule 5 of the Wildlife and Countryside Act 1981. Eight Acre Pond lies within the Hurst Castle and Lymington River Estuary SSSI and is owned by Hampshire County Council. This pond supports two other species listed in Schedule 5, *Nematostella vectensis* Stephenson and *Gammarus insensibilis* Stock, and the stonewort *Lamprothamnium papulosum* (Wallr.) J. Groves, which is included in Schedule 8. In view of this rich assemblage, the conservation of these lower forms of life should take precedence when decisions on the management regime are made. A study of the ecology of *A. cirrhosa* is proposed, to be funded by the NCC. Any moves to increase the recreational use of the pond need to be carefully assessed for their potential effects on the pond's wildlife. The desirability of continuing to drain the pond in winter also needs to be examined.

Author   J.H. Bratton, using information from Sheader & Sheader (undated), R. Capaccioni-Azzati, S. Chambers, P. Garwood, A.S.Y. Mackie, C.J. Mettam and R. Mitchell (pers. comms) and an information sheet prepared for the NCC by M. Sheader.

PLACOBDELLA COSTATA   INSUFFICIENTLY KNOWN

Phylum ANNELIDA   Order RHYNCHOBDELLIDA
Class HIRUDINEA   Family GLOSSIPHONIIDAE

Placobdella costata (Fr. Muller, 1846), formerly known as *Haementeria costata*.

Identification   Elliott & Mann (1979).

Distribution   In 1975 a single female was found upstream of Rickney pumping station on the Hurst Haven, East Sussex, which takes water from a number of lowland streams draining the Pevensey Levels. The leech could have drifted from these streams. The second British record was from flooded pasture in Ridham Marshes, East Kent, in 1989. Abroad, *P. costata* has been recorded from around the Baltic, Mediterranean, Black and Caspian Seas, and in Poland, Hungary and Holland.

Habitat and ecology   In Europe, this species has been found in almost all types of fresh water, including ponds, ditches, lakes, springs, streams and rivers. It usually occurs where aquatic macrophytes are present. It is a blood-sucking leech, reported to feed on terrapins, frogs, waterbirds and mammals, including man. It has been used as a medicinal leech in the Crimea. Feeding can take up to two hours, and the process can increase the leech's weight by a factor of seven. Satiated leeches and those carrying eggs tend to remain amongst stones on the bottom, whilst hungry leeches and those carrying young are usually attached to the leaves of aquatic plants and are thus in a position to attack a host. This would suggest that leeches carrying young could be dispersed by waterfowl. Breeding takes place in summer. The life cycle in the field can take one, two or three years, and specimens have survived for up to two and a half years in the laboratory.

Status

Only one adult specimen was found in the Pevensey Levels. This was a female carrying seventy-eight young, so possibly there is a breeding population in the vicinity. An alternative explanation is that it had recently arrived in the area, having been transported by a bird. The Kent specimen could also have been a recent arrival and it remains in doubt whether *P. costata* is an established British species. The Pevensey Levels have been extensively surveyed for aquatic invertebrates without further specimens of *P. costata* being found.

Threats

The Pevensey Levels drainage system receives high inputs of nutrients from arable run-off and sewage works. This may have an adverse effect on the fauna and flora of the drainage ditches. Ridham Marshes are threatened by industrial development.

Conservation

Parts of the Pevensey Levels are protected as an SSSI and NNR. The ditches in this area are isolated as much as possible from eutrophication and continue to support a rich community of aquatic plants and animals. Ridham Marshes lie within the Swale SSSI. Lack of hosts is unlikely to be a problem at either site in view of the wide range of vertebrates used by *P. costata*.

Authors

J.H. Bratton and J.M. Elliott, using information from Elliott, Mugridge & Stallybrass (1979), who cite the studies of Wilkialis (1970, 1973), and from E.G. Philp (unpublished).

HIRUDO MEDICINALIS   RARE

Medicinal Leech

Phylum ANNELIDA   Order GNATHOBDELLIDA
Class HIRUDINEA   Family HIRUDINIDAE

Hirudo medicinalis Linnaeus, 1758.

Identification

Elliott & Mann (1979).

Distribution

Records are scattered throughout Great Britain. There are post-1980 records from Islay, South Ebudes; Main Argyllshire;

Hatchet Pond, New Forest SSSI, South Hampshire. Shallow warm weedy pools support the internationally threatened Medicinal Leech *Hirudo medicinalis*. The grazing stock of the New Forest may act as hosts to the leech, though waterfowl and amphibians are also important food sources. Such base-poor pools also support the snail *Lymnaea glabra*. (Photo by P. Wakely.)

Westmorland (two sites); Glamorgan; Anglesey; East Norfolk; Dorset; the New Forest, South Hampshire; East Sussex; and East Kent (several water bodies, two sites). *H. medicinalis* is known in recent years from 24 European countries but is very scarce in France and Belgium and probably extinct in Ireland (Elliott & Tullett 1984; Wells, Elliott & Tullett 1984). Distribution maps for Great Britain are given by Elliott & Tullett (1982, 1984). The latter paper also shows the European distribution.

Habitat and ecology The typical habitat is a eutrophic lake or pond with dense stands of waterplants. Adults feed on the blood of mammals, birds, amphibians and small fish, but the degree of reliance on each type of host is not known. Their feeding behaviour has long been utilised in medical practice for drawing blood from a patient (phlebotomy). At Lydd, East Kent, waterbirds and amphibians are the main hosts. The leeches are attracted to disturbances in the water and it is by this means that the hosts are located. A large mammal such as a cow or deer is unlikely to suffer harm from a leech, but, in the case of toads and newts, death has been reported. A leech can take blood up to five times its own weight in a meal which is then digested slowly over several months; thus blood meals need only be very infrequent. Egg cocoons are laid on the shore just above the water line and have been found in July and August. At Lydd, cocoons were laid just below the ground surface among the roots of *Epilobium hirsutum* in a band 60-95 cm from the water line. One leech can lay up to seven cocoons, and up to thirty eggs can develop in a cocoon. Hatching takes four to ten weeks depending on temperature. Optimum conditions for activity, growth and breeding include quite high water temperatures, above 19°C (see Elliott & Tullett 1986). Tadpoles are an important food source for young Medicinal Leeches. Breeding is unlikely to occur before two years of age and the life span is thought to be at least four years.

Status Though it has been declared extinct in Britain twice this century (Harding 1910 and by implication in Sawyer 1981), there are recent confirmed records from several sites, with the population at Lydd thought to number several thousand. There are probably no more than twenty isolated populations remaining in Great Britain. The release of imported leeches has boosted British populations in the past. *H. medicinalis* is classed as Indeterminate in *The IUCN Invertebrate Red Data Book* (Wells, Pyle & Collins 1983), meaning that it is unclear which of categories 1 to 3 is the correct designation. The European status is given as Vulnerable by Collins & Wells (1987).

Threats British hospitals used medicinal leeches in thousands in the nineteenth century. A dealer in Norwich kept a stock of about 50,000. Most were imported from abroad, often packed in damp grass in large sacks, and there was a high mortality rate (Harding 1910). It has been suggested that the leech trade is partly responsible for the wide distribution of *H. medicinalis*, since satiated leeches were often released into nearby ponds. However, this trade undoubtedly had a severe impact on the population levels, and several countries introduced export controls at that time. There is currently an upsurge in interest in the use of leeches in medicine. Live leeches are required for phlebotomy, whilst drug extraction involves destroying the leech. Sustained collecting for either purpose from most British populations could quickly eliminate them. Very little is known of the levels of international trade at present, but the pharmaceutical industry is potentially more damaging than the nineteenth century usages in that extraction of the anticoagulant hirudin requires the destruction of the leech. Other factors have probably contributed to the decline of this species. Many lowland cattle ponds have disappeared in recent decades, either because of the shift to arable agriculture or because cattle troughs and piped water have been supplied to pastures. In such instances, farm ponds frequently change to marsh or are infilled. Ponds surviving in arable areas are isolated from livestock which previously supported the adult leeches, deer possibly being the only suitable mammalian hosts remaining. Some of the Lake District tarns have been deepened to provide coldwater conditions suitable for brown trout *Salmo trutta* L., and, in view of the high temperature requirements of *H. medicinalis* for activity, growth and breeding, this lowering of the temperature regime probably accounts in part for the decline of the leech in the Lake District (see Elliott & Tullett 1986). Commercial forestry has been suggested in the catchment of the Islay site, which could lead to acidification and other forms of pollution. There are also proposals to re-establish a small reservoir using water pumped from the loch that contains leeches (E.H. Bignal pers. comm.). This would be likely to cause fluctuations in the water level in the loch, which might be detrimental to the leech colony, particularly if it eliminated the warm marginal shallows. There were plans to increase the use of the Lydd gravel pit for water sports, which would have disturbed the waterbirds upon which this largest British population of *H. medicinalis* feed. However, the conservation importance of the site was upheld at a public inquiry in 1988. Other pools near Lydd Airport which also support *H. medicinalis* are threatened with infilling as part of runway modification. A further problem at Dungeness is excessive water abstraction which is causing shallow pools to dry up more frequently.

Conservation   *Hirudo medicinalis* is protected by inclusion in Schedule 5 of the Wildlife and Countryside Act 1981. It is also included in Appendix II of the Convention on International Trade in Endangered Species of Wild Fauna and Flora (CITES) (Almada-Villela 1988), which controls by licences trade in the species when a signatory nation is involved, and in Appendix III of the Bern Convention, which offers protection in parts of Europe. There are post-1960 records from nine SSSIs. At one of these, Bookham Commons, Surrey, the leech may no longer occur, as the site is well studied and there have been no definite records since 1961, despite searches in the 1980s. (The identity of specimens seen there in 1986 remains in doubt

(Beven 1988).) Most of the water bodies near Lydd which support *H. medicinalis*, including the gravel-pit with the largest British population, lie within Dungeness SSSI, and specimens have been found within the Dungeness RSPB reserve. Other SSSIs supporting this species are Walland Marsh, East Kent; Rye Harbour, East Sussex; the New Forest, South Hampshire; Kenfig Pool (within an NNR), Glamorgan; Cors Goch (a North Wales Trust reserve) and Newborough Forest, Anglesey; the two Scottish sites; and Moccas Park NNR, Herefordshire. At the last, it was abundant in the lake in 1973 ([Foster] 1977; R.B. Angus pers. comm.). The use of the Moccas Park lake by cattle, sheep and deer probably makes it an ideal site for *Hirudo*. Formal protection for some other populations should perhaps be negotiated. Management of such sites should aim at the maintenance of submerged and marginal vegetation, strong amphibian populations to provide tadpoles on which the juvenile leeches can feed, and the availability of larger vertebrate hosts for the adult leeches. To allow the water to reach optimum breeding temperature, shading from surrounding trees should be avoided and shallow areas should be present. Sawyer (1981) suggested that mass rearing should be started to meet pharmaceutical needs or that the industry should switch to other species such as the Amazonian leech *Haementeria ghilianii* de Filippi, for which large-scale rearing is feasible.

Authors   J.H. Bratton and J.M. Elliott, using information from Sawyer (1981, 1988), Elliott & Tullett (1984), Wells, Elliott & Tullett (1984), Elliott & Tullett (1986), Morgan (1987), Wilkin (1987, 1988), Wilkin & Scofield (1990) and B. Banks, E.H. Bignal, J.G.M. Cuppen, R.A. Findon, M.J. Morgan, J.B. Ratcliffe and R.T. Sawyer (pers. comms).

MYRIAPODA

The Myriapoda consist of four groups of invertebrates given the rank of subclass or class depending on whether the Myriapoda are designated a class or an informal category. Two of these groups, the Diplopoda (millipedes) and the Chilopoda (centipedes), are dealt with here. The Symphyla and Pauropoda constitute the other two groups, but their British members have not been studied in detail and they are not assessed in this Red Data Book.

The greatest variety of millipedes is found in woodlands on base-rich soils, though they can be found in most terrestrial habitats including acid woodlands, grasslands, arable areas, sand-dunes and, in the case of *Thalassisobates littoralis* (Silvestri), the intertidal zone. The soil/litter layer boundary is the commonest micro-habitat of millipedes, vegetable detritus forming the food of most species. They thus play an important role in nutrient cycling. A few also eat living plant material such as seedling roots and can occasionally be a pest of crops. A number of millipedes can reproduce by parthenogenesis but sexual reproduction is more usual. Some females build an elaborate nest of faecal material or silk, while others coat each egg with an earthy substance. Development proceeds as soon as the egg is laid in the spring. After hatching the animal passes through up to fourteen moults, gradually increasing its number of component rings until reaching maturity. This usually takes a year and a half, being attained in the second autumn after hatching. An interesting facet of millipede biology is the ability to secrete a range of chemical defences against predation, including quinones and hydrocyanic acids.

The centipedes are predatory, feeding on other invertebrates which they immobilise by the use of powerful poison claws. The surface-dwelling species, in contrast to the millipedes, are fast-moving and agile. Other centipedes hunt in the soil crevices, a habitat to which they are adapted by having very long flexible bodies and the ability to move backwards as rapidly as forwards. Many of these subterranean species are blind. A few species are found on the shore, often intertidally, where they live in such micro-habitats as rock crevices or buried driftline litter. Two orders of centipedes, the Geophilomorpha and the Scolopendromorpha, tend their eggs until hatching and brood the young through the early stages of development, whereas in the Lithobiomorpha the eggs are camouflaged with soil particles and abandoned. The earliest stages are passed through in a matter of days after hatching, but moults then become less frequent. The full number of body segments and maturity may not be attained for two years in lithobiomorphs or three years in geophilomorphs, and the total life span may be five to six years. The chilopods are represented in most terrestrial habitats, but their greatest diversity in natural situations occurs in woodlands.

Both millipedes and centipedes colonise synanthropic sites very successfully. Refuse tips and derelict urban areas are often rich in species. Several species found in natural habitats in the south of England become exclusively synanthropic further north.

The study of myriapods has never attracted a following comparable to entomology, but there is now a growing interest in the centipedes and millipedes, co-ordinated by the British Myriapod Group. The standard identification work for British centipedes is Eason

(1964), while for millipedes Blower (1985) has now superseded Blower (1958). The BMG *Newsletter* and *Bulletin* include descriptions of additions to the British fauna. They also contain much biological and ecological information, as do Camatini (1979) and Lewis (1981). Distribution atlases have been prepared (Barber & Keay 1988; British Myriapod Group 1988), based on records submitted to the centipede and millipede recording schemes.

Despite this burgeoning data bank, the myriapods proved very difficult to assess for RDB status. Very few appear to be restricted to a particular habitat except for the coastal species, and these are in the main difficult to collect and thus probably under-recorded. While several species have seldom been found, there is often no apparent cause for their rarity and it is suspected in some cases that they are alien species accidentally imported with, for example, pot plants. *Lithobius peregrinus* Latzel, currently known only from the port of Sheerness, East Kent, is omitted for this reason. It is a Balkan species but known from several sites around the world, presumably owing to having been introduced. The dearth of information concerning the myriapod fauna of mainland Europe compounds the difficulty of judging which species occurring in Britain are within their natural world range and which are likely to be introductions. *Nesoporogaster souletina* Brolemann, recorded from the French Pyrenees, also occurs in a derelict ornamental park in Cornwall. There is the added complication in this case that the Cornish specimens differ from the typical *N. souletina* and were raised to specific status as *N. brevior* Eason by Matic & Darabantu (1969). However, as the only British record originates from an artificial habitat, there are considerable doubts about its being a native species. Also, the characters used to separate the 'species' of *Nesoporogaster* may be no more than intraspecific variations within *N. souletina* (E.H. Eason pers. comm.). In the light of these points, the Cornish *Nesoporogaster* has not been given Red Data Book status.

Several species appear to qualify for RDB status on the grounds of paucity of records but have been excluded because they are certainly under-recorded. The centipede *Brachyschendyla dentata* Brolemann & Ribaut had been found at only four sites up to September 1986 and one of these is known to have been destroyed. However, since it is an inconspicuous species living within the soil and best collected by Tullgren extraction, it is likely that only a tiny proportion of its sites have been discovered. *Pachymerium ferrugineum* (C.L. Koch), *Geophilus pusillifrater* Verhoeff and *Hydroschendyla submarina* (Grube), three coastal species with few records, have been excluded from the RDB because their habitat makes them difficult to find and there is no reason to suppose that they are rare. *P. ferrugineum* was discovered at Cuckmere Haven, East Sussex, in 1960 and then not seen again in Britain until 1989, when it was found at two other coastal shingle sites, Walberswick in East Suffolk and Newtown Bay on the Isle of Wight (Corbet 1989; Keay 1989b). In 1990 it was found again, at Porth Hellick, Isles of Scilly (A.P. Fowles pers. comm.).

One further centipede deserves mention. *Chalandea pinguis* (Brolemann) has a very restricted range in Britain, being recorded only from North Devon. (For a distribution map, see Barber 1987.) It has been found in the litter layer, in *Luzula* rhizomes and under the bark of fallen trees, always in deciduous woodland. In 1989, members of the British Myriapod Group found it in a further seven locations, making a total of nine 10 km squares from which it has been recorded, all to the north and east of Torrington. While clearly uncommon, this species cannot be considered to be a threatened member of our fauna and it is therefore not given Red Data Book status. Some of its populations are within SSSIs.

TRACHYSPHAERA LOBATA

INSUFFICIENTLY KNOWN

Phylum UNIRAMIA
Class DIPLOPODA

Order GLOMERIDA
Family TRACHYSPHAERIDAE

Trachysphaera lobata (Ribaut, 1954).

Identification Jones & Keay (1986); Demange (1981); Ribaut (1954).

Distribution In Britain, known only from the Isle of Wight, where it was discovered in 1984. It has been found at East Cliff near Bembridge and at the Duver. This species is also known from central France.

Habitat and ecology At East Cliff it was found abundantly in the soil of a small, mainly deciduous, coastal woodland within a few metres of the high tide mark. The wood is dominated by mature sycamore and has a ground flora of ivy, common nettle *Urtica dioica* and small patches of dog's mercury. The soil is acidic (pH 5.5 to 6.0) sand with shingle overlying clay at about 30 cm depth. One specimen was also found in dead wood on the woodland floor and another sieved from litter. *T. lobata* was most abundant at about 15 cm depth, where a density of 28 per 0.005 cubic metres was recorded. Only a single specimen has been found at the Duver. It was sieved from below leaf litter on sand in an area of scrub. No males have been found in Britain, so this species is probably parthenogenetic. Males are present in France.

Status There are no indications of synanthropy and no reason to think that this species is not native. Although recently discovered, being small and soil-dwelling, it could easily have been overlooked in the past. Clearly, if this is the case, it could still be escaping attention in other parts of the country and it would be premature to give the species a higher category than Insufficiently Known.

Conservation The Duver is an SSSI and a National Trust property.

Author J.H. Bratton, in consultation with P.T. Harding and D.T. Richardson and using information from Jones & Keay (1986) and Keay (1987).

CHORDEUMA SYLVESTRE

INSUFFICIENTLY KNOWN

Phylum UNIRAMIA
Class DIPLOPODA

Order CHORDEUMATIDA
Family CHORDEUMATIDAE

Chordeuma sylvestre C.L. Koch, 1847.

Identification Blower (1985).

Distribution	Known in Britain only from two areas of East Cornwall, Trelill, from where the first British record came in 1961 and where it has been found on several occasions since and Widlake Wood, Hessenford, where it was found in 1982. The British Myriapod Group have produced a distribution map (Barber & Keay 1988). It has also been recorded in France, Holland, Belgium, Switzerland, Germany and Italy. Records from Czechoslovakia and the Soviet Carpathians are thought to refer to *Orthochordeumella germanicum* (Verhoeff), which was at one time considered synonymous with *C. sylvestre*.
Habitat and ecology	Around Trelil this species occurs in deciduous woodland among leaf litter. At Hessenford it was found under pieces of wood in a coniferous plantation. Several juvenile stadia and adults have been found in the spring and subadults in the autumn. From this, it is inferred that egg-laying occurs from early in the year until April and that this species has an annual life cycle. Courtship involves secretion of a pheromone by the male to attract the female (Haacker 1971, cited in Blower 1985). Use of a Tullgren funnel has shown this species to be abundant at sites around Trelill. The Chordeumatidae found in Britain have a range mainly with a west maritime climate, with cool (not cold) winters, warm summers and rain throughout the year. However, in the Italian part of the range of *C. sylvestre* these conditions do not prevail.
Status	Though the known distribution in Great Britain is very restricted, there are no obviously unusual features of its sites to indicate the presence of an exceptional fauna. Thus its apparent rarity may only reflect the low intensity of recording effort for millipedes in the southwest.
Conservation	Provided that its woodland sites do not undergo felling and a change of land-use, the survival of this species is unlikely to be a cause for concern. Survey work to determine the full range is desirable and would perhaps show RDB status to be unwarranted for this species.
Author	J.H.Bratton, in consultation with P.T. Harding and using information from Blower (1984, 1985) and G. Blower and D.T. Richardson (pers. comms).

GEOPHILUS PROXIMUS   INSUFFICIENTLY KNOWN

Phylum UNIRAMIA
Class CHILOPODA

Order GEOPHILOMORPHA
Family GEOPHILIDAE

Geophilus proximus C.L. Koch, 1847.

Identification	Brolemann (1930); Enghoff (1971).

Distribution	A single specimen has been identified from Unst, Shetland Islands, the locality being marked on a distribution map compiled by the British Myriapod Group (Barber & Keay 1988).
Habitat and ecology	It was found under boulders in the bottom of a nettle-grown hollow on a limestone hillock.
Status	A widespread Scandinavian and north European species which would seem to represent a northern element in Britain's chilopod fauna. Very few myriapod surveys have been carried out in mainland north Scotland, Orkney or Shetland.
Author	A.D. Barber

LITHOBIUS LAPIDICOLA   INSUFFICIENTLY KNOWN

Phylum UNIRAMIA   Order LITHOBIOMORPHA
Class CHILOPODA   Family LITHOBIIDAE

Lithobius lapidicola Meinert, 1872, synonymous with *L. pusillus* Latzel, 1880 (Eason, 1982). The species recorded as *L. lapidicola* in Eason (1964) is *L. borealis* Meinert, 1968.

Identification	Similar to *L. borealis* but without projections on tergite 13 and with fewer ocelli. Included in an identification key in Eason (1982).
Distribution	Recorded as an outdoor species only from Sandwich Bay, East Kent, but also reported from hothouses in Edinburgh (Rawcliffe 1987). Its European distribution is difficult to establish because of nomenclatural confusion, but it is probably quite widespread in northwest Europe (Eason 1982).
Habitat and ecology	The Sandwich Bay shore consists of bare sand giving way to patches of marram and later to a grass sward. *L. lapidicola* has been found under wood and stones in both the marram and grass sward areas. *L. melanops* Newport is also present.
Status	The true status is unclear. *L. lapidicola* could have been mistaken for another species in Kent and elsewhere.
Conservation	An extensive area of Sandwich Bay is an SSSI and much is protected as nature reserves. The locality from which *L. lapidicola* is recorded is within and close to the reserve of the Kent Trust and is not under immediate threat.
Author	A.D. Barber.

LITHOBIUS TENEBROSUS

INSUFFICIENTLY KNOWN

Phylum UNIRAMIA
Class CHILOPODA

Order LITHOBIOMORPHA
Family LITHOBIIDAE

Lithobius tenebrosus Meinert, 1872, formerly known as *L. nigrifrons* Latzel & Haase, 1880.

Identification
Eason (1964), as *L. nigrifrons*. Superficially very similar to *L. melanops* Newport.

Distribution
Two specimens of *Lithobius* collected in 1911 from Gibside, Co. Durham, were identified as *L. nigrifrons* by E. Ellingsen "with some hesitation" (Bagnall 1913). Turk (1945) recorded it from Reskadinnick, West Cornwall, in 1944. Eason (1964) considers that both these records should be "treated with reserve" owing to the possibility of confusion with *L. muticus* C.L. Koch. The only modern and reliable record is from Constitution Hill, Aberystwyth, Cardiganshire, where it was found during the 1988 British Myriapod Group meeting (Keay 1989a). Turk (1945) described its European distribution as "wide but seemingly discontinuous", listing central Europe, Corsica and Scandinavia, to which Eason (1982) added Austria, Germany and Switzerland.

Habitat and ecology
The first two British records give the habitat as fields. The Aberystwyth specimen was found in the splash zone of a sea-cliff in a soil-filled rock crevice. Open or sparse vegetation, possibly including arable land, would seem to be a common theme of the British records of this species.

Status
Clearly an elusive species, with no further records at any of its reported British sites after the initial discovery. There must therefore be an element of doubt about its being under threat in Great Britain.

Threats
Intensification of agriculture, with loss of rough grazing and widespread use of pesticides, may have affected this species, but this can only be speculation, in view of the doubts about the two records from fields.

Conservation
Constitution Hill is protected as an SSSI, as are similar cliffs to the south of Aberystwyth.

Author
J.H. Bratton, using information from Barber (1988 and pers. comm.) and Keay (1988 and *in litt.* to A.P. Fowles).

CRUSTACEA

The Crustacea show a range of forms far more diverse than any other phylum and include, for example, waterfleas, woodlice, crabs, barnacles and numerous ectoparasites scarcely recognisable as animals. Crustaceans have never commanded the same degree of attention from naturalists or the general public as have the insects, Chater (1988b) notwithstanding, possibly owing to Crustacea being mostly dull grey or brown in colour (until cooked), fewer in number of species, and predominantly aquatic. The range of life histories and feeding methods exhibited by the Crustacea is too diverse for a summary to be given here, and the texts of Schmitt (1973) and Green (1961) are recommended as sources. The relevant identification works are referred to in the data sheets and microcrustacea text. Isopods are the only group for which distribution atlases have been published, based on a national recording scheme (Moon & Harding 1981; Harding & Sutton 1985). The journal *Isopoda*, which was first produced in 1987, carries papers dealing mainly with British woodlice, while the newsletter of the Isopod Survey Scheme carries less formally presented information. The latter is sent to all contributors to the survey.

This Red Data Book includes data sheets for representatives of five orders: Anostraca, Notostraca, Mysidacea, Isopoda and Amphipoda. Three groups of microcrustacea (Cladocera, Copepoda and Ostracoda) are also discussed. Of these, only the Isopoda and Cladocera have national recording schemes. However, the British representatives of the Anostraca and Notostraca are few in number and sufficiently unusual often to evoke a published comment when found, so there is a usable database of records for these. Three rather harsh habitats support the majority of the crustaceans described in this book: brackish waters, seasonal pools and subterranean waters.

Harding & Sutton (1985) presented a Red Data List of woodlice which includes four species for Great Britain. Despite their choice of species and categories being based on a very comprehensive database of modern records, further recording of woodlice between 1983 and 1990 has led to the revision of the status of two of these species. *Armadillidium album* Dollfus was classed as Rare by Harding & Sutton, but the number of dune systems from which it is now known places it outside the terms of this book. The increase in the number of known sites is not a result of successful conservation measures, merely of further survey, so *A. album* does not qualify for category 4, Out of Danger. *Metatrichoniscoides celticus* Oliver & Trew was placed in the Vulnerable and Endemic categories by Sutton & Harding. Again, more sites have been found since their statement was published and this species has proved extremely difficult to find even at sites where it is known to occur. For these reasons it has been placed in a lower threat category and has been removed from the Endemic category. *Halophiloscia couchi* (Kinahan) was placed in category 4, Out of Danger, by Harding & Sutton and is not considered further here. The fourth of Harding & Sutton's species, *Armadillidium pictum* Brandt, remains in category 3, Rare.

There is unfortunately a dearth of distribution data for amphipods and it is this weakness which has caused several to be graded no higher than RDB K. Others have been omitted completely despite a paucity of records. At the time of publication of the standard text on British amphipods (Lincoln 1979), the sand-hopper *Orchestia remyi roffensis* Wildish was known only from Chatham Ness in the Medway estuary, Kent, though the nominate subspecies *O. remyi remyi* Schellenberg was perplexingly recorded from a subterranean freshwater lake in Corsica. Wildish (1987) accorded the former specific status, *O. roffensis* (Wildish), as well as describing a new species, *O. aestuarensis* (Wildish), which has been found in the Medway, Kent, the Tamar, South Devon, and the Duddon, Cumberland. There is clearly much to be learnt about the composition and distribution of British *Orchestia* species and, until there is a firmer basis of recording, the idea that these are threatened taxa is untenable.

The omission of Britain's only native freshwater crayfish, *Austropotamobius pallipes* (Lereboullet), from this Red Data Book may be considered surprising by some. Its world status is given as Rare by Wells, Pyle & Collins (1983) and its European status as Vulnerable by Collins & Wells (1987). It is included in Appendix III of the Bern Convention. Populations are being lost throughout Europe owing to the crayfish plague. This is a fungal infection, *Aphanomyces astaci* (Schikora), which has been transmitted from introduced American Signal Crayfish *Pacifastacus leniusculus* Dana. If unchecked, this fungus could possibly wipe out the British populations of *A. pallipes*. The situation in Britain is being monitored. According to the latest report (Holdich & Reeve 1989), outbreaks of crayfish plague have eliminated native crayfish from seven separate river systems but the status of most native crayfish populations outside the south of England appears to be healthy. *A. pallipes* is now protected against collection or sale without a licence by the Wildlife and Countryside Act 1981, as amended in 1988, and the Act also prevents the release of foreign crayfish into the wild. Goddard & Hogger (1986) reviewed the causes of the decline of this species and presented a key to crayfish likely to be found in British fresh waters and some distribution data. *A. pallipes* is not considered to fall within the bounds of any Red Data Book category at present, but the contraction of its range currently occurring is obviously of great concern. It is hoped that remedial measures can be taken before this species reaches the stage of qualifying for an entry in a British Red Data Book.

Wells, Pyle & Collins (1983) list another crayfish, *Astacus astacus* (L.), as a threatened British species with Vulnerable status internationally. It is widely distributed in northern and eastern Europe but has been severely depleted by crayfish plague. According to Goddard & Hogger (1986), there are no substantiated records of *A. astacus* in the wild in Great Britain, while Holdich & Reeve (1989) refer to two records of this species in the wild. It is definitely not native to this country.

MICROCRUSTACEA:
CLADOCERA, COPEPODA AND OSTRACODA

Despite a long history of study in Britain, the freshwater microcrustaceans are still poorly known. Their intricacy and diversity attracted much attention from the Victorian microscopists and several major works were published at that time, such as Baird (1850), Brady (1868, 1878, 1880) and Brady & Norman (1889, 1896). The classification, biology and ecology of the copepods were updated by Gurney (1931, 1932, 1933), and identification works for cyclopid and calanoid copepods (Harding & Smith 1974), parasitic copepods (Fryer 1982) and Cladocera (Scourfield & Harding 1966) have been published by the Freshwater Biological Association. Additional useful identification works for the Cladocera include Flossner (1972), Amoros (1984) and Margaritora (1985), all of which are well illustrated. Unfortunately there is no recent account of the British harpacticoid copepods, so that students of these are forced to consult foreign works such as Klie (1938), Lang (1948) or Sars (1903-1911, 1922-1928). The marine and brackish-water Ostracoda can be identified using Athersuch, Horne & Whittaker (1989) and a companion volume dealing with the freshwater Ostracoda is awaited. Cladocera are the only group to be covered by a national recording scheme, and this has few active contributors, so it is difficult to assess the British microcrustacea for rare and threatened species. There are a small number of candidates for Red Data Book status, but it was decided not to give the detailed treatment used for other groups of invertebrates in view of the poor state of knowledge.

Many Cladocera and Ostracoda produce drought-resistant resting eggs, by which means they survive in seasonal ponds and pools. These eggs also facilitate dispersal from pool to pool and may allow occasional colonisation of Britain by continental species. The surface-dwelling cladoceran *Megafenestra* (=*Scapholeberis*) *aurita* (Fischer) is seldom recorded in Britain but its few sites include Leighton Moss wildfowl reserve, West Lancashire, and Borough Fen duck decoy, Northamptonshire, suggesting that aquatic birds may play a role in distributing this species. Such species are undoubtedly uncommon in this country, but two factors make Red Data Book status inappropriate. The first is the lack of recording coverage for microcrustacea. Secondly, if a species is subject to periodic reintroduction from abroad, its status is more akin to a vagrant than to a rare native and conservation measures may not be possible.

Only one site in Great Britain is known for the large chydorid cladoceran *Eurycercus glacialis* Lilljeborg, this being Morrich More, near Tain, East Ross-shire (Duigan 1988). (A record from Ronas Hill, Shetland, requires confirmation.) This species is often found in seasonal pools and regularly produces resting eggs (ephippia), so it could feasibly be distributed by waterfowl. However, *E. glacialis* was recorded in the Tain area in 1957 (Scourfield & Harding 1966), suggesting that the populations found by Duigan may be permanent and worthy of conservation effort. This species has also recently been discovered in Ireland (Duigan & Frey 1987).

Two British cladocerans are absent from the key of Scourfield & Harding (1966). *Daphnia rosea* Sars is widespread in Europe but has only recently been confirmed in Britain, from Wicken Fen, Cambridgeshire (Hearn in prep.). The features distinguishing this species from *D. longispina* O.F. Muller are not compellingly obvious, so it may exist unrecognised elsewhere in Britain. Secondly, the chydorid *Dunhevedia crassa* was reported from two Breckland sites in the 1970s. *Kurzia latissima* (Kurz) is another chydorid known only from East Anglia, at East Ruston Common in East Norfolk.

There are northern elements of the British microcrustacea which may be under threat. *Holopedium gibberum* Zaddach is found in deep water bodies that are low in calcium. Although it still occurs widely in Scotland, it has disappeared from several Cumbrian lakes since the 1930s, probably as a result of eutrophication (G. Fryer pers. comm.). The macrothricid cladoceran *Ophryoxus gracilis* Sars is known in Great Britain only from Lochs Ness and Oich, Inverness-shire, and, while there is scope for more populations to be found in other lochs, it is generally accepted to be rare and on the southern edge of its range in Scotland.

Ennerdale Water, an oligotrophic lake in Cumberland, supports three crustaceans thought to have been isolated in this water body since the last glacial retreat. One, *Mysis relicta* Loven, is discussed below. The other two species are copepods. *Limnocalanus macrurus* Sars is, like *M. relicta*, known in Great Britain only from Ennerdale Water. It has on occasion been a major component of the zooplankton, but has not been found since 1956, so its survival must be in doubt. The lake has been subjected to extensive conifer afforestation in its catchment, acid precipitation, and manipulation of the water levels, any of which could have had subtle detrimental effects on the ecosystem. *Salmincola edwardsii* (Olsson) is a copepod parasitic upon Char *Salvelinus alpinus* (L.) and is known from four Scottish lochs in addition to Ennerdale. However, the Ennerdale population differs from the Scottish ones in certain characteristics and may prove to be a different taxon. Fryer (1981) discusses the possible origins of this Ennerdale assemblage. *L. macrurus* and *S. edwardsii* are strong contenders for Red Data Book status.

The Ostracoda are a neglected branch of British natural history and it has not been possible to obtain the information needed to propose, even tentatively, a list of threatened species. Species new to Britain are occasionally reported from our fresh waters (e.g. Fox 1964, 1967) but subsequent records and site inventories are rarely published.

ARTEMIA SALINA

EXTINCT

Brine Shrimp

Phylum CRUSTACEA
Class BRANCHIOPODA

Order ANOSTRACA
Family ARTEMIIDAE

Artemia salina (Linnaeus, 1758).

Identification

It has recently been shown that *A. salina* as originally conceived actually embraces a species complex. Britain is the type locality for *A. salina* (L.), so it follows that British specimens are correctly named, unless more than one species was present. However, it is impossible to say whether any of the extant species are identical to the British material, as identification relies not only on morphological differences but also on behavioural and biochemical traits. *A. salina sens. lat.* can be identified by using Flossner (1972) or Fitter & Manuel (1986).

Distribution

Known only from Hayling Island and Lymington, South Hampshire. These were among the most northerly sites in Europe for brine shrimps. *A. salina sens. lat.* has a virtually worldwide distribution.

Habitat and ecology

Occurs in landlocked, strongly saline water bodies. The Hampshire sites were tanks where brine was produced from sea water by natural evaporation as a preliminary to salt production. *Artemia* was most abundant where the brine had the strength of a quarter pound of salt per pint of water. Some brine always remained in these tanks. In others which were emptied fortnightly, *Artemia* never occurred. *Artemia* is a filter-feeder, ingesting microscopic algae and presumably Protozoa and bacteria, and occasionally feeding on smaller specimens of its own species. The tanks at Lymington where it occurred were called 'clearers' because the liquor became clear whilst in them. The saltworkers attributed this clearing to the actions of *Artemia* and would add a few brine shrimps to a tank if they failed to arrive by natural means. This practice still occurs in regions where salt is produced by solar evaporation. Waddington (1913) commented that *A. salina* could be reared from ova contaminating packs of Tidman's sea-salt. Efficient oxygen uptake, using haemoglobin, allows *A. salina* to survive in waters of low oxygen tension. Eggs of *Artemia* are resistant to desiccation, and it is by means of these eggs that populations can survive the periods when saltpans are dry. Such eggs now form the basis of an industry, since they can be hatched rapidly to provide a source of food for captive fish and other aquatic predators. French populations of *Artemia* are reported to lay eggs before July and after September but to be ovoviviparous during the summer. Eggs are laid two to three weeks after they are formed, a batch varying from 50 in autumn to 160 in summer. Three or four batches are produced during the life of a female. No predators are reported from the brine tanks at Lymington, but in

France a waterbeetle in the Dytiscidae has been seen to attack *Artemia*.

Status   First noted in 1755 and present in the mid nineteenth century. The Rev. T.R.R. Stebbing wrote in the Victoria County History for Hampshire (Doubleday 1900) that the Lymington salterns "have now been turned into places of amusement, and there is reason to fear that *Artemia salina* is now missing from the fauna of Hampshire". In 1907 Canon Norman visited the Lymington brine pans to search for *Artemia* but was unsuccessful and was convinced that it had disappeared. It has not been found since. If populations are found in the wild in the future, they are more likely to be introductions from stock used in the fish- and prawn-rearing industries than descendants of the native population. If the latter were to be discovered, their origin would be impossible to verify.

Threats   Cessation of salt production in the Hampshire salt-pans eliminated the only known British habitat of this species. Suitable natural saline lagoons are likely to have always been very scarce, probably occurring only where the highest of spring tides would leave a pool which could then be concentrated by evaporation. Such conditions have largely been lost from British coasts owing to sea defences truncating saltmarshes below the highest tidemarks.

Author   J.H. Bratton, using information from Baird (1850), Slack (1863), Waddington (1913), Mitchell & Geddes (1977), Fryer (1986) and G. Fryer (pers. comm.).

CHIROCEPHALUS DIAPHANUS   VULNERABLE

A fairy shrimp

Phylum CRUSTACEA   Order ANOSTRACA
Class BRANCHIOPODA   Family CHIROCEPHALIDAE

Chirocephalus diaphanus Prevost, 1803.

Identification   Flossner (1972); Fitter & Manuel (1986).

Distribution   It has been recorded from much of England north to York (in 1862). Most recent records come from Devon, Cornwall and the New Forest, South Hampshire, with a well documented population surviving in pools in Cambridgeshire (Walters 1972, 1978; Preston 1989). There is one Welsh record (Whiting 1978). *Chirocephalus diaphanus* is essentially a circum-Mediterranean species not extending as far north as Fennoscandia.

Habitat and ecology   *Chirocephalus* is an inhabitant of temporary pools ranging from cart ruts to weedy ponds. Its distribution in Britain corresponds well with the area having a deficit of precipitation over evapotranspiration in the period April to September (Bratton & Fryer 1990), this being the area where temporary pools are most likely. It is usually found in pools receiving regular disturbance by trampling livestock, ploughing or vehicles. An important prerequisite is an absence of predators, as *Chirocephalus* is eaten by various insect larvae and in its early stages by ostracods, and it never coexists with fish. In mountainous areas of southern Europe *Chirocephalus* is found in permanent water bodies, which are probably fishless and harbour few other predators. *C. diaphanus* has been found at all months of the year in England and has been taken from ice-covered ponds. It is tolerant of a wide range of water chemistry, temperature and oxygenation. Its food consists of particulate detritus and microscopic life, filtered from suspension or scraped from the bottom deposits. Periods of drought are passed as eggs. Not all resting eggs hatch at the first wetting, so that, if the duration of the inundation is on one occasion too short for the life cycle to be completed, a residue of viable eggs remains. Eggs do not necessarily require a period of desiccation before they hatch. The hatching process and the conditions controlling it are reviewed by Webster (1987). In the New Forest, ponies, cattle and deer are probably the main agents of dispersal of *Chirocephalus* eggs. Unlike many crustaceans found in seasonal pools, *C. diaphanus* is not parthenogenetic.

Status

Enquiries and survey work for this data sheet have brought to light a number of previously unrecorded colonies. *Chirocephalus* has been recorded from at least eighty pools since 1900 and, excluding the New Forest, eleven pools since 1980. The New Forest contains a large number of seasonal pools, some of which will support permanent populations of *Chirocephalus*, while others may occasionally be colonised but not maintain viable populations. Throughout its British range, pools supporting *Chirocephalus* are being destroyed or damaged or are under threat. Although there are undoubtedly *Chirocephalus* colonies yet to be discovered, the fragility of the habitat occupied by this species justifies its Vulnerable status.

Threats

Of the eleven *Chirocephalus* colonies mentioned above, two have been infilled (both on SSSIs, one within a County Trust reserve), but it is hoped that careful excavation will reinstate the habitat for *Chirocephalus*; one has been partly bulldozed and it remains to be seen whether the *Chirocephalus* has been affected; one in a woodland ride is likely to become overgrown; and the future of the Cambridgeshire colony (in an SSSI) is in doubt owing to a lowering of the water table caused by groundwater abstraction. The fate of the remaining six colonies is unknown but none can be considered safe. *Chirocephalus* colonies are also being lost in the New Forest: at Hatchet Green a population has been eliminated by its pool being deepened and lined with concrete, making a permanent pond of no conservation value; at Hyde Common a road gravel store now stands on what was a *Chirocephalus* colony; and at Cadnam Green pools are threatened by the building of gravel

Coxe's Cliff, Sidmouth to Beer Coast SSSI, South Devon. Upper photograph opposite: 28 March 1986. Lower photograph opposite: 3 July 1986. This seasonal pool near the cliff-top contained a colony of the fairy shrimp *Chirocephalus diaphanus*, currently a protected species in Britain. In 1989 the land was sold and the new owner removed the hedgerow and partially filled in the pool with subsoil from a nearby building site (photograph above), despite the pool being within an SSSI. Ancient seasonally flooded hollows can support an assemblage of uncommon Crustacea, including *Triops cancriformis*. (Photos by J., M.E. and S.D. Webster.)

tracks to paddocks and by ditch excavation to prevent car access to the verges. In the first half of this century, *Chirocephalus* was recorded on several occasions from common land in the Home Counties, particularly in Buckinghamshire and Hertfordshire. Urban expansion, the commuter society and road building, causing the collapse of the traditional grazing of commons, has led to most of these commons converting to scrub and secondary woodland. Few, if any, of these sites now have suitable habitat for *Chirocephalus*.

Conservation   Though several colonies, including most of those in the New Forest, are within SSSIs, this does not appear to provide adequate protection to this species. Its pools are often viewed as unsightly muddy hollows which should be infilled or deepened to create a 'proper' pond. Seasonal pools can support a range of scarce species, including insects and plants, and their wildlife value needs to be more widely appreciated. It needs stressing that *Chirocephalus* can complete its life cycle very rapidly and a pool which lasts for only a month can be adequate for its needs. Even where an inundation is more long-lived, *Chirocephalus* are unlikely to be present throughout the whole period and the absence of active *Chirocephalus* from a pool should not lead to the conclusion that the pool has become unsuitable. Active management of *Chirocephalus* pools is often vital to prevent their becoming overgrown and filling with leaf litter. Heavy grazing and poaching by cattle or horses appear to be ideal. In addition to maintaining a sparse vegetation cover, livestock replenish the fertility of the pool through their dunging, and their trampling of the sediments helps to maintain a viable reserve of resting eggs. In 1988 *C. diaphanus* was given protection by its addition to Schedule 5 of the Wildlife and Countryside Act 1981.

Author   J.H. Bratton, using information from Fryer (1986), Spooner & Spooner (1988) and J. Biggs, A. Bolton, C. Chatters, K. Halstead, S.J.J. Lambert, R.L. Manuel, G.C. Matthews, C.D. Preston, S.M. Turk and S.D. Webster (pers comms).

TRIOPS CANCRIFORMIS   ENDANGERED

Apus, Tadpole Shrimp

Phylum CRUSTACEA   Order NOTOSTRACA
Class BRANCHIOPODA   Family TRIOPSIDAE

Triops cancriformis (Bosc, 1801), formerly *Apus cancriformis* and *Monoculus apus* L.

Identification   Flossner (1972); Fitter & Manuel (1986).

Distribution

There are old records from Kent (*ca* 1738 and mid nineteenth century); Hampshire (*ca* 1816); Glanvilles Wootton, Dorset, where it was described as "abundant" by Dale (1878); near Powick (1841 and 1842) and between Tewkesbury and Upton-on-Severn (1861 or 1862), both Worcestershire; and Bristol, Somerset or Gloucestershire (before 1837). In 1907 it was found in two pools at Preston Merse, Kirkcudbrightshire, and again in 1948 in several pools on the merse about a mile from the former site. There are recent records only from the New Forest, South Hampshire. In one pool there, it has been recorded at varying intervals since 1934. There are records from other pools but they are less well documented and none are known to represent long-lived colonies. Reports of *Triops* on a nature reserve in West Gloucestershire have not been substantiated and are likely to be in error. The world distribution of *T. cancriformis* is western Europe from Spain to Sweden and east to Russia; North Africa; the Balkans; Asia Minor; and the Middle East to India. It does not extend beyond 60°N, and the range in Russia is obscure, but there are no authenticated records for eastern Asia (Longhurst 1955).

Habitat and ecology

Thought to be restricted to seasonal pools because of the need to avoid predators such as fish which occur in permanent water bodies. Its rapid development from drought-resistant eggs after inundation allows maturity to be reached within 2-3 weeks. It has been suggested that two types of egg are produced, one able to hatch soon after production if the conditions remain favourable, the other only hatching after one or more periods of desiccation. In the extreme north of its range, including Britain, males are unknown, and here females contain ovotestes (Longhurst 1955). *Triops* is omnivorous, feeding on oligochaetes, other crustaceans and insects, particularly if the prey is disabled; leaves of waterplants such as *Callitriche*; and microscopic food extracted from the sediments. Enrichment of the pool by dung from grazing animals is thought to be beneficial (T. Gledhill pers. comm.). The functional significance of many aspects of the morphology of *T. cancriformis* (and other Notostraca) have been described by Fryer (1988). At the main New Forest site it is found with the threatened anostracan *Chirocephalus diaphanus* Prevost.

Status

Triops has not been found at the Kirkcudbrightshire locality for over thirty years, so it is possibly now restricted to the New Forest. In Britain, *Triops* is near the lower temperature limit of its distribution, which could account for its rarity here. What have been thought of in the past as merely racial differences in Notostraca are shown by Fryer (1988) to have functional significance, suggesting that the taxonomy of the group may be over-simplified at present. This raises the possibility of the British *Triops* population being internationally important (*cf Artemia salina* (L.)).

Threats

The Forestry Commission, which manages the New Forest, is aware of the importance of the pool supporting the main colony.

There has been an attempt to drain the pool but this has been remedied. There is also the risk of pollution from a nearby road. *Triops* may be highly susceptible to bird predation (Balfour-Browne 1962) and, if the New Forest site were to be occupied by domestic ducks, these could make serious inroads into the *Triops* population. Deepening of any pools it inhabits, thereby changing them to permanent water bodies (for instance to provide drinking for stock or in a misguided attempt to improve the site), would probably cause the extinction of *Triops*.

Conservation

The New Forest is an SSSI. The long history of *Triops* in the main New Forest site suggests that no extra management is required, the heavy grazing being sufficient to prevent loss of the pool through vegetational succession. Vigilance is needed to ensure that no change to the water regime occurs. Preston Merse is part of the Southerness Coast SSSI, but the exact location at which *Triops* was last found may have been lost to the sea (G. Fryer pers. comm.). Casual investigations of the pools on Preston Merse in recent years have failed to find *Triops*, but a systematic survey including attempts to rear this species from mud may be successful. In 1988 *Triops* was given protection by inclusion in Schedule 5 of the Wildlife and Countryside Act 1981.

Author

J.H. Bratton, using information from Evans (1841, 1842), Page (1908), Fox (1949), Fryer (1986), Galliford (1967) and A. Bolton, C. Chatters and G. Fryer (pers. comms).

MYSIS RELICTA ENDANGERED

An opossum shrimp

Phylum CRUSTACEA   Order MYSIDACEA
Class MALACOSTRACA   Family MYSIDAE

Mysis relicta Loven, 1862.

Identification

Tattershall & Tattershall (1951); Gledhill, Sutcliffe & Williams (1976).

Distribution

In Great Britain, known only from Ennerdale Water, Cumberland. Also recorded from several loughs in Ireland; north German lakes; widespread in Scandinavia; Spitzbergen; Russia; Denmark; Italy; and North America. Widely introduced in Europe and North America as a food for trout. Riddoch, Jones & Ward (unpublished) have studied the chemotaxonomy and morphometry of *Mysis* and suggested that *M. relicta* contains four sibling species. Specimens from Ennerdale were not available for their study, but would probably correspond to the most southerly distributed

Scandinavian species, which has been identified from the Baltic, southern Sweden, Denmark and Ireland.

Habitat and ecology A detritivore, feeding on the surface layers of the sediments, which also catches small planktonic animals such as *Daphnia*. *Mysis* has been taken in the plankton, especially at night. It is a winter breeder, at temperatures not exceeding 7°C, and most active at temperatures between 0°C and 3°C. In Ennerdale Water, gravid females are found in December. They incubate the eggs in a marsupium. Males die after copulation and females at the end of the breeding season. Nowhere in its range does it occur where the summer water temperature exceeds 14°C. In fresh waters it requires at least 4 ml oxygen per litre, which limits its distribution in eutrophic lakes. In brackish waters 1.6 ml oxygen per litre will suffice.

Status *Mysis relicta* was discovered in Ennerdale Water in 1941 (Scourfield 1941) and last seen in 1952 or 1953 (G. Fryer pers. comm.). It is infrequently caught, so there may be only a small population present. The Ennerdale population of *Mysis* is thought to date from water bodies forming in the period of thaw following the last glaciation, but whether the species evolved at this time from a marine mysid or is a much older species is open to question (Vainola 1986). Ennerdale Water supports other species thought to have colonised at the end of the Pleistocene glaciation. This aspect of its fauna has been discussed by Fryer (1981).

Threats Eutrophication, which would lead to low summer oxygen levels in deep water, and other forms of water pollution are probably the most serious threats to this species. As the second most oligotrophic lake in the Lake District, Ennerdale Water is vulnerable to acidification which may ensue from the establishment of Ennerdale Forest and from acidic precipitation. *M. relicta* has disappeared from a number of small acidified lakes in Sweden (Riddoch, Jones & Ward unpublished). Ennerdale Water has long been used as a reservoir and in periods of drought is subject to drawdown of 1.5 metres or more (T.T. Macan *in litt.*). However, water abstraction preceded the discovery of *M. relicta* there by many decades (Berry 1982), so present levels of use may not be a serious threat. Trout are known to prey on *M. relicta*, and so artificial stocking of the lake with fish should be avoided.

Conservation Ennerdale is an SSSI and *Mysis* is mentioned in the citation. Part of the surrounding farmland is the property of the National Trust. Intensification of agriculture in the lake catchment should be avoided, to prevent the run-off of nutrients into the lake.

Author J.H. Bratton, using information from Tattershall & Tattershall (1951).

METATRICHONISCOIDES CELTICUS   INSUFFICIENTLY KNOWN

Phylum CRUSTACEA   Order ISOPODA
Class MALACOSTRACA   Family TRICHONISCIDAE

Metatrichoniscoides celticus Oliver & Trew, 1981.

Identification   Oliver & Trew (1981); Harding & Sutton (1985).

Distribution   Recorded from seven sites along a 48 km stretch of the Glamorgan
                           coast (Harding & Sutton 1985); an inland site in Carmarthen
                           (Chater 1986); and St Bees beach, on the Cumberland coast
                           ([Hopkin] 1987), although this last record requires confirmation as
                           only a female specimen was found (S.P. Hopkin pers. comm.). A
                           female almost certainly of this species was found by A.G. Irwin on
                           the Giant's Causeway, Antrim, in 1989.

Habitat and ecology   Initial records were from a zone five metres wide inland from the
                           highest strandline at the top of rocky shores, on limestone or
                           calcareous conglomerate where soil and vegetation are subject to
                           erosion. In 1986 it was found in an overgrown disused limestone
                           quarry 7 km inland, 170 metres above sea level, near Crwbin,
                           Carmarthen. The animals were under rocks in damp stony soil
                           (Chater 1986). In Cumberland, it was found among damp Old Red
                           Sandstone rubble on the beach. Five previous visits to this site had
                           failed to reveal *M. celticus* ([Hopkin] 1987). This species may move
                           deep into the soil during dry conditions.

Status   Discovered new to science in 1979. Harding & Sutton (1985)
                           placed this species in Red Data categories 2 and 5 (Vulnerable and
                           Endemic). The subsequent discoveries of specimens inland in
                           Wales and on the English coast have led to its being demoted to
                           category K in this volume. It is also felt that Endemic status is not
                           justified in this case, as levels of isopod recording in Europe lag
                           behind Britain and a species which evaded discovery for so long in
                           Britain could easily still be doing so in Europe. Surveys of
                           apparently suitable sites in southwest England and Ireland have
                           failed to find it. Even searches at its known sites have on occasions
                           failed to reveal the species, so repeated visits to suitable habitat
                           are necessary to provide reliable distribution data.

Threats   The Welsh coastal sites are at present subject to only slight human
                           disturbance but, if the recreational potential was exploited, it would
                           be likely to cause much disturbance of the strandline and might
                           prompt major engineering works, such as beach stabilisation,
                           which would be very damaging to the habitat of *M. celticus*. This
                           species is also likely to be adversely affected by pollution or
                           industrial development. There are plans to reopen the Carmarthen
                           quarry for further limestone extraction (I.K. Morgan pers. comm.).

| Conservation | One Welsh record is from within Southerndown Coast SSSI, Glamorgan. St Bees beach is part of an SSSI and RSPB reserve. Further survey work should be carried out in similar habitats elsewhere. |

Conservation

One Welsh record is from within Southerndown Coast SSSI, Glamorgan. St Bees beach is part of an SSSI and RSPB reserve. Further survey work should be carried out in similar habitats elsewhere.

Author

J.H. Bratton, using information from Harding & Sutton (1985).

ARMADILLIDIUM PICTUM RARE

RARE

A pill woodlouse

Phylum CRUSTACEA
Class MALACOSTRACA

Order ISOPODA
Family ARMADILLIDIIDAE

Armadillidium pictum Brandt, 1833.

Identification

Sutton (1972).

Distribution

A 1917 record for Catrigg Force, Midwest Yorkshire, has been confirmed by examination of voucher material. It was refound at this site in May 1985 and near Grassington, also in Midwest Yorkshire, in 1988. Other recent valid records are from five localities in Westmorland and West Lancashire and one locality in each of Breconshire and Radnorshire. Several previously published records have proved to be misidentifications (Harding 1977), while a further eight remain unsubstantiated. Harding & Sutton (1985) and Richardson (1989) give distribution maps. *A. pictum* is also known from France, Switzerland, Germany, the Benelux countries, Denmark and southern Scandinavia.

Habitat and ecology

Most British records are from rocky terrain, including rock pavement, scree and dry stone wall, within woodland or scrub or adjacent to woodland. It is found on a variety of rock types and may burrow to a depth of up to two metres. At Coed Aber Edw, Radnorshire, it was associated with living and dead oak trees in an oak wood. Specimens were found under bark, within dead wood and under moss on tree trunks, some specimens 1.5 metres above ground level. Very few were found under wood lying on the ground and none under stones. This Welsh habitat is similar to the woodland and dead wood habitat which is usual for this species in mainland Europe.

Status

Rare. Thought to be the least common of the British woodlice. It is not under immediate threat, but most of its sites are small and surrounded by unfavourable habitat.

Threats

Removal of rock for ornamental use could become a problem. Sites such as at Catrigg Force, Midwest Yorkshire, and Tarren yr Esgob, Breconshire, could be subject to greater human disturbance in future if they become widely known as beauty spots.

Conservation	There are post-1968 records from five SSSIs, including Gait Barrows NNR, West Lancashire, and the National Trust's properties at Low Wood, Hartsop, and Arnside Knott, both in Westmorland. Habitat management for this species may require the prevention of vegetational succession on rock pavement and screes. At Coed Aber Edw SSSI, the importance of retaining standing dead wood should be recognised.
Author	J.H. Bratton, using information from Harding & Sutton (1985), Chater (1988a), Richardson (1989) and P.T. Harding (pers. comm.).

COROPHIUM LACUSTRE   RARE

Phylum CRUSTACEA   Order AMPHIPODA
Class MALACOSTRACA   Family COROPHIIDAE

Corophium lacustre Vanhoffen, 1911, previously confused with *C. crassicorne* Bruzelius and *C. grossipes* Templeton.

Identification	Lincoln (1979).
Distribution	Has been known for many years from sites in the Norfolk Broads, such as the River Bure, River Thurne, River Yare and Heigham Sound, including records under the name *C. crassicorne* (Scherren 1896). Sheader & Sheader (undated) record it from Little Anglesey, South Hampshire. Also occurs on the European coast of the North Sea and English Channel and the Atlantic coast of North America.
Habitat and ecology	Found in shallow water and the lower intertidal zone in waters of very low salinity. In Norfolk it can occur in waters where there is no tidal effect but which are kept brackish by a subterranean saltwater table (Crawford 1937a). The Hampshire locality is a brackish pool. It constructs tubes in marshy banks and ditches and on submerged weeds or the hydroid *Cordylophora caspia* (Pallas).
Status	Long thought to be restricted in Britain to the Norfolk Broads, but the recent Hampshire record makes its true status less certain.
Threats	Eutrophication of the Norfolk Broads rivers has long been a problem and causes loss of the aquatic plants and deoxygenation of the lower layers of water. Both these effects are likely to be harmful to *C. lacustre*. Other forms of river pollution would also be damaging. A tidal barrage has been proposed for the River Yare, which could alter the salinity regime of the Broads rivers, though less drastic flood prevention measures are also being considered. Whether these would adversely affect *C. lacustre* remains to be seen.

Conservation

Much effort is being put into lowering the nutrient-loading of the Norfolk Broads and rivers, mainly by removing phosphate from sewage works effluent before it discharges into the rivers, which will benefit most invertebrate groups. The Norfolk Broads are designated an Environmentally Sensitive Area and it is hoped that, among other benefits, this will lead to less fertiliser use within their catchment. Under the Norfolk and Suffolk Broads Act 1988, the Broads Authority acquired additional powers to ensure sensitive management of the area, though some responsibility for the rivers has been retained by the water authority. However, the importance given to conservation in the new legislation is felt by some to be inadequate (Mayes 1987). The Bure Marshes are an SSSI and in part an NNR. Heigham Sound is part of Hickling Broad NNR and Norfolk Trust reserve.

Author

J.H. Bratton, using information from Crawford (1937a), Driscoll (1980), Lincoln (1979), Turner & Brooke (1988) and P.A. Wright (pers. comm.).

GAMMARUS INSENSIBILIS   RARE
Lagoon Sand Shrimp

Phylum CRUSTACEA   Order AMPHIPODA
Class MALACOSTRACA   Family GAMMARIDAE

Gammarus insensibilis Stock, 1966.

Identification

Lincoln (1979). A very similar species to *G. locusta*. The distinctions between these two are amplified by Sheader & Sheader (1985). Also very similar to *G. crinicornis* Stock, of which there are not yet any confirmed British records (M.J. Costello pers. comm.).

Distribution

Known from over a dozen sites on the east and south coasts of England from North Lincolnshire to Dorset (Howes 1939 and Spooner 1947, cited in Lincoln 1979; Williams 1972; Sheader & Sheader 1984, 1987a, 1987b, undated). Also found in Lough Hyne, Ireland (Kitching 1987), on the Atlantic coast of Europe and in the Mediterranean and Black Seas.

Habitat and ecology

The sites in Great Britain are waters of reduced salinity, either landlocked or with only a restricted connection with the sea, but in all cases showing no more than a small tidal range, allowing the development of beds of attached and free-floating plants. In the Mediterranean this species is also found in fully marine habitats at depths from 0 to 15 metres (Stock 1967), and in Lough Hyne the salinity differs little from full strength sea water (Kitching 1987). A major food source in the British south coast lagoons is the alga *Chaetomorpha linum* Kutzing, and *G. insensibilis* typically forms part of a weed-associated fauna including the isopods *Idotea*

chelipes (Pallas) and *Sphaeroma rugicauda* Leach, the amphipod
Corophium insidiosum Crawford, the chironomid midges
Chironomus salinarius Kiefer and *Halocladia varians* (Fabricius), the
molluscs *Cerastoderma glaucum* (Poiret), *Hydrobia ventrosa*
(Montagu), *H. ulvae* (Pennant) and *Littorina saxatilis tenebrosa*
(Olivi), and the uncommon anthozoan *Nematostella vectensis*
(Stephensen). Studies at Fort Gilkicker Moat, South Hampshire,
have shown that *G. insensibilis* breeds throughout the year, though
at a reduced rate during the winter. In laboratory conditions, male
Gammarus locusta (L.) can be induced to mate with female
G. insensibilis, and the eggs pass through the first stages of division
before development halts.

Status

There are old records only from the Fleet, Dorset, and New
England Creek, South Essex, but a recent coastal lagoon survey
organised by the NCC has revealed this species in a number of
sites. The intention of the survey was to examine all coastal
lagoons, so the majority of populations of this species should now
be documented. Stock (1967) suggests that *G. insensibilis* and
G. inaequicauda Stock are the southern and northern ends
respectively of a cline within a single species ranging from the
Mediterranean to Scandinavia, but, since so few Atlantic localities
are known which could provide intermediate populations, the two
taxa have not been synonymised. The name *G. inaequicauda* has
been retained for the type series from Norway and a population in
the Baltic, these having a few features not present in the British,
French or Mediterranean populations.

Threats

Landlocked coastal pools are vulnerable to pollution, reclamation,
drying-out, and infilling by hydroseral succession. The Fleet is
being invaded by the introduced alga *Sargassum muticum* (Yendo)
Fensholt, which could have deleterious effects on the several rare
invertebrates found there. The number of brackish pools at
Gilkicker Point, South Hampshire, has been reduced by infilling,
but those remaining support *G. insensibilis* and are now protected
as an SSSI. Cockle Pond at Gosport, Hampshire, is a concrete pond
used for model boating events, and algicides are frequently used
there, but this has not eliminated *G. insensibilis* to date. This species
appears to have been lost from Widewater Lagoon, West Sussex.
The reason for this is unclear, though it could be linked to the low
oxygen levels which are prevalent during warm summers, as the
period during which it disappeared included the exceptionally hot
summer of 1976. Titchwell Lagoon, West Norfolk, where it was
found in 1969, was drained in 1971 (Williams 1972).

Conservation

Most sites known to support this species lie within SSSIs and it is
found in at least two ponds within the North Solent NNR, South
Hampshire. Several of the SSSIs have been notified on account of
their brackish-water flora and fauna, so *Gammarus insensibilis*
should be well catered for. It is important that the salinity regimes
of its sites should not be altered (for example by conversion to
freshwater fishing lakes or by increasing the marine influence).

Chesil and the Fleet SSSI, Dorset. This lagoon supports six of the threatened brackish-water invertebrates, and three threatened spiders are recorded from the shingle beach which forms the far bank. Though it is almost landlocked, the salinity of the lagoon is maintained by sea water seeping through the shingle. (Photo by P. Wakely.)

In 1988 *G. insensibilis* was given protection by inclusion in Schedule 5 of the Wildlife and Countryside Act 1981.

Author   J.H. Bratton, using information from Sheader & Sheader (1985, 1987a, 1987b, undated) and J.H. Stock (pers. comm.).

NIPHARGELLUS GLENNIEI   INSUFFICIENTLY KNOWN ENDEMIC

Phylum CRUSTACEA   Order AMPHIPODA
Class MALACOSTRACA   Family NIPHARGIDAE

Niphargellus glenniei (Spooner, 1952), formerly called *Niphargus glenniei*.

Identification   Gledhill, Sutcliffe & Williams (1976).

Distribution   Known from fourteen sites in seven 10 km squares, all in South Devon except for one, Napps Cave, Berrynarbor, North Devon.

Habitat and ecology   Recorded from caves, wells, springs and river gravels. The main habitat is interstitial groundwater (Glennie 1967).

Status   This species has the most restricted distribution of all the British subterranean Malacostraca. Moreover, it is replaced on the French Channel coast by *Niphargus boulangei* Wichers and is not recorded elsewhere in Europe; thus there are good grounds for considering *N. glenniei* to be endemic to England (J.H. Stock pers. comm.).

Threats   Pollution of groundwaters is the most serious threat to this species. Fiers & Wouters (1985), discussing the threats to the Belgian stygiofauna, mention pollution from sewer pipes emptying into caves and calcium carbide from cavers' lamps being poured away in caves. Water abstraction could also have deleterious effects, by drying out the porous rock strata or allowing the inflow of marine water. River engineering projects which remove river gravels will disrupt some sites where *Niphargellus* can be found, but these activities are unlikely to affect the main populations.

Conservation   Some of the sites from which this species has been recorded are SSSIs. However, its conservation depends not on preserving isolated sites but on safeguarding the groundwater catchment areas from pollution and allowing the recharge of aquifers to continue. This is more likely to be achieved through concern for public health than by a desire to safeguard subterranean amphipods, but the latter will benefit nonetheless.

Author   J.H. Bratton, using information from Harding & Greene (1988).

118

ALLOMELITA PELLUCIDA

INSUFFICIENTLY KNOWN

Phylum CRUSTACEA
Class MALACOSTRACA

Order AMPHIPODA
Family MELITIDAE

Allomelita pellucida (Sars, 1882), formerly called *Melita pellucida*.

Identification

Lincoln (1979), as *Melita pellucida*. Stock (1984) also provides a description and figures of this species.

Distribution

There are records from the River Bure between Acle Bridge and Six Mile House, East Norfolk (Gurney 1907, 1929); Oulton Broad, East Suffolk (Gurney 1907); Benfleet, South Essex; Afon Water, South Hampshire (Goodhart 1941); the Rivers Towy, Taw, Tamar and Tavy and Dawlish Warren, South Devon (Crawford 1937b); the Bristol Channel area (Lincoln 1979); and Silverburn Estuary, Isle of Man (Jones 1948). It is also recorded from southern Norway, northwest France and Portugal (Stock 1984).

Habitat and ecology

A brackish-water species found mostly in harbours or ditches. Crawford (1937b) found it chiefly among freshwater vegetation or where there was "much decayed land", and Gurney (1907) wrote that it burrows in the soft mud under stones and in the bark of submerged wood. The salinity tolerance of this species is given as 0.6-3.0 parts per thousand by Goodhart (1941). Stock (1984) describes a population of this species at Etretat, France. Here it was living 50-100 cm down in the interstices of a gravel beach in the intertidal zone, in an area of freshwater discharge. The salinity regime at this depth in the beach was not known. This population lacked body pigment but had pigmented eyes.

Status

Often abundant when it is recorded, but no published records have been found from Britain relating to recent years. It is thought to be rare throughout its range (Stock 1984).

Threats

Agricultural reclamation and industrial development have destroyed many areas of grazing marsh with brackish ditch systems in recent decades. When such grazing land is converted to arable agriculture, the drainage is invariably improved, with the elimination of the vegetation-rich ditches. Maintenance and improvement of sea defences frequently alter the salinity regime of coastal ditch systems. Pollution in harbours, including the use of anti-fouling paints on boat hulls, may have had an impact on this species.

Conservation

Numerous areas of coastal marsh are now protected as nature reserves and SSSIs, and survey of the more brackish regions may reveal this species. There is sometimes the desire to lower the salinity of such areas in order to encourage a more diverse freshwater fauna. This needs to be resisted, as the brackish-water elements are equally deserving of conservation despite the fewer species involved. Dawlish Warren is now an SSSI, part LNR and part Devon Trust reserve.

Author   J.H. Bratton, using information from Lincoln (1979).

ARACHNIDA

Arachnida constitute the bulk of this Red Data Book. Representatives of two orders contain species qualifying for Red Data Book status. The pseudoscorpions have one species in category K and one in category 3, and there are 86 species of spiders distributed between the categories.

Pseudoscorpions are seldom encountered by the general naturalist. They are mainly crevice-dwellers, being found under loose bark, inside rotting trees or among leaf litter. The name pseudoscorpion refers to the proportionately large chelicerae, which are reminiscent of those of true scorpions. The chelicerae of pseudoscorpions are used to catch other small invertebrates and inject them with poison. The entomologist occasionally finds pseudoscorpions in his pooter without having intentionally collected them. This is because several species achieve dispersal by clinging to insects, a habit known as phoresy. A few are coastal species which live in rock crevices in the upper shore where an air supply is trapped during periods of submersion. *Kewochthonius halberti* (Kew) was discovered in 1915 under stones around high water mark on the Dublin coast and was recorded the following year from Axmouth, South Devon. However, there are suspicions that the Devon specimens may have been misidentified deutonymphs of another species, and so, as no further British specimens have come to light, *K. halberti* has not been given RDB status. A few pseudoscorpions are strongly synanthropic, inhabiting haystacks, manure heaps, barns and houses. *Allochernes powelli* (Kew) is one such which may be under threat, as its habitat of barn and stable refuse is becoming increasingly scarce in today's high-technology agriculture. However, it has not been given RDB status because it is probably under-recorded and is thought by some to be an introduced species.

The pseudoscorpion recording scheme has been in operation for a number of years, and a provisional atlas has been produced (Jones 1980b). The recent publication of a new monograph (Legg & Jones 1988) will undoubtedly encourage further study of this group. It includes updated distribution maps.

Spiders form the largest order covered by this Red Data Book. Merrett, Locket & Millidge (1985) and Roberts (1987) both list 622 British species despite the composition of their lists differing slightly. It is thus not surprising that spiders contribute the most species with RDB status. Spiders are ubiquitous in the terrestrial habitats of the British Isles. The orb web spiders are probably the most familiar, but many British species use other techniques to catch their prey, including a range of other web forms, active hunting as practised by the wolf spiders and jumping spiders, and lying in ambush in flower heads to catch pollinating insects, a method employed by some crab spiders. Most spiders feed on insects, but *Dysdera* spp. catch woodlice, and other spiders can be the prey of some species. All spiders gain their nourishment by external digestion, injecting or pouring digestive juices over the prey and ingesting the resulting soup.

Courtship is a well-known phenomenon in spiders, males of many species performing a ritual dance of palp-waving and leg-vibrating which is thought to reduce the predatory tendencies of the female before mating takes place. The fertilised egg sac may be attached to vegetation or some other substrate or may be carried by the female spider, and in nearly all species the female guards the eggs to some extent. Hatching is usually within a few days or weeks. No species has a long dormant egg stage and some achieve two generations in a year. Larger spiders such as *Dolomedes* spp. may have a three- or four-year life cycle. Dispersal over long distances can be achieved by ballooning. Here, the freshly emerged spiderling extrudes silk threads into the wind from a suitable vantage point, eventually being lifted into the air, with the potential to drift many miles. Most British habitats furnish examples of spiders under threat, with the faunas of heathland, the coastal zone, wetland and undisturbed grassland featuring prominently.

Merrett, Locket & Millidge (1985) announced the deletion of a number of species from the British list, owing to improved understanding of spider taxonomy or doubts about the validity of the records. Three of the species are known from only single specimens found in the nineteenth century, and there are doubts about whether these species were ever truly established in Britain (P. Merrett pers. comm.). The species concerned are *Salticus mutabilis* Lucas, 1846, *Heliophanus melinus* L. Koch, 1867 and *Aculepeira ceropegia* (Walckenaer, 1802). If wild populations of any of these were to be found in Britain, the species concerned would probably qualify for Red Data Book status.

The main identification work for British spiders was for many years Locket & Millidge (1951, 1953), which was updated by Locket, Millidge & Merrett (1974). Roberts (1985a, 1985b, 1987) has now superseded these and is unlikely to be surpassed in the foreseeable future. Jones (1983) provided a useful photographic guide. The spider recording scheme has recently been relaunched in collaboration with the Biological Records Centre at Monks Wood Experimental Station, a welcome aim being "to record the arachnofauna of selected sites of particular concern to nature conservation".

The harvestmen (Opiliones) were assessed for this book, but it was decided that none qualified for RDB status. The newly discovered *Sabacon viscayanum ramblaianum* Martens is known from a small but growing number of sites (I.K. Morgan pers. comm.) and cannot be considered to be under threat. Nor does it qualify on grounds of endemism, as this taxon is also found in the Pyrenees (Martens 1988). Distribution maps resulting from the Opiliones recording scheme have recently been published (Sankey 1988).

Of the mites, only the watermites (Hydracarina) were considered for inclusion, and it was decided that recording of this group was at too early a stage for Red Data Book categories to be justifiable. There are undoubtedly some uncommon species within the watermites. For example, *Wandesia racovitzai* Gledhill is a bizarre elongate species discovered in the interstitial water of a Cumbrian river shingle bed in 1966. No further specimens have come to light despite much work on the interstitial fauna in Cumbria and Scotland. However, the lack of further records from the original site suggests that it occurs at very low density and mitigates its apparent rarity. An identification key to watermites is being prepared by the Freshwater Biological Association.

NEOBISIUM CARPENTERI

Phylum CHELICERATA
Class ARACHNIDA

Order PSEUDOSCORPIONES
Family NEOBISIIDAE

Neobisium carpenteri agg., originally known as *Obisium carpenteri* (Kew).

Identification

Legg & Jones (1988). *N. carpenteri* (Kew, 1910) was described from Irish material. Specimens from Great Britain may not belong to the same species; see below.

Distribution

In 1950 specimens believed to be *N. carpenteri* were found at Colne Point, North Essex, where this form is easily obtained. Other records are from another North Essex locality; South Essex; the coast of the Isle of Grain, West Kent; and Spurn Point, Southeast Yorkshire. In 1984-85 specimens resembling this species were found in a quarry in Carmarthen. The type material was collected in 1909-10 at Glengariff, West Cork, Ireland, and there are more recent records from this site. It has not yet been found outside the British Isles. For map, see Legg & Jones (1988).

Habitat and ecology

At Colne Point the habitat is marsh debris and litter among shingle. However, at the type locality, Glengariff, it was found under the flaking bark of strawberry-trees *Arbutus unedo* and in the *Sphagnum* moss and leaf litter beneath the trees.

Status

Rare. The odd distribution suggests either that it is under-recorded or that more than one species is involved (see Legg & Jones 1988), a view supported by the widely different habitats reported in Ireland and Great Britain. Specimens from the east coast of England are clearly all of one species. R.E. Jones (pers. comm.) has suggested that the Welsh specimens could belong to a third species in the *carpenteri* aggregate. *N. carpenteri* agg. may be endemic to the British Isles.

Threats

Alteration of land-use, such as seashore and other coastal recreational development. Marine pollution such as oil spills could be a danger to the east coast colonies. Loss through tidal action and erosion could destroy the Yorkshire colony, as Spurn Point is predicted by some to be on the verge of being lost to the sea during severe winter storms.

Conservation

Colne Point is an SSSI and in part an NNR and reserve of the Essex Trust, and Spurn Point is an SSSI and reserve of the Yorkshire Trust. The importance of the sites supporting this species is enhanced by the presence of other restricted and uncommon invertebrates.

Author

G. Legg, using information from Beier (1963), Legg & Jones (1988) and R.E. Jones and A.J. Rundle (pers. comms).

123

DENDROCHERNES CYRNEUS

RARE

Phylum CHELICERATA
Class ARACHNIDA

Order PSEUDOSCORPIONES
Family CHERNETIDAE

Dendrochernes cyrneus (C.L. Koch, 1873), formerly known as *Chernes cyrneus* and *Chelifer cyrneus*.

Identification

Legg & Jones (1988).

Distribution

There is a 1957 record from West Gloucestershire, and there are post-1960 records (in most cases in addition to earlier records) from sites in Northamptonshire, Nottinghamshire, Oxfordshire, Berkshire, Surrey and Leicestershire. A record has also been published from Suffolk (Gilbert 1951) but there is doubt about its validity (Mendel 1981). Legg & Jones (1988) present a distribution map. *D. cyrneus* is widely distributed in Europe, in France, Germany, Austria, Bulgaria, Hungary, Italy, Corsica and Albania, and also recorded from Cyprus and Algeria.

Habitat and ecology

The majority of records of this species are from ancient woodland or ancient parkland. It usually occurs under bark and in dry sapwood of dead, decaying or overmature trees or parts of trees. Oak is favoured, but it has been found associated with other species including ash, beech, elm and hawthorn. The condition of the wood is more important than the tree species. It appears to prefer timber heated by the sun and shuns the shaded side of branches and tree trunks. It was found in debris in a hole in an oak growing in an open meadow at Maisemore, West Gloucestershire. Long-horn beetles (Cerambycidae) may be important for its dispersal, by phoresis. It overwinters in silken chambers from November to March; consequently free-living individuals cannot be found during the winter. At other times of year it may be difficult to find because of its having withdrawn into beetle borings. Kew (1929) found that specimens in Richmond Park emerged onto the tree trunks on calm warm summer evenings about an hour after sunset.

Status

Jones (1980a) considered that viable populations remained at only four sites in England. In view of the difficulty of finding specimens, this may be an over-pessimistic view and *D. cyrneus* may still be present at sites where it has not been seen for many years. In 1989 it was discovered in two fragments of woodland close to Castor Hanglands, Northamptonshire. However, in view of its strong association with ancient woodland, the rigorous examination which this habitat receives from coleopterists, and the large size of *D. cyrneus*, it is unlikely to be grossly under-recorded and the status of Rare is justified.

Threats

Alterations of land-use, including intensification of forestry. Commercial forestry frequently involves the replacement of native

Sherwood Forest, Birklands and Bilhaugh SSSI, Nottinghamshire. The aged stag-headed oaks support a renowned assemblage of invertebrates, including the pseudoscorpion *Dendrochernes cyrneus* and the spiders *Lepthyphantes midas* and *Tuberta macrophthalma*. The area of ancient forest has been greatly reduced by expansion of conifer plantation, arable agriculture and housing. (Photo by P. Wakely.)

broadleaved woodland with conifers (as in much of Sherwood Forest), and conifers do not support this pseudoscorpion. Even where native broadleaved woodland remains, the trees are cropped long before reaching the overmature stage which this species requires. Ancient trees generally form the most valuable invertebrate habitat in an ancient woodland, but felling is all too often carried out to make way for younger timber trees. A similar threat is the removal of dead wood (by tree surgery or boughs being shed naturally) from ancient woodland, parkland and hedgerows. The last two habitats are susceptible to loss of dead wood through a desire for tidiness. The presence of overmature trees is often not tolerated in areas open to the public because the loss of limbs from such trees is seen as a hazard. Coleopterists and other naturalists frequently remove the bark from dead wood while searching for specimens, and this could destroy a significant proportion of the habitat where dead wood is scarce. Restraint is necessary when studying the fauna of dead wood. One of the sites listed by Jones (1980a) as supporting a viable population is a narrow strip of woodland between a road and clay-diggings and there are now very few trees remaining in a suitable condition for this species, partly owing to vandalism (Jones 1979; J.H. Bratton pers. obs.). Most of the mature trees were felled at Castor Hanglands in 1952, shortly before the site was leased to the NCC, and adjacent woodland not within the boundary of the NNR has been converted to conifer plantation; thus the habitat available to *D. cyrneus* at this site has been severely reduced.

Conservation

Several of its sites are protected. Castor Hanglands (records from 1954 to 1978) is an NNR. Birklands and Bilhaugh (Sherwood Forest Country Park), Nottinghamshire, Blenheim Park, Oxfordshire, and Windsor Forest and Great Park, Berkshire, are SSSIs. Richmond Park, Surrey, is protected to the extent that it is a Royal Park and thus safe from drastic land-use change. It is important to ensure the continuity of the dead wood habitat at its known sites.

Authors

G. Legg and J.H. Bratton, using information from Beier (1963), George (1961), Jones (1980a), Legg & Jones (1988), W. Turner (unpublished) and M. Beeson, D.N. Carstairs, A.O. Chater, R.S. George, R.E. Jones, P. Kirby and A.J. Rundle (pers. comms).

ERESUS NIGER   ENDANGERED

Ladybird Spider

Phylum CHELICERATA   Order ARANEAE
Class ARACHNIDA   Family ERESIDAE

Eresus niger (Petagna, 1787).

Identification

Locket & Millidge (1951); Jones (1983); Roberts (1985a, 1985b).

Distribution	Formerly recorded from several heathland areas in the Poole/Bournemouth area, Dorset, and may have been seen at Kynance Cove, West Cornwall, in 1932 (Bristowe 1958). Now known only from one site in Dorset. This species is rare in northern Europe (Denmark and Germany) but widespread and fairly frequent in parts of southern Europe. There is, however, some doubt as to whether the southern European form is a separate subspecies or species, as the appearance of the male is very different.
Habitat and ecology	Found on dry sandy heathland with some bare or lichen-covered patches. Shelter from wind is probably necessary, and a south-facing slope is an advantage. It builds a silk-lined burrow about 10 cm deep covered by a small silk and debris 'roof'. Well-drained soil is essential. The burrows are usually found in open patches. The life cycle takes at least four years. One batch of eighty to ninety eggs is laid. The young remain in the mother's burrow over the first winter, until the sixth instar. Males are active in early May. Females and young feed from April to early June and in August and September, aestivating in late June and July. The food is mainly beetles and spiders, and ants when the spider is young.
Status	One of the rarest and most spectacular of British spiders, thought to be extinct in Britain until rediscovered in 1979. The population size is believed to vary between fifteen and forty adults, with unknown numbers of juveniles.
Threats	The site is a small isolated fragment of heath. Threats to the habitat include encroachment onto the heathland by the surrounding rhododendrons and pine trees, fire and loss of heather from infestations of the Heather Beetle *Lochmaea suturalis* (Thomson). The population is so small that even limited collecting of this species is not acceptable.
Conservation	There is an agreement with the Forestry Commission on the conservation and management of the site. A fence has been erected around the site by the NCC. Some pine trees and rhododendrons have been removed, and this should be continued, leaving just a few to provide shelter. Further research into the biology and habitat requirements of the species is desirable. This species is protected by inclusion in Schedule 5 of the Wildlife and Countryside Act 1981, which prohibits, among other things, taking specimens without a licence.
Author	P. Merrett, using information from Locket & Millidge (1951) and personal observations.

DICTYNA MAJOR

VULNERABLE

Phylum CHELICERATA
Class ARACHNIDA

Order ARANEAE
Family DICTYNIDAE

Dictyna major Menge, 1869, formerly known as *D. arenicola* O. P.-Cambridge.

Identification   Locket & Millidge (1951); Roberts (1985a).

Distribution   Recorded from Aberlady Bay, East Lothian; from Loch Morlich, East Inverness-shire, in 1893; and from Morayshire. It has been found throughout much of northern Europe, including France, Belgium, the Netherlands, Germany, Denmark and Finland, and in the Balkans, Hungary and Poland.

Habitat and ecology   At Aberlady Bay, the males were found running over warm sand and the females were concealed with their egg cocoons in pieces of dried seaweed and withered leaves on the sand. At Loch Morlich, specimens were found on the shore at an altitude of about 320 metres. It is not unusual for coastal species to be found on loch shores.

Status   No reliable recent records, despite much searching at Aberlady Bay and Gullane (D. Horsfield pers. comm.).

Threats   Possibly public pressure on beaches, disturbing the strandline.

Conservation   Aberlady Bay is an LNR and SSSI. There is not undue public pressure on the site and the drift line is left undisturbed, so the habitat of this species would seem to be still present (R.S. Key pers. comm.), though this may not have been the case throughout the period since *D. major* was recorded.

Author   P. Merrett, using information from Locket & Millidge (1951).

LATHYS STIGMATISATA

RARE

Phylum CHELICERATA
Class ARACHNIDA

Order ARANEAE
Family DICTYNIDAE

Lathys stigmatisata (Menge, 1869).

Identification   Locket & Millidge (1951); Roberts (1985a).

Distribution   Recorded early this century from the Lizard and Kynance, West Cornwall, and Lundy Island, off the North Devon coast. In the 1960s it was found at Chapel Porth, East Cornwall, and Dungeness, East Kent (also recorded at the latter site in 1982 and found to be quite numerous there in the late 1980s during an NCC survey); in the mid-1980s and 1989 at Rye Harbour, East Sussex; and in the late 1980s at the Crumbles, East Sussex. Also known from France, Belgium, the Netherlands, Germany, Austria, Switzerland, Denmark, Sweden, Russia, Czechoslovakia, Hungary, Poland, Yugoslavia and the Balkans.

Habitat and ecology Found under stones, among heather and grass, and among sparse vegetation on shingle. Both sexes are adult in April and females have also been found in June.

Status Apparently rare, but as it matures early in the season it may have escaped detection in some localities. At most known sites several specimens have been found.

Threats The loss of coastal heathlands in Cornwall and public pressure on the remaining ones. Accidental fire is a risk at Kynance. Dungeness is being degraded by a number of activities including gravel extraction, vehicle damage and trampling. The last two cause disturbance to the fragile vegetation and the thin covering of soil, resulting in the creation of areas of bare shingle. The shingle habitat at the Crumbles has been largely destroyed by building and marina development.

Conservation Chapel Porth, Kynance Cove and Lundy are National Trust properties, the last two also being SSSIs. The National Trust now controls public access at Kynance Cove and the previously serious damage from trampling of the cliff-top vegetation has eased. The National Trust and the NCC are reintroducing grazing to this site, which should benefit the heathland and grassland communities. The Cornwall Trust have a reserve at Kynance Cliffs. The Lizard is an SSSI and in part an NNR. The Rye Harbour records are from within the LNR. Dungeness is an SSSI and in part an RSPB reserve.

Author P. Merrett, using information from Locket & Millidge (1951), Maidstone Museum Biological Records Centre, and G. Legg and J.A. and F.M. Murphy (pers. comms).

ALTELLA LUCIDA   ENDANGERED

Phylum CHELICERATA   Order ARANEAE
Class ARACHNIDA   Family DICTYNIDAE

Altella lucida (Simon, 1874).

Identification Locket & Millidge (1951); Locket, Millidge & Merrett (1974); Roberts (1985a, 1985b).

Distribution Known from Morden Bog, Dorset, since 1971. A male was

Morden Bog NNR, Dorset. Two extremely rare spiders are to be found on the exposed stony areas of this heath. This microhabitat is easily lost without active management to prevent the vegetation closing over the bare areas. Wet heath can be seen in the background which supports the Large Marsh Grasshopper *Stethophyma grossum* and other threatened invertebrates. (Photo by P. Wakely.)

recorded from a house at Hoddesdon, Hertfordshire, in 1880. This was possibly a chance importation, though there were sizeable areas of wet heath in the Hoddesdon area at that time. This species is rare in France and Germany; also recorded from Italy, Spain, Austria and Belgium.

Habitat and ecology Found in cavities in the soil under small stones embedded in dry algal mats on bare sandy areas of dry heathland. Adults are found in April and May, occurring in small colonies.

Status Currently known from only a few square metres of heath, with a population of possibly less than fifty. There is the possibility of its having been overlooked in other areas, in view of its small size, specialised micro-habitat and early maturation season. However, the lack of disturbance or burning at Morden Bog makes the habitat at this site very unusual and few other sites are likely to be suitable for this spider.

Threats The fragility of the micro-habitat is such that even widely used heathland management practices such as controlled burning could cause damage. In the absence of such management, seral progression is a threat.

Conservation Morden Bog is an NNR. The bare areas were caused by military training during the war and, because the area is very gravelly, they have not revegetated. It may eventually become necessary to create new disturbed areas. In the meantime, management should concentrate on removal of pine and other tree seedlings with minimum disruption to the *A. lucida* colony. All burning should be avoided.

Author P. Merrett, based on personal observations, Locket & Millidge (1951), Locket, Millidge & Merrett (1974) and E. Duffey (pers. comm.).

ULOBORUS WALCKENAERIUS   RARE

Phylum CHELICERATA   Order ARANEAE
Class ARACHNIDA   Family ULOBORIDAE

Uloborus walckenaerius Latreille, 1806.

Identification Locket & Millidge (1951); Roberts (1985a).

Distribution Has been found in large numbers at a few places in the New Forest, South Hampshire; Chobham Common and Thursley Common, Surrey; and Lavington Common, West Sussex. Also recorded from Crookham, North Hampshire; Ambersham Common, West Sussex; Ash Ranges, Surrey; and many years ago

131

from Bloxworth, Dorset, and Wokingham, Berkshire. Widespread in central and especially southern Europe. Also recorded from the Canary Islands.

Habitat and ecology Found among mature heather, where it spins an almost horizontal orb web about midway between the ground and the top of the heather. A burnt area of Chobham Common was recolonised after four or five years (F.M. Murphy pers. comm.). Both sexes are adult in June, females also in July and occasionally in August.

Status Abundant in a few places but has disappeared from or become scarce at some former strongholds.

Threats Loss of heathland to other land-uses has decreased the area of potential habitat. For example, most of Bloxworth Heath has now been planted with conifers and forms Wareham Forest, though a small portion remains as Morden Bog NNR. A large area of Thursley Common was damaged by fire in 1976. Few specimens of *U. walckenaerius* have been found there since then, and none recently. Fires have also occurred at Ambersham Common in recent years, but the most serious damage at this site is from motorcycle scrambling. Birch and pine invasion is a problem at Chobham Common, and some parts are subjected to too frequent accidental fires, which are leading to replacement of the heath by purple moor-grass *Molinia caerulea*. Locally, grazing levels in the New Forest are too high to permit the development of tall, mature heather in many areas, though with falling numbers of grazing cattle and ponies this may change in coming years. If the number of commoners exercising their grazing rights continues to fall, lack of grazing, causing loss of heath to scrub, could be a more serious problem (Chapman, Rose & Basanta 1989). Overuse by horse-riders is a major cause of damage to the New Forest heath, with a proliferation of horse tracks eroding the vegetation and soil (New Forest Review Group 1987).

Conservation Occurs within the New Forest SSSI, Chobham Common SSSI (in part also an LNR), Ash Ranges to Pirbright SSSI and the National Trust property at Lavington Common SSSI. Thursley Common is an NNR and Surrey Trust reserve. Ambersham Common is an SSSI and part is a reserve of the Sussex Trust. A burning regime, whereby small areas are burnt each year on a long rotation of 20 years, backed up by manual scrub clearance where necessary, should ensure the continuity of the correct habitat for this species. Unfortunately, this is difficult to achieve even on nature reserves because accidental fires tend to occur more frequently than this. In the New Forest the *Calluna* heath is maintained by grazing, but this option is not available on some other heaths because common rights prevent the erection of fences and busy roads present a danger to unfenced livestock. There are proposals to increase the area of heath in the New Forest by up to 943 ha by not replanting areas currently under conifers (New Forest Review Group 1987). Lavington Common has been described as one of the finest

132

Calluna heaths in Sussex since scrub control has been carried out by the National Trust (Rose 1987), though rhododendron invasion is likely to continue to be a problem at this site.

Author   P. Merrett, using information from Locket & Millidge (1951), Lovesey (1988) and R. Jones and F.M. Murphy (pers. comms).

HYPTIOTES PARADOXUS   RARE
Triangle Spider

Phylum CHELICERATA   Order ARANEAE
Class ARACHNIDA   Family ULOBORIDAE

Hyptiotes paradoxus (C.L. Koch, 1834).

Identification   Locket & Millidge (1951); Roberts (1985a, 1985b).

Distribution   First found in Britain in Borrowdale, Cumberland, in the 1860s and since recorded from West Walk Wood and various places in the New Forest, South Hampshire; Box Hill and Wallis Wood, Surrey; Bagley Wood, Berkshire; Buttler's Hangings and Hearnton Wood, Buckinghamshire; and Grubbins Wood, Westmorland. Widespread in southern and central Europe but not common.

Habitat and ecology   Mainly found on yew or in the vicinity of yew trees, also other evergreens (especially box and holly). It spins a triangular segment of orb web among tree branches. Both sexes are adult from July to September. At Buttler's Hangings it was first found in scrub on chalk grassland, but it has since been found in nearby yew woodland.

Status   Known from fewer than ten sites. Abundant at Box Hill, Bagley Wood (still there in the 1970s) and some places in the New Forest.

Threats   Bagley Wood was an ancient deciduous woodland, but large areas have now been planted with conifers. It is not known whether the spider is utilising the conifers or the remaining broadleaved woodland, but it has been found on several occasions since the conifers were planted, so it has not been eliminated by the changes in the wood. West Walk Wood has similarly fallen victim to planting with conifers and the current status of *H. paradoxus* there is not known.

Conservation   Several sites are protected as SSSIs. Box Hill is National Trust property, Buttler's Hangings, Grubbins Wood and Wallis Wood are County Trust nature reserves. However, the presence of an established population at Buttler's Hangings remains to be proved. The specimen found there may have been a stray from the adjacent Hearnton Wood, which fits the usual habitat of the spider.

133

Author P. Merrett, with additional information from Britten (1912), Locket & Millidge (1951), Parker (1977) and M. Askins, R.B. Coleman, J.A.L. Cooke, C. Hambler, J.A. and F.M. Murphy, J.R. Parker and R. Thomas (pers. comms).

HAPLODRASSUS UMBRATILIS   RARE

Phylum CHELICERATA   Order ARANEAE
Class ARACHNIDA   Family GNAPHOSIDAE

Haplodrassus umbratilis (L. Koch, 1866).

Identification Locket, Millidge & Merrett (1974); Roberts (1985a).

Distribution Recorded from five sites in east Dorset: Cranborne Common, Stephens Castle, Holt Heath, Knighton Heath and Horton Common; and from Vales Moor on the western edge of the New Forest, South Hampshire, all since 1969. This pattern of distribution is similar to that of *Ero aphana* (Walckenaer), a more seriously threatened species. In 1990 the British range of *H. umbratilis* was found to include Hadleigh Downs, South Essex (Harvey 1990). It is widespread in Europe.

Habitat and ecology In Dorset and Hampshire it has been found on dry heathland in the building and mature phases. In Essex it occurred on steep south-facing grassland with scrub. Adult males have been found in May and June, females from May to August.

Status Abundant at Vales Moor and Cranborne Common and probably occurs in several sites on the eastern side of the Avon Valley on the western fringes of the New Forest.

Threats Uncontrolled heathland fires and the loss of heathland to building development and agriculture. Previously abundant at Horton Common, but much of this site (100 ha) has now been ploughed up and is used for agriculture. Knighton Heath is now a golf course with only a few banks of heath left, and even the golf course is now under threat of building development. Much of Cranborne Common has been planted with conifers, only strips of heathland remaining. If the density of scrub at Hadleigh Downs is increasing, it may overrun the grassland required by this spider.

Conservation Occurs on Holt Heath NNR. The remaining heath at Cranborne Common is now an SSSI and in part a Dorset Trust reserve. There is pressure for some of the conifers outside the SSSI to be removed for the benefit of the herpetological interest and, if this should occur, the invertebrates would be likely to benefit as well. Heath at Stephens Castle lies within Verwood Heaths SSSI. The surviving twenty hectares of heath at Horton Common now have the protection of SSSI status. Management to accommodate this spider requires patches of the heath to be regularly returned to the early stages of heather development on a long rotation, preferably well over a decade. This should ensure the permanent presence of the building and mature stages. It could be achieved by small-scale burning, or, where nearby pine plantations preclude this, heavy grazing for a short period or manual stripping of the vegetation could be attempted. At Hadleigh Downs, sufficient grazing is required to maintain patches of short sward and to prevent scrub encroachment. Some scrub clearance may also be necessary.

Author   P. Merrett, using personal observations and Locket, Millidge & Merrett (1974), with additional information from Haskins (1988) and D. Elton, L. Farrell, R.G. Snazell and J.R. White (pers. comms).

HAPLODRASSUS SOERENSENI   VULNERABLE

Phylum CHELICERATA   Order ARANEAE
Class ARACHNIDA   Family GNAPHOSIDAE

Haplodrassus soerenseni (Strand, 1900).

Identification   Locket & Millidge (1953); Locket, Millidge & Merrett (1974); Roberts (1985a).

Distribution   In Britain, recorded only from Abernethy Forest, East Inverness-shire, in 1948, 1959 and 1961, and from the Black Wood of Rannoch, Mid Perthshire, in 1966. It has also been found in Sweden, Norway, Finland, Russia, Poland, Czechoslovakia, Switzerland and Austria.

Habitat and ecology   In Britain, apparently confined to Caledonian pine forest. Found among ground vegetation in open pine woods. Females with eggs have been noted in July and adults also occur in June.

Status   Few specimens have been found, but little collecting has been carried out in this area in recent years.

Threats   The loss of Caledonian pine forest, often to more intensive blanket forestry. At least 25% of native Caledonian pine forest extant in 1957 and described by Steven & Carlisle (1959) had been lost by 1987 and the greatest losses (13% of the 1957 area) are due to ploughing and underplanting with exotic conifers. These losses include 1,308 ha clear-felled in Abernethy Forest, of which only 60 ha have not been ploughed and replanted. Planting is usually at a density of 2,500 trees per hectare, and this produces 'blanket' forest with little light reaching the ground and virtually no ground flora. Such conditions eliminate *H. soerenseni* along with most of the other fauna and flora. Similarly, in the Black Wood of Rannoch there has been planting of conifers, both on adjacent unforested ground and in 214 ha of scattered mature native pine. The establishment of plantations adjacent to native forest precludes the natural expansion of the forest and threatens existing forest through allowing its invasion by the exotic species. The exotics frequently outcompete the native Scots pine *Pinus sylvestris.*

Conservation   Abernethy Forest is an SSSI, part NNR, and a large area has recently been purchased by the RSPB. The Black Wood of Rannoch is also an SSSI. Part is an FNR and the Forestry Commission have a management plan aimed at conserving and expanding the native component. While this will ensure the future of the native pine, closing-in of the forest canopy needs to be avoided. Fencing and deer-culling are promoting strong regeneration of pine in parts, and much thinning with the creation of glades may need to be implemented if the ground vegetation is to be maintained in a state suitable for *H. soerenseni.*

Author   P. Merrett, using information from Locket & Millidge (1953), Locket, Millidge & Merrett (1974), Bain (1987) and G.H. Locket (pers. comm.).

HAPLODRASSUS MINOR   RARE

Phylum CHELICERATA   Order ARANEAE
Class ARACHNIDA   Family GNAPHOSIDAE

Haplodrassus minor (O. P.-Cambridge, 1879), formerly known as *Drassodes minor.*

Identification   Locket & Millidge (1951); Locket, Millidge & Merrett (1974); Roberts (1985a).

Distribution   Recorded from the Portland end of Chesil Beach, Dorset; Hayling Island, South Hampshire; Wootton Creek, Isle of Wight; Rye Harbour, East Sussex; Colne Point, North Essex; Havergate Island, East Suffolk; and Foryd Bay, Caernarvonshire. European distribution includes Germany, Switzerland, Hungary, Czechoslovakia, Poland, the Balkans and Russia

Habitat and ecology   Among tide litter and sparse vegetation and on shingle on the seashore. Both sexes are adult from April to June.

Status   Apparently fairly numerous at Colne Point, but most populations are very localised and the habitat is vulnerable to disturbance.

Threats   Public pressure can disturb the habitat by trampling. In some areas, holiday development and gravel extraction are also threats.

On some beaches used for recreation the strandline is regularly removed by machine as it is considered unsightly and a source of pests. This is not known to take place on any beaches supporting this spider, but it could pose a threat to this and other strandline-dwelling invertebrates.

Conservation   Havergate Island is an NNR and RSPB reserve. Colne Point is a reserve of the Essex Trust and within an NNR. A small part of Hayling Island is a County Trust reserve and includes some shingle workings. Rye Harbour, Chesil Beach and Foryd Bay are SSSIs, the first being in part also an LNR. Accumulations of tideline litter are likely to be of value to this spider and should be left undisturbed.

Author   P. Merrett, using information from Locket & Millidge (1951), Locket, Millidge & Merrett (1974) and J.R. Parker and S.A. Williams (pers. comms).

GNAPHOSA OCCIDENTALIS   ENDANGERED

Phylum CHELICERATA   Order ARANEAE
Class ARACHNIDA   Family GNAPHOSIDAE

Gnaphosa occidentalis Simon, 1878.

Identification   Locket & Millidge (1951); Locket, Millidge & Merrett (1974); Roberts (1985a).

Distribution   The British records are from West Cornwall: Kynance Cove in 1922 (one male and two females) and Cadgwith in 1935. Also known from Italy, France and Switzerland.

Habitat and ecology   The habitat in Britain is apparently not recorded. The two localities are well-known for their cliff-top heather and grassland. The spider would possibly be found under stones in this vegetation. Both sexes are adult in June.

Status   Few specimens have been found in this country, and none since 1935 despite a considerable amount of collecting effort at Kynance and Cadgwith Coves in recent years.

Threats   The cliff-tops at Kynance have suffered badly from heavy trampling, but public access is now controlled by the National Trust and the heath and grassland communities are recovering very well. Accidental fires are possibly the main threat at this site now. At Cadgwith there has been no grazing on the cliffs for many years and the coastal heath and grassland have been largely lost to rank vegetation including scrub and bracken. It is unlikely that *G. occidentalis* will have survived at Cadgwith.

Conservation	Part of Kynance Cove and much of the area of cliffs around Cadgwith are National Trust properties. Kynance Cove is within an SSSI and some of the cliffs are a reserve of the Cornwall Trust. It is not known whether these protected areas encompass the sites where *G. occidentalis* was found. Grazing is being restored by the National Trust and the NCC on the cliff heathland at Kynance.
Author	P. Merrett, using information from Jackson (1924), Bristowe (1939), Locket & Millidge (1951), Locket, Millidge & Merrett (1974) and K.N.A. Alexander (pers. comm.).

CALLILEPIS NOCTURNA   ENDANGERED

Phylum CHELICERATA   Order ARANEAE
Class ARACHNIDA   Family GNAPHOSIDAE

Callilepis nocturna (Linnaeus, 1758).

Identification	Locket, Millidge & Merrett (1974); Roberts (1985a, 1985b).
Distribution	Found in 1969 and subsequently at and near Deckler's Cliff, East Prawle, South Devon. In 1990 it was found about 2 km away along the cliff to the east at Signalhouse Point (K.N.A. Alexander pers. comm.). This species is widespread in Europe.
Habitat and ecology	Near Deckler's Cliff the habitat is a steep sandy bank ('head' deposits) on a raised beach below sea-cliffs, sparsely vegetated with a sedge (probably *Carex arenaria*) and various herbs, including bloody cranesbill *Geranium sanguineum*. At Signalhouse Point it was found on sunny rock outcrops sheltered by scrub. Adults have been found in May and June.
Status	Well-established in this small length of coast.
Threats	Coastal defence work has degraded soft-rock cliffs on many stretches of coast but is unlikely to be carried out at Deckler's Cliff. Further growth of scrub at Signalhouse Point could overshade the habitat (K.N.A. Alexander pers. comm.).
Conservation	Deckler's Cliff is under the protection of the National Trust and lies within an SSSI and Area of Outstanding Natural Beauty. Much of the head deposit has been eroded away from this part of the coast, but some continual slight erosion is probably important for maintaining the sparsely vegetated conditions on the sandy bank near Deckler's Cliff. Scrub development at Signalhouse Point needs to be monitored and controlled if necessary. Control could be by moderate grazing being introduced or by manual scrub clearance.

Author   P. Merrett, using information from K.N.A. Alexander, R.G. Snazell and F.M. Murphy (pers. comms), Murphy (1971) and Locket, Millidge & Merrett (1974).

MICARIA ALPINA   **RARE**

Phylum CHELICERATA   Order ARANEAE
Class ARACHNIDA   Family GNAPHOSIDAE

Micaria alpina L. Koch, 1872.

Identification   Locket & Millidge (1951); Locket, Millidge & Merrett (1974); Roberts (1985a).

Distribution   Recorded from Y Lliwedd and Clyder Fawr, Caernarvonshire; Cader Idris, Merionethshire; Creag Meagaidh, West Inverness-shire; An Teallach, West Ross; and between Loch an Fheoir and Loch Gaineamhach, East Sutherland. In Europe, known from France, Austria, Switzerland, Hungary and Sweden.

Habitat and ecology Under stones, among grass and moss, etc., usually above 750 metres. On Creag Meagaidh it was found in *Vaccinium myrtillus* heath, while on An Teallach the habitat was *Nardus/Racomitrium* grassland (D. Horsfield pers. comm.). Near Loch an Fheoir it was found in a hummock of *Racomitrium* in the middle of a *Sphagnum* bog. Males are adult from May to July, females in June and July.

Status   Very few specimens have been found but it has a wide range in Britain.

Threats   Some populations are likely to suffer damage from hill-walkers and skiers. Forestry is a potential threat to populations below the tree line.

Conservation   Occurs in Creag Meagaidh and Snowdon NNRs and probably in Cader Idris NNR. An Teallach is an SSSI. Part of Glyder Fawr is owned by the National Trust.

Author   P. Merrett, using information from Locket & Millidge (1951), Locket, Millidge & Merrett (1974) and D. Horsfield and J.E.D. Milner (pers. comms).

CLUBIONA SUBSULTANS   VULNERABLE

Phylum CHELICERATA   Order ARANEAE
Class ARACHNIDA   Family CLUBIONIDAE

Identification	*Clubiona subsultans* Thorell, 1875. Locket & Millidge (1951); Roberts (1985a).
Distribution	Recorded from Abernethy Forest several times between 1945 and 1970 and near Coylumbridge in 1979, both in East Inverness-shire, and from the Black Wood of Rannoch, Mid Perthshire, in 1913, 1948, 1966 and 1987. This species is widespread in Europe, being known from Italy, France, Belgium, the Netherlands, Germany, Austria, Switzerland, Denmark, Sweden, Norway, Finland, Poland, Hungary, Czechoslovakia and Russia.
Habitat and ecology	Associated with Caledonian pine woods, having been found under bark, on branches, in pine litter, once among young pines and, near Coylumbridge, on juniper growing as an understorey within a pine wood. Adults of both sexes have been found in June, males also in September.
Status	Fairly plentiful in Abernethy Forest, widespread but sparse in the Black Wood of Rannoch.
Threats	Loss of Caledonian pine forest through conversion to intensive plantation forestry. Both Abernethy Forest and the Black Wood of Rannoch have suffered from planting of Scots pine and non-native conifers in large blocks, sometimes preceded by clear-felling of the native pine. 30 ha of Abernethy Forest were felled in 1984 before it was renotified as an SSSI, and in all 226 ha of this forest have been lost since 1977.
Conservation	The Black Wood of Rannoch is an SSSI and part is an FNR. The Forestry Commission has produced a management plan aimed at conserving the pine and other native trees. This includes a 384 ha zone in which there are no exotic conifers and which will not be subject to planting or felling and a further 526 ha in which exotics will be gradually felled and replaced with local Scots pine. Abernethy Forest is an SSSI and part is an NNR. Much of the Forest was acquired by the RSPB in 1988. At both sites, natural regeneration of Scots pine is occurring and this should be allowed to proceed to give the typical open forest structure. In the Black Wood of Rannoch, regeneration in parts is so dense as to be "almost impenetrable" (Bain 1987) and such areas are likely to suffer the same shortcomings as areas of plantation, perhaps necessitating early thinning of the saplings to create glades.

Author   P. Merrett, using information from Locket & Millidge (1951), Bain
                    (1987) and N.P. Ashmole, G.H. Locket, J.A.L. Cooke and
                    M.J. Roberts (pers. comms).

CLUBIONA ROSSERAE   ENDANGERED

Phylum CHELICERATA   Order ARANEAE
Class ARACHNIDA   Family CLUBIONIDAE

Clubiona rosserae Locket, 1953.

Identification   Locket & Millidge (1953); Roberts (1985a).

Distribution   Found in 1951 and on several subsequent occasions at
                        Chippenham Fen, Cambridgeshire, most recently in 1988
                        (D.A. Procter pers. comm.). In 1969 it was recorded at Tuddenham
                        Fen, West Suffolk (J.R. Parker pers. comm.). Otherwise known only
                        from Czechoslovakia.

Habitat and ecology Found among cut sedge and around tussocks in fen. Adults have
                        been found in February, May, June and September.

Status   There appears to be a well-established population at Chippenham
                        Fen.

Threats   Dredging of the River Lark since 1964 has lowered the water table
                        in the region of Tuddenham Fen and greatly reduced the amount of
                        fen along the river valley. However, part of Tuddenham Fen is
                        spring-fed and this is to a large extent independent of the state of
                        the river. Unfortunately, water abstraction in the vicinity may affect
                        the flow of the springs. Water abstraction in the area of
                        Chippenham Fen is thought to be reducing the input of water from
                        the springs at this site as well.

Conservation   Tuddenham Fen is part of Cavenham Heath NNR. It is hoped that
                        the fen can be maintained by ponding back the outflow of the
                        springs. Chippenham Fen is also an NNR. Management here is
                        geared to produce a high water table and maintain the areas of
                        sedge-bed free from carr encroachment by annual mowing.

Author   P. Merrett, using information from Locket & Millidge (1953)
                        and J. Crocker, G.H. Locket, I.F.G. McLean, F.M. Murphy,
                        N.M.C. Twyman-Musgrave and R.M. Wright (pers. comms).

Chippenham Fen NNR, Cambridgeshire. Scrub would rapidly cover the remaining areas of reed and sedge if active management such as cutting was not carried out. The resulting habitat supports a rich spider and mollusc fauna, including several threatened species. (Photo by I.F.G. McLean.)

CLUBIONA SIMILIS

RARE

Phylum CHELICERATA
Class ARACHNIDA

Order ARANEAE
Family CLUBIONIDAE

Clubiona similis L. Koch, 1867.

Identification Locket, Millidge & Merrett (1974); Roberts (1985a).

Distribution British records are all from the east and southeast coasts of England: Holme, Scolt Head and Holkham, West Norfolk; Blakeney Point, Cley and Winterton, East Norfolk; Sizewell, East Suffolk; and Sandwich, East Kent. Also known from Italy, France, the Netherlands, Belgium, Germany, Denmark, Switzerland, Austria, Czechoslovakia, Hungary, Poland, Russia and the Balkans.

Habitat and ecology Occurs in marram *Ammophila arenaria* tussocks on sand dunes.

Status Well-established on coastal dunes in East Anglia.

Threats Public pressure can cause damage to the fragile dune vegetation, destroying it by too much trampling or by climbing in the steeper dunes. Possibly holiday development has destroyed some habitat, and this is always a threat to coastal dunes which lack statutory protection. Sand dunes also form a popular site for golf courses, Sandwich Dunes now supporting three, and the associated buildings, roads, reprofiling and reseeding cause damage to the natural dune ecosystem.

Conservation Scolt Head Island, Holkham Dunes and Winterton Dunes are NNRs. Holme Dunes, Blakeney Point and the coastal strip at Cley are within the North Norfolk Coast SSSI and are under the protection of the Norfolk Trust or the National Trust. The Kent Trust, National Trust and RSPB own or manage parts of Sandwich Dunes, which are also an SSSI.

Author P. Merrett, using information from Locket, Millidge & Merrett (1974) and P. Harvey (pers. comm.).

CLUBIONA JUVENIS

VULNERABLE

Phylum CHELICERATA
Class ARACHNIDA

Order ARANEAE
Family CLUBIONIDAE

Clubiona juvenis Simon, 1878.

Identification Locket & Millidge (1951); Roberts (1985a).

Distribution	Recorded from Keysworth, Poole Harbour, Dorset, in 1962-63; the Bure Marshes, Reedham Marsh and Meadow Dyke near Horsey Mere, East Norfolk, in 1970-71; Barton Turf, about three miles north of Reedham Marsh, in 1983; Stanford Warren, South Essex, in 1987; and sedge-beds at Reedham, Catfield, Sutton, Woodbastwick and Hickling, all East Norfolk, during an extensive survey in 1988 and 1989. Also reported from southeast Ireland, France, Germany, Austria, Switzerland and Romania.
Habitat and ecology	Found among ground vegetation in brackish *Phragmites* marsh in Dorset, and under cut saw-sedge *Cladium mariscus*, among reeds and ground vegetation in *Phragmites/Cladium* fens in Norfolk. The Essex specimens, three females, were in silk retreats in *Phragmites* heads in an area of wet grass and reed. In Ireland this species has been found on sand dunes. Adults of both sexes have been found in July and September, females also in May.
Status	Appears to be well-established in several places in the Norfolk Broads.
Threats	There has been serious loss of reed-beds in the Norfolk Broads in recent decades, caused by various aspects of the eutrophication problem. The best Broads are now those few which are isolated from the Broads rivers. Succession to carr is also occurring in several places where reed-cutting has ceased.
Conservation	All the Norfolk specimens are from NNRs or SSSIs. Reinstatement of reed- and sedge-cutting on several nature reserves in the Norfolk Broads should prevent the habitat of this species being lost to carr. In addition, efforts are being made to reduce the nutrient-loading of the Broads rivers by more effective sewage treatment, including phosphate-stripping. The Essex specimens were found just outside Stanford Warren, an Essex Trust reserve. *C. juvenis* probably also occurs inside the reserve.
Author	P. Merrett, using information from Locket & Millidge (1951), Carter (1972) and E. Duffey, P. Harvey, D.A. Procter and M.R. Shaw (pers. comms).

CLUBIONA GENEVENSIS   RARE

Phylum CHELICERATA   Order ARANEAE
Class ARACHNIDA   Family CLUBIONIDAE

Clubiona genevensis L. Koch, 1867.

Identification	Locket & Millidge (1951); Roberts (1985a).
Distribution	Recorded from the Isles of Scilly, Kynance Cove and Beagles Point,

West Cornwall; Lulworth and Ringstead, Dorset; and Ramsey and Skokholm Islands, Pembrokeshire. It is possibly widespread in southern and central Europe, but there has been some confusion with closely related species on the Continent.

Habitat and ecology   Found under stones and among grass and heather near the coast. Adults of both sexes have been found in April, females also in March, May and June.

Status   May be under-recorded owing to its early season of maturity. Abundant at Kynance Cove.

Threats   Public pressure at its sites and loss of coastal grassland and heathland to other land-uses. The loss of vegetation due to trampling can be very severe at famous beauty spots such as Lulworth Cove and Kynance Cove. Accidental fires are also thought to be a risk to the latter site.

Conservation   Kynance Cove is a National Trust property and lies within an SSSI. The National Trust now controls public access to the site and the impact of trampling by visitors is now less damaging than formerly. Grazing is being restored, which will help to maintain the cliff heath and grassland. Beagles Point and the Ringstead site are also National Trust properties, the latter partly leased to the Dorset Trust and within an SSSI. The habitat at Ringstead is self-maintaining owing to regular landslips and light grazing by rabbits and roe deer.

Author   P. Merrett, using information from Locket & Millidge (1951), F.M. Murphy and K.N.A. Alexander (pers. comms) and personal observations.

CHEIRACANTHIUM PENNYI   VULNERABLE

Phylum CHELICERATA   Order ARANEAE
Class ARACHNIDA   Family CLUBIONIDAE

Cheiracanthium pennyi O. P.-Cambridge, 1873.

Identification   Locket & Millidge (1951); Locket, Millidge & Merrett (1974); Roberts (1985a).

Distribution   Abundant on Chobham Common, Surrey, where it was first found in 1968 and has been recorded on many subsequent occasions. Other records are from Wokingham, Berkshire, in 1872, when both sexes were found; a female near Mark Ash in the New Forest, South Hampshire, in 1958; nine specimens including both sexes from Whitmoor Common, Surrey, in 1970; a male from Horton Common, Dorset, in 1980; and Cobbetthill Common, Surrey, in

1989. Its European distribution includes the Balkans, Crete, Italy, Spain, France, Belgium, the Netherlands, Germany, Denmark, Hungary, Romania and Russia.

Habitat and ecology Occurs on mature dry heathland and is closely associated with the heather. Females, either with eggs or heavily gravid, have been found in cells on cross-leaved heath *Erica tetralix*, several dead flower heads having been drawn together and the cell made in their middle. On heather *Calluna vulgaris*, an immature female has been found in a cell, with the male waiting outside. Males have been found from June to August and females from May to August.

Status Apparently thriving on Chobham Common and possibly on Whitmoor Common, but scarce elsewhere.

Threats Accidental fire or too frequent use of fire as a management tool on the heathland habitat, and loss of habitat through changing land-use. A hundred hectares of Horton Common were ploughed up and turned over to agriculture in 1980. In the absence of burning, grazing or other active management on areas of heath, birch and pine invasion is a threat. This is currently a problem in the spider's habitat on Chobham Common.

Conservation The New Forest, Cobbetthill Common, Whitmoor Common and the surviving area of heath at Horton Common are, or are within, SSSIs. Chobham Common is an SSSI and in part an LNR. Reversal of the birch and pine invasion at this site is included in the management plan. Whilst fire is a valuable management tool for maintaining *Calluna* heath, it should be used at long enough intervals to allow the mature phase in the *Calluna* growth cycle to be reached and burning should be carried out on a rotation which allows this phase to be ever present on the site. If grazing is used in management, it may be necessary to fence off exclosures in which the *Calluna* can develop ungrazed for a number of years.

Author P. Merrett, using information from Locket & Millidge (1951), Locket, Millidge & Merrett (1974), Clark & Jerrard (1972), Haskins (1988), E.J. Lovesey (unpublished) and E. Duffey and F.M. and J.A. Murphy (pers. comms).

AGROECA LUSATICA   ENDANGERED

Phylum CHELICERATA   Order ARANEAE
Class ARACHNIDA   Family LIOCRANIDAE

Agroeca lusatica (L. Koch, 1875).

Identification Locket & Millidge (1951); Locket, Millidge & Merrett (1974); Roberts (1985a).

| Distribution | Recorded in Britain only from Sandwich Dunes, East Kent. Its European distribution includes Spain, France, Belgium, the Netherlands, Germany, Hungary, Poland, Russia and Sweden. |

Distribution
Recorded in Britain only from Sandwich Dunes, East Kent. Its European distribution includes Spain, France, Belgium, the Netherlands, Germany, Hungary, Poland, Russia and Sweden.

Habitat and ecology
Occurs on sand dunes. An adult male has been found in September, and females in May and September.

Status
It was first found at Sandwich Dunes in 1938 and subsequently on a number of occasions at this site, so it is apparently well-established.

Threats
The habitat may be threatened by erosion and disturbance of the dunes through intense public use. The Sandwich dune system now has three golf courses, and their associated buildings, roads, drains and fairways have caused loss of natural dune habitat. The dunes form the sea defence for their strip of coast, and some low points have been artificially built up to reduce the risk of flooding, and this has caused disturbance to the habitat.

Conservation
Sandwich Dunes are within an SSSI and different areas are owned and/or managed by the Kent Trust, the RSPB and the National Trust.

Author
P. Merrett, using information from Locket & Millidge (1951), Locket, Millidge & Merrett (1974) and A.P. Foster and G.H. Locket (pers. comms).

APOSTENUS FUSCUS   ENDANGERED

Phylum CHELICERATA   Order ARANEAE
Class ARACHNIDA   Family LIOCRANIDAE

Apostenus fuscus Westring, 1851.

Identification
Williams & Locket (1982); Roberts (1987).

Distribution
Recorded only from Dungeness, East Kent, first in 1981. Common and widespread on the Continent.

Habitat and ecology
Found at Dungeness on shingle covered with a thin layer of soil and bearing vegetation composed of mixed grasses, mosses, lichens, spring ephemerals and wood sage *Teucrium scorodonia*. Males have been found in May and once in November, females from May to July. This species is at the edge of its range and possibly is restricted to Dungeness by the need for open sun-baked conditions and associated high summer temperatures.

Status
This species was found in some numbers during an NCC survey of Dungeness in the late 1980s.

| Threats | Dungeness is being extensively damaged by gravel extraction, which is causing significant alteration of the hydrology, and thereby ecology, in addition to the obvious loss of shingle area to gravel-pits. Gravel extraction may accelerate with increasing demand for aggregates in Southeast England. The likelihood of further nuclear power station construction at Dungeness is unclear at present but still poses a threat. Irrevocable damage is being caused by motorcycles and other vehicles crossing the shingle, damaging the vegetation and the shingle ridges. The extension of holiday centres and other recreational activities are also causing damage. |

Conservation Parts of Dungeness are an SSSI. Part is an RSPB reserve, though this area is extensively affected by gravel extraction.

Author P. Merrett, using information from Williams & Locket (1982).

ZORA ARMILLATA   RARE

Phylum CHELICERATA   Order ARANEAE
Class ARACHNIDA   Family ZORIDAE

Zora armillata Simon, 1878.

Identification Locket & Millidge (1951); Locket, Millidge & Merrett (1974); Roberts (1985a).

Distribution Recorded from Wicken Fen, including the portion known as St Edmund's Fen, Cambridgeshire; Woodwalton Fen, Huntingdonshire (record requires confirmation); and Hartland Moor and Morden Bog, Dorset. Also known from Spain, France, Greece and Sweden.

Habitat and ecology Known from two rather dissimilar habitats in Britain: among litter and cut reeds in fens in East Anglia, and in wet heath and bog in Dorset. Adults of both sexes are found between April and September. Despite the major fire at Hartland Moor in 1976, the site has revegetated well and this spider still occurs there in good numbers.

Status Fairly frequent at all known sites except Woodwalton Fen.

Threats Lowering of the water table, such as by drainage of adjacent land and/or water abstraction, would damage all the listed localities of this species. A lower water table often leads to scrub invasion, which increases the drying process and shades out the fen and bog plant communities. The effects of drainage on the fenland sites are well known (e.g. Godwin 1978; Darby 1983). It is only through much manual and mechanical scrub clearance that the fenland vegetation is maintained on these sites, and even this probably differs markedly from what would be present if drainage of the surrounding area had not been carried out. The catchment of Morden Bog has also been greatly modified by the extensive conifer forestry in the area this century.

Conservation Wicken and Edmund Fens are National Trust property with SSSI status. The other three sites listed are NNRs, Woodwalton Fen being owned by the RSNC. Mowing and sedge-harvesting are part of the management of Wicken Fen with the aim of maintaining scrub-free areas. Also much scrub clearance has been accomplished in recent years, restoring former sedge and litter beds. This should ensure the continuity of the spider's habitat at this site.

Author P. Merrett, using information from Locket & Millidge (1951), Locket, Millidge & Merrett (1974) and T.J. Bennett, E. Duffey and J.A. and F.M. Murphy (pers. comms).

ZORA SILVESTRIS   VULNERABLE

Phylum CHELICERATA   Order ARANEAE
Class ARACHNIDA   Family ZORIDAE

Zora silvestris Kulczynski, 1897.

Identification Locket, Millidge & Merrett (1974); Roberts (1985a).

Distribution Recorded from Hurt Wood, Surrey, in 1953; Iken Heath, East Suffolk, in 1955; Ambersham Common, West Sussex, in 1969; and Sherwood Forest Country Park, Nottinghamshire, in 1987. Also known from France, the Netherlands, Germany, Denmark, Sweden, Finland, Switzerland, Poland, Hungary and the Balkans.

Habitat and ecology In Britain, it occurs on dry heathland, mainly in mature heather. In Sherwood Forest it was found with larger numbers of *Z. spinimana* (Sundevall) in mixed heather and grassland from which encroaching scrub and trees had been cleared. Both sexes are found from May to July and a female has been recorded in September.

Status Apparently rare but may have been overlooked owing to its similarity to the widespread and abundant *Z. spinimana*. Several specimens were found at Hurt Wood.

Threats Fires in the mature heather habitat are a threat to this species. Management to reduce the fire risk by preventing the heather reaching the mature phase, such as by grazing or burning on a short rotation, is often used on nature reserves, but would probably

149

result in very little heather being at the desired stage for this spider. Small unmanaged areas rapidly succumb to scrub encroachment, with loss of heather. Heathlands are also at risk from urban expansion and conversion to arable land. At Ambersham Common, motorcycle scrambling is damaging the areas of heath (R. Jones pers. comm.). At Iken Heath, the spider was found on a thin margin of *Erica* at the roadside, and such a site is at risk from traffic pollution, road salt and roadworks.

Conservation
Ambersham Common is an SSSI and three acres are a Sussex Trust reserve. The Sherwood Forest site lies within Birklands and Bilhaugh SSSI. The scrub and tree clearance at the latter site had been carried out as part of the conservation management and further work of this sort is clearly what is needed. Ideally it should be followed by a grazing regime which will maintain the heathland vegetation with *Calluna* at a variety of heights.

Author
P. Merrett, using information from Locket, Millidge & Merrett (1974) and E. Duffey and M.J. Roberts (pers. comms).

PISTIUS TRUNCATUS   ENDANGERED

A crab spider

Phylum CHELICERATA   Order ARANEAE
Class ARACHNIDA   Family THOMISIDAE

Pistius truncatus (Pallas, 1772).

Identification
Locket & Millidge (1951); Roberts (1985a).

Distribution
Recorded from the New Forest near Brockenhurst, South Hampshire, in 1896. The precise locality is not known. A female was recorded from a wood in the Blean area, East Kent, in 1985. Also known from Portugal, Spain, Italy, France, Belgium, the Netherlands, Denmark, Austria, Switzerland, Czechoslovakia, Hungary, Poland, Romania and Russia.

Habitat and ecology
The Blean specimen emerged in May from pieces of dead wood collected in the previous March, which suggests that dead wood is an overwintering site. The specimen survived for some weeks in captivity, being fed on flies. In France, this species is found on bushes, especially small scrubby oaks. Adults occur in May and June.

Status
Was thought to be extinct in Britain but recently rediscovered.

Threats
Many broadleaved woodlands in southeast England have been cleared for agriculture or converted to conifer plantations in recent decades, and both activities are still real threats to the surviving woods. Development pressures are also increasing in Kent with the

prospect of the Channel Tunnel, and further woods are likely to be lost to housing, industry and roads.

Conservation   The New Forest is an SSSI. The Kent record is from a private nature reserve within East Blean Woods SSSI. The main block of East Blean Wood is a reserve of the Kent Trust.

Author   P. Merrett, using information from Simon (1932), Locket & Millidge (1951) and E. Bradford and J.A. Murphy (pers. comms).

XYSTICUS LUCTATOR   VULNERABLE

A crab spider

Phylum CHELICERATA   Order ARANEAE
Class ARACHNIDA   Family THOMISIDAE

Xysticus luctator L. Koch, 1870.

Identification   Locket & Millidge (1951); Locket, Millidge & Merrett (1974); Roberts (1985a).

Distribution   Recorded only from Bloxworth Heath, Dorset (a single male in 1854 and a female soon after); Beaulieu Road Heath, New Forest, South Hampshire (a male and female in 1958 and several times previously); and High Standing Hill, Windsor Forest, Berkshire (a single male in 1978). Fairly widespread in central and northern Europe.

Habitat and ecology   Found in mature dry heathland and under dead wood among heather and beech litter. Both sexes are adult in May.

Status   Few individuals have been found, and it appears to be very rare.

Threats   The grazing pressure, particularly from ponies, is too high in much of the New Forest for mature heath to develop. This is despite the fact that current grazing levels are much below that allowed by the bye-laws. However, in the long term a more serious threat is posed by the decline of grazing as the population of the New Forest loses interest in exercising the commoners' rights to graze livestock. A marked lessening of the grazing pressure would allow scrub encroachment on the areas of heath. Bloxworth Heath has been largely lost to conifer forestry, only a small part of the original surviving as Morden Bog NNR.

Conservation   High Standing Hill is within Windsor Forest and Great Park SSSI and the New Forest is also an SSSI.

Author   P. Merrett, using information from Locket & Millidge (1951), Locket, Millidge & Merrett (1974) and D.R. Nellist (pers. comm.).

THANATUS FORMICINUS

VULNERABLE

Phylum CHELICERATA
Class ARACHNIDA

Order ARANEAE
Family PHILODROMIDAE

Thanatus formicinus (Clerck, 1757).

Identification   Locket & Millidge (1951); Roberts (1985a).

Distribution   Recorded from Beaulieu Heath near Brockenhurst, New Forest, South Hampshire, in 1894; and Legsheath and Duddleswell, in Ashdown Forest, East Sussex, this century. Adults were found at Legsheath in the 1930s and juveniles at both Sussex sites in 1969. This species is widespread in Europe.

Habitat and ecology   Found in boggy areas with *Sphagnum*, tall *Molinia caerulea* and mature *Calluna vulgaris* and *Erica tetralix*. Adult in March or April.

Status   The paucity of records may partly be due to this species being mature early in the year when little recording of spiders is carried out. It is apparently well-established in Ashdown Forest.

Threats   Fire on heathland and loss of the heathland habitat to other land-uses. Drainage of some New Forest bogs has been carried out in the past in order to increase the area and quality of grazing land. There is now very little grazing in Ashdown Forest, partly because the main roads crossing the unfenced common land are a danger to livestock. Consequently, scrub and bracken invasion of the heath is a problem.

Conservation   Occurs within Ashdown Forest SSSI and the New Forest SSSI. Ashdown Forest has recently been bought by East Sussex County Council, and it is hoped that this will safeguard the site. Scrub clearance has been carried out in some places but more is needed.

Author   P. Merrett, using information from Locket & Millidge (1951), B. Banks (pers. comm.) and personal observations.

HELIOPHANUS AURATUS

VULNERABLE

A jumping spider

Phylum CHELICERATA

Order ARANEAE

Class ARACHNIDA

Family SALTICIDAE

Heliophanus auratus C.L. Koch, 1835.

Identification

Locket, Millidge & Merrett (1974); Roberts (1985a).

Distribution

In Britain known only from Essex. First recorded in 1961 at Colne Point, North Essex, and in 1987 found at Shinglehead Point, North Essex, and Steeple Creek, South Essex, both on the Blackwater Estuary. Widespread in central and southern Europe.

Habitat and ecology

Found at Colne Point among sparse vegetation on shingle, just below the line of the spring tide litter, near old gravel-workings. The Blackwater sites consisted of a shingle strip and a shell bank, both adjacent to the sea wall. *H. auratus* is found running on shingle during periods of sunshine. Both sexes are adult in June and a male has been found in early July.

Status

Found in some numbers in 1961 and 1987.

Threats

Construction and maintenance of sea defences frequently destroy the strip of habitat in front of the sea wall, so, where possible, work should be carried out from the landward side of the existing bank.

Conservation

Colne Point is an Essex Trust reserve, and all three sites are within SSSIs. Special management is unlikely to be necessary for this species.

Author

P. Merrett, using information from Cooke (1961), Locket, Millidge & Merrett (1974) and P. Harvey (pers. comm.).

NEON VALENTULUS

VULNERABLE

A jumping spider

Phylum CHELICERATA

Order ARANEAE

Class ARACHNIDA

Family SALTICIDAE

Neon valentulus Falconer, 1912.

Identification

Locket & Millidge (1951); Roberts (1985a).

Distribution

Known from Wicken and Chippenham Fens, Cambridgeshire; Foulden Common, West Norfolk; Pashford Poors Fen, West Suffolk;

and Redgrave Fen, East Suffolk. The single melanic female reported in Essex (Hull 1948) requires verification. A record from Box Hill, Surrey, (Locket, Millidge & Merrett 1974) has proved, on re-examination of the specimen, to be *N. reticulatus* (Blackwall). The European distribution of *N. valentulus* includes the Netherlands, Germany, Poland and Sweden.

Habitat and ecology Found amongst moss and grass in sedge fens. At Redgrave Fen a specimen was found among *Molinia*, *Cladium* and *Juncus* by the edge of a pool. Adults are found in May and June.

Status Restricted to a few fens in a small area of East Anglia. Reported to be not uncommon at Wicken Fen, Chippenham Fen and Foulden Common.

Threats Loss of fen habitats. Drainage of the East Anglian fenland for agriculture has lowered the water table over a large area. Water abstraction for irrigation and the public water supply is decreasing the output from many of the springs on which many valley fens depend. The maintenance of fen conditions on nature reserves thus poses great problems. Diverting water from fenland rivers to reserves can cause eutrophication because of the high nutrient-loading of rivers flowing through agricultural areas. The lack of a suitable water source is especially acute at Pashford Poors Fen, where irrigation boreholes adjacent to the fen have lowered the water table and willow and birch invasion is exacerbating the problem. It is uncertain whether fen conditions can be maintained at this site.

Conservation Wicken Fen is a National Trust nature reserve and SSSI. Chippenham Fen is an NNR. Pashford Poors Fen and Redgrave Fen are reserves of the Suffolk Trust and SSSIs. Foulden Common is a Norfolk Trust reserve and SSSI. At some sites, hydrology is being manipulated where possible to maintain a high water table and revival of sedge-cutting is reversing the encroachment of scrub which has occurred in recent decades.

Author P. Merrett, using information from Locket & Millidge (1951) and E. Duffey and J.A. and F.M. Murphy (pers. comms).

EUOPHRYS BROWNINGI   RARE

A jumping spider

Phylum CHELICERATA   Order ARANEAE
Class ARACHNIDA   Family SALTICIDAE

Euophrys browningi Millidge & Locket, 1955.

Identification Locket, Millidge & Merrett (1974); Roberts (1985a).

Colne Point, North Essex, within Colne Estuary NNR. A number of spiders are found only on the sparsely vegetated shingle. Several are associated with the drift line (inset) and one inhabits empty whelk shells. (Photos by P. Wakely and (inset) I.F.G. McLean.)

155

Distribution	Recorded from Blakeney Point, East Norfolk; Orford Beach and Shingle Street, East Suffolk; Colne Point and Walton Naze, North Essex; Bradwell, South Essex; Lydd Ranges and near Faversham, East Kent; and Rye Harbour, East Sussex, all since 1953.
Habitat and ecology	Among tide litter, in empty whelk shells and in the open on shingle. Adults of both sexes are found from April to June and from August to October.
Status	Apparently restricted to shingle beaches in the southeast but numerous at some sites, for example Bradwell, Colne Point and Shingle Street. There are uncertainties about the taxonomy of this species. It is very similar to the mid-European *E. obsoleta* (Simon), but, if it is truly a different species, it is possibly endemic to Britain.
Threats	Public pressure, causing erosion by trampling, may degrade its sites. The use of vehicles on shingle, as at Lydd Ranges, certainly causes irreversible disruption to the habitat. Holiday development may be a threat outside nature reserves.
Conservation	The East Anglian records are all from within SSSIs. Blakeney Point is owned by the National Trust. Bradwell Cockle Spit, Colne Point and Walton Naze are Essex Trust reserves, the first two also having NNR status. Lydd Ranges lie within the Dungeness SSSI. Rye Harbour is an SSSI and in part an LNR.
Author	P. Merrett, using information from Locket, Millidge & Merrett (1974), Maidstone Museum Biological Records Centre, and P. Harvey and S.A. Williams (pers. comms).

SITTICUS FLORICOLA   RARE
A jumping spider

Phylum CHELICERATA   Order ARANEAE
Class ARACHNIDA   Family SALTICIDAE

Sitticus floricola (C.L. Koch, 1837).

Identification	Locket & Millidge (1951); Roberts (1985a).
Distribution	Well-established at four sites in the Delamere Forest area: Flaxmere, Black Lake, Abbots Moss (where it has been found several times since 1914) and Little Budworth Common. Also found more recently at Wybunbury Moss. In addition to these Cheshire sites, it was discovered in 1981 in marsh by Loch Ken near New Galloway, Kirkcudbrightshire, and has since been found several times in this area and at Loch Stroan a few miles away. This species is fairly widespread in Europe.

Habitat and ecology	In the Delamere area it has been found in bogs on *Sphagnum*, and at Wybunbury Moss in two fen meadows and in an area of abundant *Eriophorum vaginatum* in the *Sphagnum* bog. It spins a cocoon in tall vegetation such as seed heads of *Eriophorum* and flower heads of *Lychnis flos-cuculi* and *Cirsium palustre*. It overwinters deep in the *Sphagnum*. In the Scottish sites it also occurs on *Deschampsia cespitosa* at the side of the loch and in drier areas in dead leaves lying in the grass. Adults are found from March to September.
Status	Abundant at all its known sites.
Threats	Wybunbury Moss suffered severe eutrophication for many years prior to 1986 owing to pollution from a septic tank and road drainage. Agricultural run-off still threatens further damage of this sort. The eutrophication has caused marked changes in the vegetation, with loss of *Sphagnum* lawn. There has been further loss of *Sphagnum* owing to birch and pine invasion. Woodland encroachment is also a problem at Abbots Moss. The first Scottish specimens of *S. floricola* were discovered on an RSPB reserve in an area due to be flooded to attract wildfowl. Flooding was postponed until the spider's range in this area could be clarified. *S. floricola* is now known to be abundant in parts of the area not to be affected by the flooding and is thus not thought to be threatened by the RSPB's plans.
Conservation	Wybunbury Moss is an NNR. Since 1986 the main sources of eutrophication have been diverted away from the moss and work on removing the invading trees has progressed. In 1989 *S. floricola* was found in an area of bog where the tree cover had recently been removed, resulting in a good growth of *Sphagnum* and *Eriophorum*. The four other Cheshire sites are all SSSIs, Abbots Moss and Black Lake also being Cheshire Trust reserves. Both Scottish sites are within SSSIs and the Ken Dee marshes are also an RSPB reserve (see above).
Author	P. Merrett, using information from Locket & Millidge (1951), Dobson (1982, 1987) and M.P. Bailey, S. Dobson, R.A. Lindsay and D.W. Mackie (pers. comms).

PHLEGRA FASCIATA   RARE

A jumping spider

Phylum CHELICERATA   Order ARANEAE
Class ARACHNIDA   Family SALTICIDAE

Phlegra fasciata (Hahn, 1826).

Identification	Locket & Millidge (1951); Roberts (1985a, 1985b).

Distribution	Recorded from Studland, Arne and the Portland end of Chesil Beach, Dorset; Hayling Island and doubtfully from the New Forest, South Hampshire; Hastings, Rye Harbour and Camber, East Sussex; and Sandwich, Dungeness and Lydd Ranges, East Kent. Fairly widespread in Europe. Also found in the U.S.A.
Habitat and ecology	Found mainly on sand dunes and sometimes in other dry coastal habitats such as shingle. Adults of both sexes are found between April and July, females also in September.
Status	This species is not as common as it may first appear from the above list of localities. Of the ten localities listed, four are within one continuous area of shingle and dunes between Rye Harbour and Dungeness and for some sites the records are over fifty years old. It was recorded in small numbers at several sampling points at Rye Harbour and Dungeness during an NCC survey in the late 1980s.
Threats	Erosion caused by high public use, particularly the use of motor vehicles on shingle, and possibly holiday development threaten the rather fragile habitats of this species.
Conservation	Chesil Beach, Lydd Ranges, Dungeness and Sandwich Dunes are within SSSIs. Parts of the last are owned or managed by the National Trust, Kent Trust and RSPB. The RSPB also has a reserve at Dungeness. Rye Harbour is an SSSI and, in part, an LNR. Studland Heath is an NNR which includes the coast, and the Arne peninsula is partly NNR and partly RSPB reserve and/or SSSI. A small part of Hayling Island is a Hampshire and Isle of Wight Trust reserve.
Author	P. Merrett, using information from Locket & Millidge (1951), Maidstone Museum Biological Records Centre, and R. Jones and J.A. and F.M. Murphy (pers. comms).

PELLENES TRIPUNCTATUS   ENDANGERED

A jumping spider

Phylum CHELICERATA   Order ARANEAE
Class ARACHNIDA   Family SALTICIDAE

Pellenes tripunctatus (Walckenaer, 1802).

Identification	Locket & Millidge (1951); Roberts (1985a).
Distribution	Numerous specimens have been found in recent years at Dungeness, East Kent. Previously it was recorded only from Folkestone, East Kent, in 1888, when both sexes were found. There is also an unconfirmed record from the Crumbles, East Sussex, in the 1980s. It is apparently widespread in central and southern Europe.

158

Habitat and ecology	Found on sparsely vegetated shingle, on one occasion in whelk shells. Adults have been found in late May and June.
Status	At Dungeness it was known from only three specimens found at long intervals until an NCC survey in the late 1980s recorded small numbers at several sampling points there.
Threats	Dungeness is being damaged by gravel extraction, and this may increase as shingle deposits are used up elsewhere in the county. Some damage to the shingle vegetation and the shingle ridges is also resulting from the passage of vehicles. The Crumbles was largely destroyed in 1988 by marina and building developments.
Conservation	Found within Dungeness SSSI. As coastal shingle is one of the few naturally maintained habitats in Britain, positive management is unlikely to be needed, but adequate safeguards are necessary to avoid the damaging operations mentioned above.
Author	P. Merrett, using information from Locket & Millidge (1951), Locket, Millidge & La Touche (1958), Jones (1982) and E. Jones and J.A. Murphy (pers. comms).

OXYOPES HETEROPHTHALMUS   VULNERABLE

A lynx spider

Phylum CHELICERATA	Order ARANEAE
Class ARACHNIDA	Family OXYOPIDAE

Oxyopes heterophthalmus Latreille, 1804.

Identification	Locket & Millidge (1951); Roberts (1985a, 1985b).
Distribution	Abundant at Chobham Common. Also recorded since 1968 at Hankley Common and around Guildford at Whitmoor Common, Blackheath, Tunnel Hill, Ash Ranges, Cobbett Hill and Pirbright Ranges. All these sites are in Surrey. There are old records (1858, 1909 and 1910) from the New Forest near Lyndhurst and Brockenhurst, South Hampshire. Widespread in central and southern Europe.
Habitat and ecology	Found on mature dry heathland, usually near the top of heather and seemingly with a preference for south-facing slopes. Adults occur in late May and June.
Status	Abundant on a few small heathland areas in west Surrey but not found elsewhere for over seventy years.
Threats	Fire and loss of heathland habitat. Because of the increased fire risk that mature heather presents, heaths are often managed to avoid

this phase, even on nature reserves. However, at Chobham Common, lack of management is resulting in birch and pine invasion. Accidental fires are also too frequent an occurrence on parts of this common, causing replacement of heath by *Molinia caerulea*. In parts of the New Forest, grazing by livestock prevents the heather developing into tall mature plants, but there are still areas of apparently suitable structure. There are worries that grazing in the New Forest may decline dramatically in coming years, as it is no longer profitable (New Forest Review Group 1987), and this could lead to widespread scrub development at the expense of heath.

Conservation   The New Forest, Blackheath, Chobham Common, Hankley Common, Whitmoor Common and Ash Ranges are, or are within, SSSIs, part of Chobham Common also having LNR status. Management needs to be geared to ensuring good representation of heather in the mature phase. Thus, if burning is to be used, small portions of the site should be treated in rotation on a cycle of about twenty years. If grazing is the favoured option, it should be at a low intensity in some areas.

Author   P. Merrett, using information from Locket & Millidge (1951) and F.M. and J.A. Murphy and E.J. Lovesey (pers. comms).

PARDOSA PALUDICOLA   RARE

A wolf spider

Phylum CHELICERATA   Order ARANEAE
Class ARACHNIDA   Family LYCOSIDAE

Pardosa paludicola (Clerck, 1757).

Identification   Locket & Millidge (1951, 1953); Roberts (1985a).

Distribution   Recorded from Shapwick Heath and Catcott Heath, North Somerset; Parkhurst Forest, Isle of Wight; Plaistow, West Sussex; Cudham, West Kent; Woodwalton Fen, Huntingdonshire; and Tarrington, Herefordshire. Fairly widespread in Europe, with rather more records from the north than the south.

Habitat and ecology   Recorded from grassy clearings in woods, running on peat near trees in fens, and among grass near a pond. It may require moderately long grass or herbage. Males are adult in late March and April, and females have been found in April and May. Both sexes have also been found in November, and some individuals may mature in late autumn and overwinter.

Status   Apparently fairly numerous at Shapwick Heath, Plaistow and Woodwalton Fen.

Threats	Shapwick Heath has been very severely damaged by peat extraction, even within the National Nature Reserve, and only a small area of the wet heath remains. Falling water tables due to agricultural drainage are a problem in the Somerset Levels sites and at Woodwalton Fen. It is difficult to maintain a high water table on the protected areas when the surrounding fields are being drained.
Conservation	Shapwick Heath and Woodwalton Fen are NNRs, the latter owned by RSNC but managed by the NCC. Catcott Heath is part of an SSSI and a small area is a reserve of the Somerset Trust. Parkhurst Forest is an SSSI. A constantly available water supply to Woodwalton Fen has been ensured by co-operation between the Middle Level Commissioners Drainage Board and NCC, but there is still concern about the water quality.
Author	P. Merrett, using information from Locket & Millidge (1951, 1953) and E. Duffey, M.E. Massey and G.H. Locket (pers. comms).

ALOPECOSA FABRILIS   ENDANGERED

A wolf spider

Phylum CHELICERATA   Order ARANEAE
Class ARACHNIDA   Family LYCOSIDAE

Alopecosa fabrilis (Clerck, 1757), previously known as *Tarentula fabrilis.*

Identification	Locket & Millidge (1951) (as *Tarentula fabrilis*); Roberts (1985a).
Distribution	Occurs in two small areas of Morden Heath, Dorset, and on Hankley Common, Surrey. It has also been recorded from Italy, France, Belgium, the Netherlands, Germany, Denmark, Sweden, Norway, Finland, Russia, Poland, Hungary, Czechoslovakia, Switzerland, Austria and the Balkans.
Habitat and ecology	Inhabits a burrow in sandy soil or holes under stones. The preferred habitat is dry sandy heathland with some open stony areas. It has also been found wandering on ploughed firebreaks but may not be resident in such habitat. Both sexes are adult in September and October, and females probably overwinter.
Status	Known to occur in three distinct populations. Each occupies a small area, and, since the spider is large, the population density is low and therefore vulnerable. There are probably no more than a hundred adults in any one population. It has been known for over a hundred years at Morden Heath. All records from Hankley Common are recent.

Threats	Pine and birch trees encroaching on the sites and probably fire.
Conservation	Morden Bog is an NNR and Hankley Common is part of an SSSI. Because of the vulnerability of the localised spider populations, fire is unsuitable as a management tool and regular removal of the invading pines by hand-pulling should be arranged. This regime may lead to a build-up of litter and humus; thus further management to restore patches of bare stony ground may be necessary, possibly by mowing or localised grazing. An area of open sand was created as part of the management on Morden Heath in 1989 (M. Tuck pers. comm.). At Hankley Common, small-scale disturbance of the vegetation in the course of army training exercises may be maintaining the desired habitat.
Author	P. Merrett, based on personal observations and information from Locket & Millidge (1951) and R. Jones (pers. comm.).

ARCTOSA FULVOLINEATA   RARE

A wolf spider

Phylum CHELICERATA   Order ARANEAE
Class ARACHNIDA   Family LYCOSIDAE

Arctosa fulvolineata (Lucas, 1846), formerly known as *Trochosa fulvolineata* and *Leaena fulvolineata*.

Identification	Locket & Millidge (1951) (as *Trochosa fulvolineata*); Roberts (1985a).
Distribution	Recorded from Scolt Head, West Norfolk; Hemley and Blythburgh, East Suffolk; Colne Point and Wrabness, North Essex; near Faversham, East Kent; Hayling Island, Beaulieu River and Lymington, South Hampshire; and an unknown locality in Dorset. Elsewhere in Europe it is recorded from Switzerland, France, Spain, Portugal, Italy and Corsica.
Habitat and ecology	Found under debris and stones at the top of saltmarshes. Cooke (1961) reported considerable numbers at Colne Point and the marshes bordering the Stour Estuary at Wrabness. In the former locality it occurred under lumps of mud and wet, tightly matted debris along the foot of the sea wall and under stones on the wet mud on the nearby marshes. At the Blythburgh Estuary it was found in cracks in the upper saltmarsh where saltpans had dried out and were unvegetated (E. Duffey pers. comm.). Adults of both sexes are found mainly from April to June, but also in September. Possibly some individuals mature in the autumn and overwinter, as in many other large lycosids.
Status	Appears to be confined to a few saltmarshes around the Solent and

on the coast of East Anglia. Such a large spider is unlikely to be overlooked. Fairly numerous at Colne Point and on the Blythburgh Estuary.

Threats

In the construction and maintenance of sea defences, the strip of land immediately in front of the sea wall is very vulnerable to being covered with spoil or at best severely disturbed. The spider's adoption of this habitat at Colne Point would suggest that the sea wall has caused a seaward contraction of its horizontal range on the shore.

Conservation

Scolt Head is an NNR and Colne Point is an NNR and Essex Trust reserve. The coast at Wrabness is within the Stour Estuary SSSI. Blythburgh Estuary lies within an SSSI and partly within an NNR.

Author

P. Merrett, using information from Locket & Millidge (1951) and Cooke (1961).

TRICCA ALPIGENA   RARE

A wolf spider

Phylum CHELICERATA   Order ARANEAE
Class ARACHNIDA   Family LYCOSIDAE

Tricca alpigena (Doleschall, 1852), previously known as *Trochosa biunguiculata* and *Arctosa alpigena*.

Identification

Locket & Millidge (1951) (as *Arctosa alpigena*); Roberts (1985a).

Distribution

Originally recorded from a mountain near Braemar, South Aberdeenshire, in 1872, as *Trochosa biunguiculata*. Found since on Cairn Toul, South Aberdeenshire, on three occasions; Cairngorm; the plateau between Cairngorm and Ben Macdui, Banffshire; and recently from Creag Meagaidh, West Inverness-shire, and Sgurr nan Clach Geala, West Ross. Also known from France, Switzerland, Austria, Hungary, Sweden, Norway, Finland and Iceland.

Habitat and ecology

Found on mountains above 1,000 metres, in silk tubes in densely matted vegetation dominated by *Empetrum* or *Nardus stricta*, with *Vaccinium*, *Cladonia*, *Racomitrium*, etc. Trapping on Creag Meagaidh showed it to be most frequent in *Nardus stricta* snow-bed grassland (which was also the habitat on Sgurr nan Clach Geala) and to a lesser extent in *Racomitrium lanuginosum* moss heath. The spiders spend much of their time below the vegetation mat and are only occasionally seen running in the open. Adults of both sexes have been found in June and July, and females also in May and until the end of August.

Status

Well-established in the Cairngorms, though probably rather local.

163

Coire an Lochan in the Northern Corries, Cairngorms SSSI, East Inverness-shire. The harsh high-altitude conditions, where snow can lie throughout the year, support a specialist invertebrate fauna including scarce spiders. The thin soil is fragile and easily destroyed by persistent trampling. (Photo by I.F.G. McLean.)

Coire Cas, Cairngorms, East Inverness-shire, close to the Northern Corries, Cairngorms SSSI. Coire Cas shows degradation of mountain wilderness caused by skiing developments. Expansion of skiing facilities is a recurring threat elsewhere in the Cairngorms and to some other montane sites in Scotland. (Photo by D.A. Ratcliffe.)

The strongest population known is on the south slopes of Cairngorm (N.P. Ashmole pers. comm.).

Threats   The high altitude vegetation which forms the habitat of this species is fragile and slow growing, and prone to damage from hill-walkers and skiers.

Conservation   Occurs within the Cairngorms and Creag Meagaidh NNRs. Sgurr nan Clach Geala is a component of the Fannich Hills SSSI.

Author   P. Merrett, using information from Locket & Millidge (1951), Horsfield, Murray & Galbraith (1989) and N.P. Ashmole and D. Horsfield (pers. comms).

AULONIA ALBIMANA   ENDANGERED

A wolf spider

Phylum CHELICERATA   Order ARANEAE
Class ARACHNIDA   Family LYCOSIDAE

Aulonia albimana (Walckenaer, 1805).

Identification   Locket & Millidge (1951); Roberts (1985a, 1985b).

Distribution   Recorded from two quarries near Dunster, South Somerset, one in 1936 and 1938 and the second on a number of occasions between 1963 and 1974; and at Newtown Ranges, Isle of Wight, in 1985. Known elsewhere in Europe from Spain, France, Germany, the Netherlands, Denmark, Austria, Switzerland, Russia, Czechoslovakia, Poland, Italy, Corsica and the Balkans.

Habitat and ecology   Found among stones at the side of a disused quarry and running on the quarry floor in Somerset. The Isle of Wight site is a damp grassy area sheltered from the wind on three sides but open to the sun. Adults were found at the end of June in a tiny hollow in the soil at the base of dense grass stems. Juveniles had previously been found in the same area in May. In Germany, this species has been observed to make a flimsy sheet web with a tubular retreat in moss (Job 1968, cited in Roberts & Roberts 1985).

Status   Currently known at only one site in Britain, and not likely to be grossly under-recorded.

Threats   The spider is thought to be lost from both Somerset sites. The quarry from which it was recorded in the 1960s and 1970s has recently been used as a rubbish tip, a common fate of disused quarries. The site of the earlier records has also apparently been destroyed.

Conservation	Newtown Ranges are Ministry of Defence property and unlikely to undergo severe change in land-use. The MOD has been notified of the precise locality and is sympathetic towards conserving the site. There are open heathland and woodland adjacent to the Dunster site which may still support this species. Survey work is required.
Author	P. Merrett, using personal observations and information from Locket & Millidge (1951), Roberts & Roberts (1985), J.R. Parker and M.J. Roberts (pers. comms).

DOLOMEDES PLANTARIUS   ENDANGERED

Fen Raft Spider, Great Raft Spider

Phylum CHELICERATA   Order ARANEAE
Class ARACHNIDA   Family PISAURIDAE

Dolomedes plantarius (Clerck, 1757).

Identification	Locket, Millidge & Merrett (1974); Roberts (1985a).
Distribution	This species was long thought to be restricted in Britain to Redgrave Fen, East Suffolk, and South Lopham Fens, East Norfolk. It was first found here in 1956 and has been recorded on many subsequent occasions. (These fens are adjacent and form one complex site straddling the River Waveney.) In 1988, however, a mature female of *D. plantarius* was found by P. Kirby in the Pevensey Levels, East Sussex. Duffey (1958) mentions speculation that *D. plantarius* may have been found in Britain in previous centuries. Collins & Wells (1987) mention Neolithic remains of this species from the Somerset Levels, but it is unlikely that Neolithic remains could be identified beyond genus and *D. fimbriatus* (Clerck) is widespread in western Britain and occurs at several sites in the Somerset Levels. *D. plantarius* is widespread in Europe, with records from Greece, Italy, France, Switzerland, Germany, Czechoslovakia, Hungary, Poland, Denmark, Sweden, Norway and Finland; also occurs in Siberia.
Habitat and ecology	*D. plantarius* has been closely studied in the South Lopham Fens, where it is found among sedges around the edges of small pools formed in old peat-cuttings. Adults are strongly territorial and males have been observed to defend a pool against other males. In the Lopham Fens saw-sedge *Cladium mariscus* plays an important part in the life cycle. The flower stems are used to support the nursery tent, the cavity in the leaf bases can be used for hibernation, and females awaiting prey are usually to be found on *Cladium*. Pools in areas of fen where fine-leaved grasses have become the dominant vegetation are less favoured, and *Dolomedes* is not found in pools among scrub. In the Pevensey Levels it was found at the water's edge on a ditch bank under

overhanging tussocky vegetation. *D. plantarius* catches its prey from the water surface, feeding on aquatic insects, mainly corixids, and on tadpoles. In captivity, craneflies, bluebottles, moths and small fish will also be taken. When it is threatened, the escape response is to submerge by crawling down aquatic vegetation, and adults can remain under water for at least fifty minutes. Female *Dolomedes* carry the egg sac for up to three weeks and, when hatching is imminent, attach it to a stem inside a nursery tent of silk. It is likely that *Dolomedes* which hatch from the egg sac in early summer mature the following year, while those hatching in late summer spend two winters as juveniles. The young may disperse by ballooning, but many probably descend into the vegetation around the nursery tent. Immatures have been found in December and January in wet *Juncus* and *Cladium* litter in the Lopham Fens. Adults live for three to five months after reaching maturity, males being more short-lived than females. Adults are found from May to August.

Status

Numerous in Little and Middle South Lopham Fens but not recorded from Great South Lopham Fen. The initial discovery of this species was in Redgrave Fen, but very few have been seen here in recent years and the habitat in this area may no longer suit the needs of the spider. The East Anglian population was estimated in 1984 to be between 7,000 and 11,000 (Kennett 1985), though these figures include juveniles; adults probably numbered no more than 1,500 in 1987 (P. Withers pers. comm.). The size of the Pevensey Levels population has not been estimated. *Dolomedes plantarius* is thought to be in decline in Europe, drainage of habitat and water pollution being the main causes, and is given Vulnerable status there by Collins & Wells (1987). This decline in Europe increases the importance of the English populations.

Threats

Falling water table and declining water quality are two major threats to the population at South Lopham Fens. Water abstraction next to the fen, drainage of the surrounding farmland and dredging of the River Waveney downstream of the fen have contributed to the fall in the water table. The consequences are that some of the pools in the fen no longer hold water throughout the summer and the character of the vegetation has altered, with grasses becoming dominant in place of sedges and invasion by grey willow *Salix cinerea* and silver birch *Betula pendula*. During the hot dry summers of 1989 and 1990 most pools on the reserve dried out and the River Waveney ceased to flow. With decreased flow from the nearby aquifer being a chronic problem, most of the water supply to the fen is now run-off from agricultural land, and this is applying unwanted nutrients to the fen. There are also occasional releases of pig slurry from nearby farms into ditches draining onto the fen. Fire is an additional threat to the spider, small outbreaks being not uncommon. In late spring, while the adults are still in hibernation above the water surface, they are very vulnerable to a fire sweeping through the areas of sedge. Parts of the Pevensey Levels have been deep-drained for arable agriculture, with consequent problems of a falling water table and eutrophication in the undrained areas.

Conservation   Redgrave and Lopham Fens are an SSSI and Suffolk Trust reserve and have been proposed for listing under the Ramsar Convention. Much of the management is geared to maintaining the habitat of *D. plantarius*. The River Waveney has been dammed to impede the drainage of water from the reserve. The falling water table allows most of the old peat-diggings to dry out in late summer, so further series of deeper small pools have been dug and are successfully colonised by the spider. Also, pools which were in areas of scrub were colonised by *Dolomedes* within three months of the scrub being cleared. The fen is mown in small blocks on a four-year rotation to prevent the fen surface being raised by the accumulation of sedge litter. This also slightly lessens the risk of fire. In East Sussex, *D. plantarius* was found within Pevensey Levels NNR. This species is protected by listing in Schedule 5 of the Wildlife and Countryside Act 1981, which prohibits the unlicensed collecting of specimens. The possibility of establishing another colony of *D. plantarius*, possibly in captivity, is being considered.

Authors   P. Merrett and J.H. Bratton, using information from Duffey (1958, 1960), Locket, Millidge & Merrett (1974), Thornhill (1985), Kennett (1985), Kirby (1990) and E. Duffey, P. Kirby, A. Rivett and P. Withers (pers. comms).

TEGENARIA PICTA   INSUFFICIENTLY KNOWN

Phylum CHELICERATA   Order ARANEAE
Class ARACHNIDA   Family AGELENIDAE

Tegenaria picta Simon, 1870.

Identification   Jones (1984); Roberts (1987).

Distribution   In Britain, recorded only from Amberley Chalk Pits Museum, West Sussex, in 1982. Widespread in France and occurs in the Channel Islands. Also known from Italy, Spain, Portugal, Belgium, Germany, Switzerland, Hungary and the Balkans.

Habitat and ecology   Found under boulders of chalk in shady parts of the chalk-pits at Amberley, though in France it is a widespread and common woodland species (Simon 1937) and it occurs in mountainous regions of Spain and Algeria. At Amberley, a sheet web is built, supported by several vertical silk tubes attached to the ceiling formed by the boulder. The females cover the egg sacs with pieces of chalk. The life cycle is thought to be as follows (Jones 1984). Spiderlings emerge from the egg sac throughout the summer, pass the winter and continue development through a second summer and winter. Maturity is attained the following spring, though in Germany the occurrence of adults in the autumn suggests that maturity can be reached sooner. At Amberley, adults of both sexes were found in May and females until July or later.

Status Only recently discovered. In view of its occurrence in France and the Channel Islands, it is not unexpected that it should be found in Britain.

Threats Amberley Chalk Pits Museum was used as the setting of a film sequence which included a number of explosions. It is not known whether the spider has survived this disturbance.

Author P. Merrett, using information from Jones (1984) and R. Jones (pers. comm.).

TUBERTA MAERENS   RARE

Phylum CHELICERATA   Order ARANEAE
Class ARACHNIDA   Family AGELENIDAE

Tuberta maerens (O. P.-Cambridge, 1863).

Identification Locket & Millidge (1953); Locket, Millidge & Merrett (1974); Roberts (1985a).

Distribution Old records are from Bloxworth, Dorset, in 1862 and 1879, and from Bagley Wood, Berkshire. Recent records include a few specimens from Wytham Woods, Berkshire, in 1953 and 1987; oaks along the boundary of Horton Common, Dorset, in 1980; Chobham Common, Surrey, in 1981; Brasenose Woods, Oxford, in 1981; Little Wittenham Wood, Berkshire, in 1986; and Savernake Forest, North Wiltshire, in 1986 and 1987. Several specimens and hundreds of presumably occupied webs of this species were found in Brasenose Wood in 1986 and 1987. It is also known from a few specimens found in Italy, France, Germany, Austria and Hungary.

Habitat and ecology The majority of records are from deciduous woodland or from near woodland. Most specimens found since 1986 were in webs comprising silken tubes in the crevices of moderately to highly textured bark on oaks, and such bark is probably its usual micro-habitat. Occupied webs were also found on cut segments of oak standing on the ground in woodland, and a few specimens, particularly adult males, were found walking on oak trunks. A single web was found on a very large Scots pine, and a few specimens have been taken under bark on oak and pine. Adult females have been found in all months, and males from July to October. Egg cocoons are built on the tree trunk. Recruitment appears to be low.

Status The micro-habitat of this species has been discovered only recently (C. Hambler in prep.), so it may prove more common than the number of records currently suggests. However, specific and intensive searches by one of us (C.H.) during 1986 and 1987 suggested that, although the species may be abundant very locally, it is often absent from what appears to be suitable habitat, both within woodland where it is known to occur and in other woods in the vicinity. This may indicate high habitat specificity and/or poor powers of dispersal. Although it has occurred in secondary woodland beside ancient woodland and has been found just outside ancient woodland, it may prove to be restricted to the vicinity of ancient woodland where there has been continuity of suitable habitat.

Threats Bagley Wood has been extensively planted with conifers, which will almost certainly have decreased the amount of habitat available to this spider at this site. Short-rotation coppice-with-standards is being revived at Brasenose Wood and, although this species has been found in areas of both young and neglected coppice, the effect of this management on this species is unclear.

Conservation Chobham Common is an SSSI, part also being an LNR. Brasenose Wood, Wytham Wood, Horton Common and parts of Savernake Forest are SSSIs. Little Wittenham Wood is a private nature reserve with no official protected status. On these sites it is important to retain trees with the necessary highly-textured bark, particularly oaks. Mature and overmature trees probably offer the best range of habitat.

Authors P. Merrett and C. Hambler, using information from Locket & Millidge (1953), Locket, Millidge & Merrett (1974), Merrett (1980) and R.B. Coleman and F.M. Murphy (pers. comms).

TUBERTA MACROPHTHALMA   RARE

Phylum CHELICERATA   Order ARANEAE
Class ARACHNIDA   Family AGELENIDAE

Tuberta macrophthalma Kulczynski, 1896, formerly known as *Tetrilus macrophthalmus* (Kulczynski). Roberts (1985a) suggested that this species is synonymous with *T. arietina* (Thorell).

Identification Locket & Millidge (1953); Roberts (1985a, 1985b) (as *Tetrilus macrophthalmus* throughout).

Distribution There are old records, dating from 1901 to 1913, from Oxshott and Weybridge, Surrey; Wellington College, Berkshire; Porlock, South Somerset; and Craig-yr-Eglwys, Glamorgan. Recently it has been recorded from six sites in Charnwood Forest and from Donington Park, Leicestershire, and from two areas in Sherwood Forest,

171

Nottinghamshire. Also known from Portugal, France, Belgium, Austria, Poland, Hungary and Yugoslavia.

Habitat and ecology   Strongly associated with ants, often but not exclusively in and around overmature trees and dead wood. Donisthorpe (1927) found egg sacs of the spider on the carton walls of the cells in nests of the ants *Lasius fuliginosus* (Latreille) and *L. umbratus* (Nylander); attached to wood in the galleries of the nests of *L. brunneus* (Latreille) in trees; and in underground passages in the nests of *Formica rufa* L. and *L. umbratus*. On Bardon Hill, Charnwood Forest, the spider's egg cocoons have been found in galleries and in the heart of the nest of *F. fusca* L., as well as attached to the underside of boulders. When *T. macrophthalma* has been encountered away from ants, it has generally been as single specimens not thought to represent breeding colonies. Observations in Charnwood Forest indicate that rocky terrain with no old trees is as acceptable a habitat as ancient woodland, provided that there are well-established ant colonies. In this situation, the spider occurs in ant nests under boulders embedded in the soil. Adults of both sexes have been recorded in all months between April and December and probably occur throughout the year.

Status   Apparently well-established and quite abundant in parts of Charnwood and Sherwood Forests, but it has not been found recently in any of its old sites in southern England, possibly because it has not been searched for sufficiently.

Threats   Some Charnwood Forest sites are threatened by quarrying. Frequent burning at Bradgate Park (part of Charnwood Forest) as part of the management plan may be the reason for this species not now being found in areas of the park where Donisthorpe recorded it. Destruction of old oaks by burning or felling is also depleting the amount of suitable habitat at Bradgate Park. Much of the ancient broadleaved woodland and parkland of Sherwood Forest has been lost to urban expansion, agriculture and afforestation with conifers. Though the current state of affairs at Sherwood Forest is not a cause for concern, the high demand for its use for recreation could lead to conservation problems in the future because there is less tolerance in public open spaces of overmature trees which may shed limbs. Arachnologists should show restraint when searching for this species under boulders, since disturbance is tolerated to some extent but, if repeated, can lead to abandonment of the nest site by the ants.

Conservation   Occurs within Sherwood Forest Country Park, where the conservation value of the dead wood and overmature trees is now appreciated by the managers. All recent records are from within SSSIs. At Donington Park, new plantings of oaks and limes are being planned to prevent there being a gap in the continuity of overmature trees in coming centuries (P. Kirby pers. comm.).

Authors   P. Merrett and J.H. Bratton, using information from Donisthorpe
                 (1927), Locket & Millidge (1953), Crocker (1973) and P. Kirby,
                 R.M. McGibbon, J.A. and F.M. Murphy and R.G. Snazell (pers.
                 comms).

TUBERTA ARIETINA   VULNERABLE

Phylum CHELICERATA   Order ARANEAE
Class ARACHNIDA   Family AGELENIDAE

Tuberta arietina (Thorell, 1871), formerly known as *Tetrilus arietinus*
(Thorell) and *Cryphoeca diversa* O. P.-Cambridge.

Identification   Locket & Millidge (1953); Roberts (1985a) (in both as *Tetrilus
                       arietinus*).

Distribution   Recorded from Oxshott, Weybridge and Woking, Surrey; from
                       Windsor Forest and Wellington College, Berkshire; and from
                       Carlisle, Cumberland, though only a single wandering female was
                       found in the last instance. A record from County Durham last
                       century under the name *C. diversa* proved to be false (Cooke
                       1967). Fairly widespread in southern and central Europe.

Habitat and ecology Only in the nests of the ants *Lasius fuliginosus* (Latreille) and
                       L. brunneus (Latreille), which inhabit tree stumps and old trees.
                       The latter species is found mostly in oaks in open country (Brian
                       1977). Adult males of the spider have been found in April and
                       October, and females in January, April, July to October and
                       December.

Status   All records are from the period 1892 to 1926. It was apparently
                       found fairly frequently in ants' nests in Surrey and Berkshire by
                       Donisthorpe in the first quarter of this century but has not been
                       recorded since. This may be because ants' nests are rarely
                       investigated by arachnologists. However, Roberts (1985a)
                       suggested that *T. arietina* and *T. macrophthalma* Kulczynski are
                       forms of the same species, as their genitalia are identical and the
                       only noticeable differences are in the eye size and arrangement.

Threats   The loss of overmature trees from woodland and parkland.
                       Unfortunately, this loss persists even within areas set aside for
                       nature conservation, largely because those responsible for
                       management do not appreciate the value of the dead wood habitat
                       and see the presence of dying trees as a sign of bad forestry.

Conservation   Windsor Forest is an SSSI, mainly on the strength of the large
                       number of overmature trees and the rich invertebrate fauna which
                       they support.

173

Author   P. Merrett, using information from Donisthorpe (1927) and Locket & Millidge (1953).

HAHNIA CANDIDA   **VULNERABLE**

Phylum CHELICERATA   Order ARANEAE
Class ARACHNIDA   Family HAHNIIDAE

Hahnia candida Simon, 1875.

Identification   Locket & Millidge (1953); Roberts (1985a).

Distribution   In Britain, recorded only from four localities in Dorset: at Portland on four occasions between 1854 and 1945; Chesil Beach near Abbotsbury in 1977; Ringstead in 1913; and Morden Park in 1913, though this last record is doubtful since the habitat is different from in the other cases. Also known from Greece, Italy, Spain, France, Belgium, southern Germany and Poland.

Habitat and ecology Most specimens were found under stones on coastal cliffs or on shingle. One female was from among heather inland. Adults of both sexes have been taken in September, and females also in February and June.

Status   It would appear to be well-established at Portland. Most of the twenty known British specimens have been found at this site.

Threats   Loss of coastal grassland habitat. There is extensive stone-quarrying on the Isle of Portland. It is not known whether this is diminishing the habitat of this spider.

Conservation   Chesil Beach, parts of Portland Bill and the cliffs at Ringstead have SSSI status, some of the last being National Trust property leased to the Dorset Trust.

Author   P. Merrett, using information from Pickard-Cambridge (1914), Locket & Millidge (1953) and P.D. Hillyard (pers. comm.).

HAHNIA MICROPHTHALMA   **INSUFFICIENTLY KNOWN**

Phylum CHELICERATA   Order ARANEAE
Class ARACHNIDA   Family HAHNIIDAE

Hahnia microphthalma Snazell & Duffey, 1980.

Identification   Snazell & Duffey (1980); Roberts (1985a).

Distribution　　One female from Lyscombe Hill, Dorset, and one female from close to Royston Heath, Hertfordshire, both in the winter of 1975/76. Not known from outside Britain.

Habitat and ecology　The Dorset example was found in chalk grassland of great age. The other was collected in a field with a clay soil overlying chalk, which had been cultivated for cereals until 1973, allowed to revert to grassland, but then ploughed and harrowed in the autumn of 1975 and which supported a sparse growth of grasses at the time that *H. microphthalma* was found. Permanent chalk grassland occurred at nearby Royston Heath. It is possible that this species lives underground in fissures in the soil or in ants' nests. Females have been found in December and January.

Status　　Only two specimens known to science.

Threats　　If old chalk grassland is important in the ecology of this species, it is likely to have suffered great loss of habitat in recent decades, as it is estimated that over 70% of chalk grassland was destroyed in Britain between 1940 and 1984 (Nature Conservancy Council 1984). Much of this loss has been the result of conversion to arable agriculture. The Royston field is now under cultivation.

Conservation　　Lyscombe Hill is a Dorset Trust reserve and part of an SSSI. Royston Heath is partly a Local Nature Reserve/Herts and Middlesex Trust reserve and SSSI (under the name Therfield Heath). Both sites are being maintained as chalk grassland, the former by grazing and the latter by mowing.

Author　　P. Merrett, using information from Snazell & Duffey (1980) and E. Duffey (pers. comm.).

ERO APHANA   **VULNERABLE**

Phylum CHELICERATA   Order ARANEAE
Class ARACHNIDA   Family MIMETIDAE

Ero aphana (Walckenaer, 1802).

Identification　　Merrett & Snazell (1975); Roberts (1985a).

Distribution　　Since 1974 recorded from five sites in east Dorset, namely Parley Common, Town Common, Ramsdown Common, Stephens Castle and Horton Common. Widespread in southern and central Europe.

Habitat and ecology　Found on dry heathland in the building and mature phases, with some patches of bare stony ground and *Ulex europaeus* and *Pinus sylvestris* present. Both sexes are found from May to July, and females also in August.

175

Status	Fairly frequent in its few known sites.
Threats	Fire and loss of heathland to building development and agriculture. Most of Horton Common has been ploughed for agriculture since the discovery of the spider. Only a small part of the once extensive heath of Parley Common survives, the rest having been lost to Bournemouth airport and housing development at Ferndown and West Parley, with further encroachment along the northern edge of the common in prospect. Pines (*Pinus sylvestris* and *P. pinaster*) have invaded substantial areas of the dry heath within Town Common SSSI, especially at Ramsdown Common.
Conservation	Town Common, Parley Common and the surviving area of Horton Common are SSSIs. The first includes Ramsdown Common, which is a Dorset Trust reserve. The Trust, helped by the Forestry Commission, is undertaking clearance of rhododendron and other invading vegetation there. Heath at Stephens Castle is within Verwood Heaths SSSI. Management of heathland, whether by grazing, mowing or burning, should allow *Calluna* to reach the mature phase. This will often necessitate the additional control of scrub and pine invasion by hand-pulling.
Author	P. Merrett, using personal observations and information from Merrett & Snazell (1975), Haskins (1988) and D. Elton, R.G. Snazell and J.R. White (pers. comms).

EPISINUS MACULIPES   RARE

Phylum CHELICERATA   Order ARANEAE
Class ARACHNIDA   Family THERIDIIDAE

Episinus maculipes Cavanna, 1876.

Identification	Locket, Millidge & Merrett (1974); Hillyard (1983); Roberts (1985a).
Distribution	A single female was recorded from Tiptree Heath, North Essex, in 1929, but *E. maculipes* has never been rediscovered there. Considerable numbers of both sexes were found in 1981 and 1982 on the undercliff between Niton and Ventnor, Isle of Wight. Searches of other Isle of Wight woodlands, including Brighstone Forest, Firestone Copse and Burnt Wood, have been unsuccessful. One male was found in 1989 at Jennycliff Bay, South Devon, and four juveniles suspected to belong to this species were found elsewhere in the Plymouth area during the same survey (R.A. Stevens pers. comm.). Also known from Yugoslavia, Greece, Italy, Spain and France.
Habitat and ecology	On the Isle of Wight, this species was found on the foliage of shrubs

176

and trees, especially sycamore, holm oak, ivy and bramble, growing on the south-facing undercliff up to 400 metres inland. Observations there showed that at nightfall it built a simple web, consisting of an inverted 'Y' frame with sticky globules. The frame could be only 5 cm long between leaves or up to 20 cm long between branches. 30 to 50% of webs of female spiders were seen to have caught prey within an hour of darkness. The prey included lacewing larvae and capsid bugs (*Phytocoris* sp.). Males tended to be found moving through the vegetation and not associated with webs. Both sexes were adult in July and August. They occurred at low density, one or two individuals per tree (Hillyard 1983). At Jennycliff Bay an adult male was found on hemp-agrimony *Eupatorium cannabinum* in a damp flush near the strandline at the base of a cliff.

Status
The old Essex record has long been considered unreliable, but the thriving colony on the Isle of Wight confirmed *E. maculipes* as a British species. It is well-established along a three-mile stretch of coastline there. Its distribution in the Plymouth area is not yet known.

Threats
Holiday development is a possible threat to the coastal populations of this spider and could be particularly damaging on the Isle of Wight, where major engineering would be needed to stabilise the soft-rock cliffs. Although the Isle of Wight coastline to east and west of the section supporting *E. maculipes* has been notified as SSSIs, the area supporting this spider has not.

Conservation
Niton Undercliff is a reserve of the Hampshire and Isle of Wight Trust. A survey to ascertain whether the spider occurs within the adjacent SSSIs is desirable. The cliff at Jennycliff Bay has been identified as a nature conservation area in the 1988 Plymouth City Plan, which offers some protection against development.

Author
P. Merrett, using information from Locket, Millidge & Merrett (1974), Hillyard (1983) and J.A. and F.M. Murphy and R.A. Stevens (pers. comms).

DIPOENA ERYTHROPUS   VULNERABLE

Phylum CHELICERATA   Order ARANEAE
Class ARACHNIDA   Family THERIDIIDAE

Dipoena erythropus (Simon, 1881).

Identification
Locket & Millidge (1953); Roberts (1985a).

Distribution
Recorded from near Tonbridge, West Kent, in the 1880s, the Lizard, West Cornwall, in 1913, and Thursley Common, Surrey, in

1971. Several specimens were found at the last site. Warwickshire is included in the distribution given in Locket & Millidge (1953), but this is probably incorrect. There are also records from Italy, France, the Netherlands, Germany, Austria, Switzerland, Hungary, Poland, the Balkans and Finland.

Habitat and ecology Found on gorse bushes on heathland. Adults occur in June.

Status Only five or six specimens have ever been found in Britain, but this apparent scarcity may partly be due to insufficient recording by appropriate methods during the season of activity.

Threats Lowland heath is widely threatened by reclamation for agriculture and other land-use and is frequently damaged by fire. Large areas of Thursley Common were accidentally burned in 1976.

Conservation Gorse is encouraged on many southern heathlands because it is the nesting site of the Dartford warbler, and this may help to ensure the survival of the spider's habitat. However, the growth form of gorse favoured by *D. erythropus* needs to be defined to enable specific management recommendations to be made. The Lizard is an SSSI and in part an NNR. The Surrey site of *D. erythropus* is probably just outside the boundary of Thursley NNR.

Author P. Merrett, using information from Locket & Millidge (1953) and A.D. Blest (pers. comm.).

DIPOENA CORACINA ENDANGERED

Phylum CHELICERATA Order ARANEAE
Class ARACHNIDA Family THERIDIIDAE

Dipoena coracina (C.L. Koch, 1841).

Identification Locket & Millidge (1953); Roberts (1985a).

Distribution Recorded from Bloxworth Heath and Morden Park, Dorset, on six occasions between 1863 and 1913, and a single male was found in Suffolk in 1904. Also known from Italy, Portugal, France, the Netherlands, Germany, Austria, Switzerland, Hungary and Bulgaria.

Habitat and ecology Mainly among heather, but also from grass in a swamp. Adults of both sexes have been found in May, and males also in August and September.

Status Only about ten specimens have been found, none for over seventy years, so this species may now be extinct in Britain.

Threats	Probably the loss and fragmentation of Dorset's heathland. For example, figures given by Webb & Haskins (1980) show that rates of heathland loss in the Poole Basin averaged 3% per year between 1960 and 1973 and that the total area of heath declined from 22,672 ha in 1896 to 5,832 ha in 1978. However, the 1978 estimate was revised to 7,000-8,000 ha (Webb 1986) to allow for the stricter definition of heath used in the 1978 survey. The former Bloxworth Heath is now mainly a Forestry Commission conifer plantation, Wareham Forest, though part survives as what is now Morden Bog NNR.
Author	P. Merrett, using information from Locket & Millidge (1953).

DIPOENA MELANOGASTER   VULNERABLE

Phylum CHELICERATA   Order ARANEAE
Class ARACHNIDA   Family THERIDIIDAE

Dipoena melanogaster (C.L. Koch, 1845).

Identification	Locket & Millidge (1953); Roberts (1985a, 1985b).
Distribution	In Britain, only known from four specimens: a female near Lyndhurst, South Hampshire, in 1858; a male from Bloxworth Heath, Dorset, in 1881; a male from Mickleham Down, Surrey, in 1970; and a female from Hackhurst Downs, Surrey, in 1976. Widespread in southern and central Europe.
Habitat and ecology	Occurs on gorse and other bushes. In Ireland, it has been found on Scots pine *Pinus sylvestris* (E. Duffey pers. comm.). Adults of both sexes have been found in June, and a female also in July.
Status	The life cycle and habits of this species, with the males being very short-lived and the females concealed in a retreat, may have led to this species being under-recorded. However, the finding of only four specimens in 130 years indicates that it must be an extreme rarity.
Threats	Most of Bloxworth Heath has been planted up with conifers by the Forestry Commission.
Conservation	Hackhurst Downs are an LNR and SSSI. Mickleham Down is a property of the National Trust. Small parts of Bloxworth Heath survive as Morden Bog NNR.
Author	P. Merrett, using information from Locket & Millidge (1953) and F.M. Murphy (pers. comm.).

DIPOENA TORVA

VULNERABLE

Phylum CHELICERATA
Class ARACHNIDA

Order ARANEAE
Family THERIDIIDAE

Dipoena torva (Thorell, 1875).

Identification   Locket & Millidge (1953); Roberts (1985a, 1985b).

Distribution   Since its first discovery in 1948 it has been recorded several times
from the Black Wood of Rannoch, Mid Perthshire, and from
Rothiemurchus Forest (near Coylumbridge and Loch an Eilein) and
Abernethy Forest, both in East Inverness-shire. Also known from
Germany, Switzerland, Austria, Poland, Russia, Finland and the
Balkans.

Habitat and ecology   Restricted to Caledonian pine forest. Found on the trunks of Scots
pine *Pinus sylvestris*. Lives in fissures in the bark and spins a small
web which catches wood ants. Both sexes have been found in June,
and females also in August and September.

Status   Apparently well-established in the Caledonian pine forests of
Rannoch, Rothiemurchus and Abernethy.

Threats   Loss of Caledonian pine forest, mainly through conversion to dense
conifer plantations of alien species for commercial wood
production. In the three forests where it is known to occur there
have been alterations to the natural forest structure over large
areas. 226 ha of Abernethy Forest have been felled since 1977.
There has been extensive planting of Scots pine and non-native
conifers in the Black Wood of Rannoch, including the underplanting
of 180 ha of scattered mature native pine. In Rothiemurchus Forest,
305 ha were ploughed and planted in 1971. Management of pine
forest for timber production is unlikely to tolerate overmature trees
with deeply fissured bark. The dense shade found in plantations
provides a much cooler habitat than the open-structured natural
forest and is unlikely to be suitable for either the spider or its main
prey, wood ants.

Conservation   Occurs in Cairngorms NNR and Black Wood of Rannoch SSSI. Part
of the latter is an FNR. Abernethy Forest is an SSSI and in part an
NNR, and a large area was purchased by the RSPB in 1988.
Management of the native pine should aim to preserve open
woodland with a varied ground flora and sunny glades, which has
been typical of Caledonian pine forest for many centuries. There is
the need to allow regeneration by lowering the deer-grazing
pressure. However, the production of dense stands of pine, even
native pine of local provenance, is unlikely to support the fauna
associated with open forest. There may be the need to thin young
pines in deer exclosures. Increased numbers of human visitors are

thought to be the cause of pine regeneration in the south of Rothiemurchus Forest, their presence disturbing the deer and lowering the grazing pressure. This probably leads to a better forest structure than the dense regeneration found within deer exclosures. While timber extraction is not totally inimical to conservation, a proportion of trees should be allowed to become senescent, as the older trees are more likely to provide the fissured bark preferred by this spider (and other micro-habitats required by many other scarce invertebrates).

Author P. Merrett, using information from Locket & Millidge (1953), Bain (1987) and N.P. Ashmole and F.M. Murphy (pers. comms).

THERIDION PINASTRI   INSUFFICIENTLY KNOWN

Phylum CHELICERATA   Order ARANEAE
Class ARACHNIDA   Family THERIDIIDAE

Theridion pinastri L. Koch, 1872.

Identification Murphy & Murphy (1979); Roberts (1985a).

Distribution Single specimens have been found on Chobham Common, Surrey, in 1977 and 1984. The species is widespread in central and southern Europe.

Habitat and ecology Found in Britain on mature heathland, though on the Continent it usually occurs in pine woods. The British examples may have been strays from nearby pine woods. A male was found at the end of June and a female in October.

Status The current evidence suggests that this species belongs in the Endangered category. If it does prove to be associated with pine woods rather than heath, its vulnerability would be diminished because its habitat would then not be scarce or threatened and the native status of the spider would also be called into question.

Threats Accidental summer fire is a threat both to the heath and to the pine woods. Too frequent burning is causing loss of heather cover and replacement by purple moor-grass *Molinia caerulea* over parts of Chobham Common. Elsewhere the heath is being invaded by birch and pine owing to lack of management.

Conservation Chobham Common is an SSSI and in part an LNR. The area in which *T. pinastri* has been found supports several other scarce spiders. A programme of heathland management, using grazing, mowing or burning on a controlled fifteen- to twenty-year rotation, needs to be implemented if the rich heathland fauna of this site is to survive.

Author   P. Merrett, using information from Murphy & Murphy (1979) and
                  P. Harvey (pers. comm.).

ENOPLOGNATHA TECTA   ENDANGERED

Phylum CHELICERATA   Order ARANEAE
Class ARACHNIDA   Family THERIDIIDAE

Enoplognatha tecta (Keyserling, 1884), previously known as
E. caricis (Fickert).

Identification   Merrett & Snazell (1975) (described as *E. caricis* (Fickert)); Roberts
                      (1985a).

Distribution   A female was discovered at Hyde, Dorset, in 1888 and a male
                      found at the Warren, Bere Regis, in 1974, about 1 km away. Also
                      known from Italy, France, Germany (where it is rare) and
                      Switzerland.

Habitat and ecology The male was found in a small area of marsh bordering a river,
                      dominated by *Phragmites australis* and *Carex riparia*. The female
                      was from "a swamp", which was probably a similar habitat. The
                      female was recorded in May and the male in July.

Status   Has persisted in this area for nearly a hundred years.

Threats   There is no threat at present to the 1974 site, but it is vulnerable to
                      drainage and possibly pollution from fertilisers on the nearby
                      agricultural land.

Conservation   Notification as an SSSI may be appropriate protection for the
                      Warren. Scrub removal may be necessary to prevent carr
                      developing in the marsh.

Author   P. Merrett, using information from Merrett & Snazell (1975) and
                      R.G. Snazell (pers. comm.).

ENOPLOGNATHA OELANDICA

RARE

Phylum CHELICERATA
Class ARACHNIDA

Order ARANEAE
Family THERIDIIDAE

Enoplognatha oelandica (Thorell, 1875). Though it was previously known as *E. mandibularis* (Lucas) in Britain, this is not a synonym but the name of a different species found in southern Europe.

Identification

Locket & Millidge (1953) (as *E. mandibularis*); Merrett & Snazell (1975); Roberts (1985a, 1985b)

Distribution

Recorded from Hayling Island, South Hampshire; Thursley, Hankley and Frensham Commons, Surrey; Sandwich, East Kent; Great Yarmouth, East Norfolk; and Alexandra Park, Middlesex. The record for Scolt Head, West Norfolk, shown in Map 282 of Locket, Millidge & Merrett (1974) is incorrect, and the South Essex record is in doubt. Reportedly widespread in northern and central Europe, but identifications of this genus can be unreliable.

Habitat and ecology

On sand dunes and dry sandy heaths, sometimes under stones or else among vegetation. In Alexandra Park, it was found in an area of old grass heath which included *Sieglingia decumbens* in the sward. Adults of both sexes have been found from May to August, and females also in September.

Status

It is rarer than once thought, owing to some older records having proved false.

Threats

Loss and fragmentation of heathland and public pressure on the coastal sites. There has been much loss of heathland and sand dunes this century, the former through conversion to other land-uses such as agriculture, forestry and building development, the latter through the spread of holiday homes and the need to strengthen sea defences. The siting of three golf courses at Sandwich Dunes has caused damage to this very important site. Surviving sand dunes tend to be favoured places for recreation and can easily suffer erosion owing to trampling. The remaining fragments of heath are very prone to scrub encroachment and outbreaks of fire.

Conservation

Some of its sites have a degree of protection. Thursley, Hankley and Frensham Commons are an SSSI. Part of Thursley Common is an NNR and Surrey Trust reserve, and Frensham Common is National Trust property managed by Waverley District Council, partly as a Country Park. Sandwich Dunes are an SSSI, various areas being under the protection of the National Trust, Kent Trust and RSPB. A small part of Hayling Island is a County Trust reserve. It is important that the heathland sites are managed, whether by grazing, mowing or controlled burning, in order to prevent scrub and tree invasion and reduce the risk of catastrophic summer fires.

Author   P. Merrett, using information from Locket & Millidge (1953),
                     Merrett & Snazell (1975) and J.E.D. Milner (pers. comm.).

ROBERTUS SCOTICUS   ENDANGERED

Phylum CHELICERATA   Order ARANEAE
Class ARACHNIDA   Family THERIDIIDAE

Robertus scoticus Jackson, 1914.

Identification   Locket & Millidge (1953); Locket, Millidge & Merrett (1974);
                         Roberts (1985a).

Distribution   Recorded from the Black Wood of Rannoch on several occasions,
                         most recently in 1988, and once from Old Wood of Meggernie,
                         which is about 10 km away. Both sites are in Mid Perthshire.
                         Elsewhere in Europe known from Belgium, Germany, Switzerland,
                         Denmark, Sweden, Finland and Poland.

Habitat and ecology Records are restricted to Caledonian pine forest, where it inhabits
                         moss and pine litter in damp areas. Males have been found in
                         August and October, and females in June, August, September and
                         October.

Status   Clearly a very rare species. It has been unsuccessfully searched
                         for in other woods, including some not far from the Black Wood of
                         Rannoch (e.g. Glen Lyon and Glen Lochay). Also rare in its
                         continental range.

Threats   The habitat of this species, Caledonian pine forest, is becoming
                         increasingly scarce as areas are turned over to intensive
                         commercial forestry using alien species, often Sitka spruce *Picea
                         sitchensis* or lodgepole pine *Pinus contorta*, in dense monocultures.
                         Many of the important features of the semi-natural forest (for
                         example an uneven age structure of trees and wide spacing with
                         numerous glades, allowing a varied ground flora) are not imitated
                         by the commercial plantations. In the Black Wood of Rannoch there
                         has been extensive planting of Scots pine and exotic conifers.
                         Planting generally involves ploughing of the ground, which
                         improves drainage and is thus liable to eliminate the habitat of this
                         spider. Plantations of Scots pine and other conifers have been
                         established adjacent to the Black Wood of Rannoch, precluding
                         expansion of the natural pine forest.

Conservation   The Black Wood of Rannoch is an SSSI and in part an FNR. The Old
                         Wood of Meggernie lies within an SSSI. The management strategy
                         adopted by the Forestry Commission for the FNR includes
                         maintaining 384 ha of native Scots pine which will be subject to no

Abernethy Forest SSSI, East Inverness-shire. A diminishing habitat supporting numerous scarce invertebrates, including threatened spiders. The open canopy, varied age structure and presence of overmature and damaged trees are important aspects of natural pine forest which are absent from commercial blanket forestry. (Photo by D.A. Ratcliffe.)

planting or felling. It is not known whether *R. scoticus* occurs in this area. Maintenance of the open structure of the forest and prevention of drainage are important for the conservation of this species. Grazing pressure from deer is suppressing pine regeneration in most areas of native pine and this can be alleviated by deer-culling or excluding deer from areas with fences. The latter option can lead to very dense regeneration, with a similar structure to a plantation and equally damaging to the fauna and flora. In such cases, thinning of the young pines to create glades may need to be carried out well before the canopy closes. At Old Wood of Meggernie, the pine woods are very heavily grazed and show no regeneration except in two deer exclosures, one of which was planted with pine.

Author P. Merrett, using information from Locket & Millidge (1953), Locket, Millidge & Merrett (1974), Bain (1987) and R.G. Snazell, D. Horsfield, E.A. Crowson and M.J. Roberts (pers. comms).

ROBERTUS INSIGNIS ENDANGERED

Phylum CHELICERATA Order ARANEAE
Class ARACHNIDA Family THERIDIIDAE

Robertus insignis O. P.-Cambridge, 1907.

Identification Locket & Millidge (1953); Merrett & Snazell (1975); Roberts (1985a).

Distribution This species was first recorded in 1907, when a male was found. The locality was given as Norwich, East Norfolk (Pickard-Cambridge 1907). In 1989 a second British specimen, another male, was identified among invertebrates collected in 1988 as part of an NCC survey in Catfield Fen, East Norfolk, about fifteen miles northeast of Norwich (D.A. Procter pers. comm.). A few individuals of both sexes have been found in recent decades in Germany, Estonia and Sweden, but it seems to be very rare throughout its known range.

Habitat and ecology Nothing appears to have been recorded of the habitat where the first British specimen was found. The second was caught in a water trap placed at ground level in a *Cladium mariscus* sedge-bed from 21 June to 5 July. In Germany a male was collected in May 1959 from a flat peaty meadow or fen meadow (Flachmoorwiese) (Wiehle 1960). In Sweden, five males and nineteen females were found in Knisa Mire, a *Cladium mariscus* mire bordered by *Carex elata* tussocks and moss (Almquist 1978).

Status The rediscovery of this species after an 80-year gap in the records gives hope that it may be surviving unnoticed in other East Anglian fenland sites or elsewhere in the country.

Threats The Broads and grazed marshes in the vicinity of Norwich have suffered much degradation since the beginning of the century, owing to eutrophication, drainage, water abstraction and lapses in long-established management regimes leading to encroachment by scrub and carr.

Conservation Catfield Fen lies within an SSSI and the sedge-beds are being maintained by mowing. This traditional management is being promoted elsewhere in the Broads by the Broads Authority and other conservation bodies, thus reversing some of the habitat loss.

Authors P. Merrett and J.H. Bratton, using information from Locket & Millidge (1953), Merrett & Snazell (1975), Roberts (1985a), Procter (1990) and D.A. Procter (pers. comm.).

GIBBARANEA BITUBERCULATA ENDANGERED

Phylum CHELICERATA Order ARANEAE
Class ARACHNIDA Family ARANEIDAE

Gibbaranea bituberculata (Walckenaer, 1802), formerly known as *Araneus bituberculatus* (Walckenaer).

Identification Locket & Millidge (1953) (as *Araneus bituberculatus*); Roberts (1985a, 1985b).

Distribution In Britain, known only from Burnham Beeches, Buckinghamshire. Records from Essex (Hull 1948) require verification. Widespread in southern and central Europe.

Habitat and ecology In Britain, it was found on bushes in open areas in woodland. In Europe, webs can be found near the ground and in hedgerows. Adult females were recorded in May in Britain.

Status Found on several occasions between 1908 and 1938 and apparently fairly numerous then, but there have been no records in recent years. Possibly now extinct in Britain.

Threats The herbage and bushes on which it was found at Burnham Beeches were mown to the ground in 1954, despite the site having been notified as an SSSI in 1951.

Conservation Burnham Beeches is an SSSI, though before the Wildlife and Countryside Act 1981 this gave very limited protection to a site.

Author P. Merrett, using information from Locket & Millidge (1953) and G.H. Locket and J.A. and F.M. Murphy (pers. comms).

ARANIELLA ALPICA

RARE

An orb-weaver spider

Phylum CHELICERATA
Class ARACHNIDA

Order ARANEAE
Family ARANEIDAE

Araniella alpica (L. Koch, 1869), formerly known as *Araneus alpicus*.

Identification   Locket & Millidge (1953); Locket, Millidge & Merrett (1974) (as *Araneus alpicus*); Roberts (1985a). This species is difficult to distinguish from two more common species, *Araniella cucurbitina* (Clerck) and *A. inconspicua* (Simon).

Distribution   Recorded from Great Kimble, Buckinghamshire; the New Forest, South Hampshire; near Box Hill, Surrey; Heyshott Down, West Sussex; Grovely Wood, near Salisbury, South Wiltshire; and Melbury Down, Dorset. The first two records are not from recent years. There are European records from Italy, Sardinia, Corsica, Spain, France, Belgium, Germany, Denmark, Sweden, Norway, Russia, Poland, Czechoslovakia, Romania, Austria, Switzerland and the Balkans.

Habitat and ecology   On trees, especially yew and beech, but also recorded from dogwood *Cornus sanguinea* near Box Hill. At Melbury Down it was found on chalk grassland, but there was woodland nearby (K.N.A. Alexander pers. comm.). Adults occur in May and June.

Status   Despite the difficulties of identification, there is no doubt that this species is very rare.

Threats   The loss of old yew and beech woods.

Conservation   Heyshott Down, the New Forest and Box Hill have the protection of SSSI status and the last is also in the care of the National Trust.

Author   P. Merrett, using information from Locket & Millidge (1953), Locket, Millidge & Merrett (1974) and R.B. Coleman, J.A. and F.M. Murphy and R. Jones (pers. comms).

HYPSOSINGA HERI

ENDANGERED

Phylum CHELICERATA
Class ARACHNIDA

Order ARANEAE
Family ARANEIDAE

Hypsosinga heri (Hahn, 1831), formerly known as *Singa heri*.

Identification   Locket & Millidge (1953) (as *Singa heri*); Roberts (1985a).

| Distribution | Single males were found at Wicken Fen, Cambridgeshire, in 1892 and 1912. It is also recorded from Berkshire but the locality and date are unknown. Widespread in southern and central Europe. |

Distribution   Single males were found at Wicken Fen, Cambridgeshire, in 1892 and 1912. It is also recorded from Berkshire but the locality and date are unknown. Widespread in southern and central Europe.

Habitat and ecology   Found on low plants near water, males in June and July.

Status   Has not been recorded for many years, despite much recording effort at Wicken Fen, and may be extinct in Britain.

Threats   Wicken Fen is known to have suffered from lowering of the water table owing to drainage of the surrounding land for agriculture (Rowell 1986) and may no longer be suitable for this species. On the Continent it is found in sites with a higher water table than that currently prevailing at Wicken Fen.

Conservation   Wicken Fen is an SSSI owned by the National Trust and managed as a nature reserve. Its surrounding banks have recently been waterproofed by the insertion of a polythene membrane to minimise the seepage of water onto the lower adjacent farmland. There is, however, little that can be done to raise the water table within the fen. An alternative approach, extracting peat in order to lower the ground surface down to the water table, has been considered for parts of the site.

Author   P. Merrett, using information from Locket & Millidge (1953) and T.J. Bennett, E. Duffey and W.J. Fojt (pers. comms).

WALCKENAERIA MITRATA   ENDANGERED

Phylum CHELICERATA   Order ARANEAE
Class ARACHNIDA   Family LINYPHIIDAE

Walckenaeria mitrata (Menge, 1868).

Identification   Locket, Millidge & Merrett (1974); Roberts (1987).

Distribution   Recorded in Britain only from Blean Woods, East Kent, in 1967. Widespread elsewhere in Europe, with records from France, Belgium, Germany, Switzerland, Austria, Czechoslovakia, Hungary, Poland, Russia, Sweden and Finland.

Habitat and ecology   In Britain, found in the litter layer of mature sweet chestnut coppice. Both sexes have been found in April and a female also in November.

Status   Only three females and two males have been found. No further records since 1967.

Blean Woods NNR, East Kent. Sweet chestnut coppice with oak standards. The litter layer and fallen boughs are home to three threatened spiders, whilst the herb, shrub and canopy layers are important insect habitats. Much Kent coppice has been converted to conifer plantation in the last 40 years. (Photo by P. Wakely.)

Threats	There has been a major decline in the area of chestnut coppice in Kent since the 1940s, much of it being lost either through neglect or through conversion to conifer forestry. The litter layer beneath conifers is unlikely to support this species, but neglected coppice may form suitable habitat.
Conservation	Occurs in Blean Woods NNR. Some other areas of the Blean Woods complex have protected status as an SSSI and nature reserves. Sweet chestnut coppice is being maintained at several sites for the benefit of the Heath Fritillary Butterfly *Mellicta athalia* (Rottemburg) (Shirt 1987).
Author	P. Merrett, using information from Swann (1971) and Locket, Millidge & Merrett (1974).

WALCKENAERIA STYLIFRONS   ENDANGERED

Phylum CHELICERATA   Order ARANEAE
Class ARACHNIDA   Family LINYPHIIDAE

Walckenaeria stylifrons (O. P.-Cambridge, 1875), formerly known as *Wideria stylifrons.*

Identification	Locket, Millidge & Merrett (1974); Roberts (1987).
Distribution	Recorded in Britain only from Weeting Heath, West Norfolk, in 1963. Its European distribution includes Corsica, France, Belgium, Germany, Austria and Switzerland, though most records are from the French Mediterranean coast.
Habitat and ecology	Found in tall dense *Festuca* turf on sandy soil. Females have been found in March and April, but males only in April.
Status	Only two females and two males have been found.
Threats	Much of Breckland has been afforested with conifers or put into permanent agricultural production, and several remaining areas of heath are fast disappearing under self-set pines.
Conservation	Occurs on Weeting Heath NNR, which is also a Norfolk Trust reserve. Though the reserve is usually heavily rabbit-grazed, myxomatosis has severely reduced the rabbit population in recent years, and thus there are areas of longer turf surviving (L. Farrell pers. comm.).
Author	P. Merrett, using information from Duffey & Denis (1967) and Locket, Millidge & Merrett (1974).

BARYPHYMA DUFFEYI   RARE

Phylum CHELICERATA   Order ARANEAE
Class ARACHNIDA   Family LINYPHIIDAE

Baryphyma duffeyi (Millidge, 1954), formerly known as *Praestigia duffeyi*.

Identification Locket, Millidge & Merrett (1974) (as *Praestigia duffeyi*); Roberts (1985b, 1987).

Distribution Recorded from Havergate Island, East Suffolk; two sites near Flatford Mill, East Suffolk/North Essex border; East Tilbury Marsh and Stanford-le-Hope saltmarsh, South Essex; and Dartford Marsh and High Halstow Marsh, West Kent. All these records are since 1953. It has been searched for at numerous places on the coast between Scolt Head, West Norfolk, and Havergate, but without success (E. Duffey pers. comm.). Its European distribution includes Belgium (Jocque 1976), the Netherlands and Germany (van Helsdingen 1980).

Habitat and ecology On wet mud in saltmarshes and brackish marshes, beneath *Halimione* and *Phragmites*, and among tide litter. Adults of both sexes are found from April to June.

Status Extremely abundant in some places, but known from few sites.

Threats Many of the Thames Marshes have been reclaimed for industrial development, with extensive use of vertical concrete-capped iron pilings along the waterfront leaving very little saltmarsh.

Conservation Tide litter should be left to accumulate, undisturbed by bonfires and beach sanitisers. Havergate Island is an RSPB reserve and forms part of an NNR.

Author P. Merrett, using information from Jerrard (1963), Locket, Millidge & Merrett (1974) and P. Harvey (pers. comm.).

BARYPHYMA GOWERENSE
INSUFFICIENTLY KNOWN

Phylum CHELICERATA
Class ARACHNIDA

Order ARANEAE
Family LINYPHIIDAE

Baryphyma gowerense (Locket, 1965), formerly known as *Acanthophyma gowerensis* and *Lasiargus gowerensis*.

Identification   Locket, Millidge & Merrett (1974) (as *Acanthophyma gowerensis*); Roberts (1985b, 1987).

Distribution   Recorded from Whiteford Burrows and Oxwich Burrows in Glamorgan in 1967 and 1971; Ruston Common, East Norfolk, in 1974; and in 1988 from Woodbastwick Fen in East Norfolk, Cors Erddreiniog on Anglesey and Cors Geirch in Caernarvonshire. Kronestedt (1979) has recorded this species from Sweden and Mackie (1970) has found it on the Dingle Peninsula, South Kerry, Eire.

Habitat and ecology   The first example was found in "seaweed drift at spring tide mark on Whiteford dunes" (Locket 1965). However, further searching failed to locate specimens in the drift material but revealed large numbers in the high intertidal zone of nearby saltmarsh. It occurred only in a narrow band on the shore in vegetation dominated by *Juncus maritimus* and *Festuca rubra*. It has been found in similar habitat at Oxwich. Ruston Common is an inland marshy area with acidic fen grading into less acidic saw-sedge *Cladium* and reed *Phragmites* stands. It is not known which vegetation type was being used by this spider. At Woodbastwick Fen a female was found in a sedge-bed managed by mowing. Adults of both sexes have been found in May and June. In Sweden, it was recorded from seasonally flooded meadows around a eutrophic lake, on wet ground under old vegetation such as *Deschampsia* tussocks (Kronestedt 1979).

Status   Apparently well-established and abundant at Whiteford and Oxwich. The 1988 records are early results from two extensive NCC surveys of East Anglian fens and Welsh peatlands. Until the full results of these surveys are known, the true status of *B. gowerense* is a matter for speculation.

Threats   At Oxwich, natural changes in the dune system have led to an increase in the accretion rate in the saltmarsh, with consequent changes in the vegetation. The habitat at Whiteford is thought to be stable. The vegetation at Ruston Common is largely the result of management by the commoners (including cutting of reed and saw-sedge for thatch), but these practices ceased in the mid-1970s and scrub invasion is a problem at this site. More efficient drainage and increased water abstraction in the vicinity of Ruston Common had a dramatic effect on the marshy area in the late 1980s, and it remains to be seen whether the wetland flora and fauna are permanently damaged.

Conservation Oxwich Burrows, Whiteford Burrows, Cors Erddreiniog and Cors Geirch are NNRs. Woodbastwick Fen is within Bure Marshes NNR. East Ruston Common is an SSSI, and the Broads Authority has recently begun conservation work at this site, consisting of scrub clearance in the reed- and sedge-beds. However, the effects of water abstraction have not yet been remedied.

Author P. Merrett, using information from Duffey (1970), Locket, Millidge & Merrett (1974), the NCC Welsh Peatland Invertebrate Survey and D. Brewster, R.B. Coleman, W.J. Fojt, M.R. Hughes and D.A. Procter (pers. comms).

GONATIUM PARADOXUM   VULNERABLE

Phylum CHELICERATA   Order ARANEAE
Class ARACHNIDA   Family LINYPHIIDAE

Gonatium paradoxum (L. Koch, 1869), formerly known as *G. corallipes* (O. P.-Cambridge).

Identification Locket, Millidge & Merrett (1974) (as *G. corallipes*); Roberts (1987).

Distribution Since 1954 recorded from two localities in Ashdown Forest, East Sussex; Limpsfield Common and Box Hill, Surrey; and Crockhamhill Common, West Kent. Also recorded from Italy, France, the Netherlands, Germany, Austria, Switzerland, Hungary, Czechoslovakia, Poland, the Balkans, Russia and Sweden.

Habitat and ecology Mainly on mature dry heathland, but also among moss and grass on Box Hill. Adults of both sexes are found in August and September, and females also in April and July.

Status Appears to be restricted to a small area of southeast England.

Threats Ashdown Forest is suffering bracken and scrub invasion because of lack of grazing, with only one of the commoners now exercising sheep-grazing rights. There are also frequent fires in some areas. Limpsfield and Crockhamhill Commons are both small and now heavily scrubbed over. It is unlikely that enough suitable habitat remains at these sites to maintain viable populations of this spider.

Conservation The Ashdown Forest sites and Box Hill lie within SSSIs. Ashdown Forest was recently bought by East Sussex County Council and it is hoped this has safeguarded the site's future. Some scrub clearance has been carried out but more is needed. As common land, it is

194

unfenced and the main roads crossing the Forest make the reinstatement of grazing unlikely. Box Hill and Limpsfield Common are National Trust properties. Scrub clearance to extend the surviving fragments of heath at Limpsfield Common was recommended in 1983 by the National Trust's biological surveyors. It is not known whether this has been acted upon (K.N.A. Alexander pers. comm.). Ideally, scrub clearance should be followed by a programme of grazing or mowing in order to keep the scrub at bay and maintain a variety of heather heights.

Author   P. Merrett, using personal observations and information from Locket, Millidge & Merrett (1974) and B. Banks (pers. comm.).

TRICHOPTERNA CITO   VULNERABLE

Phylum CHELICERATA   Order ARANEAE
Class ARACHNIDA   Family LINYPHIIDAE

Trichopterna cito (O. P.-Cambridge, 1872).

Identification   Locket, Millidge & Merrett (1974); Roberts (1987).

Distribution   Recorded from Colne Point, North Essex; Sandwich, East Kent; and Rye Harbour, East Sussex, all since 1956. Elsewhere in Europe, it has been recorded from Italy, France, Belgium, the Netherlands, Germany, Switzerland, Czechoslovakia, Hungary, Poland, the Balkans, Russia, Sweden and Finland.

Habitat and ecology   Among moss and grass on old sand dunes (at Rye) and among sparse vegetation on sandy shingle (at Colne Point). Both sexes have been found as adults in October and May, and females also in June.

Status   Although recorded from only three sites, it is apparently numerous at all of them.

Threats   Public recreation (including trampling and bonfires) can easily destroy the fragile vegetation of dunes and shingle. Outside nature reserves, this habitat is often the site of developments such as golf courses, caravan parks and chalets. There are now three golf courses at Sandwich Dunes, and this development, with its associated roads, buildings, drains, reprofiling and reseeding, has caused some damage to this fine dune system.

Conservation   Colne Point is an Essex Trust reserve, an SSSI and in part an NNR. Sandwich Dunes are within an SSSI and parts are owned or managed by the Kent Trust, National Trust and RSPB. Rye Harbour is an SSSI and in part an LNR.

Author   P. Merrett, using information from Cooke (1961), Locket, Millidge & Merrett (1974) and S.A. Williams (pers. comm.).

PELECOPSIS ELONGATA   VULNERABLE

Phylum CHELICERATA   Order ARANEAE
Class ARACHNIDA   Family LINYPHIIDAE

Pelecopsis elongata (Wider, 1834).

Identification   Locket & Millidge (1953); Locket, Millidge & Merrett (1974); Roberts (1987).

Distribution   Recorded in Britain only from Rothiemurchus Forest and Loch Garten/Abernethy Forest, East Inverness-shire, and near the south shore of Loch Rannoch, near Kinloch Rannoch, Mid Perthshire. Widespread in central and northern Europe.

Habitat and ecology In Britain, confined to Caledonian pine forest. Mainly in dry pine litter on rocks, but also on the lower branches of juniper and in moss. Adult males have been found in November, December, March and April, and females also during the summer. The main activity period is probably during the winter.

Status   Well-established in the Rothiemurchus/Abernethy area.

Threats   Loss of Caledonian pine forest. The remaining areas of Caledonian pine forest are threatened with conversion to intensive forestry using Sitka spruce *Picea sitchensis*, lodgepole pine *Pinus contorta* and other alien species. 30 ha of Abernethy Forest SSSI were clear-felled in 1984 prior to the site's renotification, and in all 226 ha were felled in the decade up to 1987. North of the Loch Garten RSPB reserve there has been a great deal of recent planting of Scots pine and lodgepole pine on land which previously supported scattered mature native pines. In Rothiemurchus Forest, 305 ha out of the 1539 ha of native pine were ploughed and planted in 1971 with Scots pine and lodgepole pine. The ecological requirements of *P. elongata* are not known in detail, but it is unlikely that conversion of open Caledonian pine forest to dense plantation forestry will maintain the habitat in a suitable state for this species.

Conservation   Abernethy Forest is an SSSI, part is an NNR, and a large area including native pine forest has recently been acquired as a nature reserve by the RSPB. Over half of the area of native pine in Rothiemurchus Forest lies within the Cairngorms SSSI and *P. elongata* occurs within the area with NNR status. At both sites, regeneration of the native pine is occurring. In Abernethy Forest this is due to protection of the felled areas from grazing, while at Rothiemurchus increased numbers of human visitors are thought to disturb the grazing deer sufficiently to reduce grazing pressure to the level at which pine regeneration can take place. In deer exclosures, natural regeneration can become as dense as a pine plantation and it may be necessary to thin the pines in order to maintain an open forest with a varied age structure and good ground flora.

Author P. Merrett, using information from Locket & Millidge (1953), Locket, Millidge & Merrett (1974), Bain (1987) and N.P. Ashmole (pers. comm.).

PELECOPSIS RADICICOLA   RARE

Phylum CHELICERATA   Order ARANEAE
Class ARACHNIDA   Family LINYPHIIDAE

Pelecopsis radicicola (L. Koch, 1875), previously known as *Lophocarenum radicicola*.

Identification Locket & Millidge (1953) (as *Lophocarenum radicicola*); Roberts (1987).

Distribution In Britain, recorded from the South Downs near Heyshott, West Sussex; the Mendips at Rodney Stoke NNR, North Somerset; Fontmell Down, Dorset; and Staverton Park, East Suffolk. All records are since 1949. Also known from France, Germany, Switzerland, Czechoslovakia, Hungary, Poland and the Balkans.

Habitat and ecology Most British records are from among grass roots in chalk or limestone grassland, but it has also been found in a glade of grass and bracken in Staverton Park, which lies on a base-poor sandy soil. Adults of both sexes are found between June and October.

Status Numerous specimens have been found at all sites except Rodney Stoke.

Threats The loss of semi-natural dry grassland to intensive farming, either arable or livestock, will have contributed to a decline in the habitat available for this species. Conversely, the neglect of suitable habitat and the decline in rabbit-grazing, with ensuing invasion by scrub or bracken, is also likely to have been damaging.

Conservation Three sites are protected. Rodney Stoke is an NNR; Fontmell Down is a National Trust/Dorset Trust reserve and SSSI; and Staverton Park is part of an SSSI.

Author P. Merrett, using information from Locket & Millidge (1953), Harding (1975), and R.G. Snazell and E. Duffey (pers. comms).

TRICHONCUS HACKMANI

VULNERABLE

Phylum CHELICERATA
Class ARACHNIDA

Order ARANEAE
Family LINYPHIIDAE

Trichoncus hackmani Millidge, 1955.

Identification
Locket, Millidge & Merrett (1974); Roberts (1987).

Distribution
Recorded from Needs Ore Point, South Hampshire; Colne Point, North Essex; and Dunwich Marshes, East Suffolk, all since 1961. There is also an unconfirmed record from Iken Marsh, East Suffolk. Elsewhere in Europe, reported from France, Belgium, Germany, Switzerland, Austria, Czechoslovakia, Poland, Sweden and Finland.

Habitat and ecology
Mainly among tide litter and sparse vegetation on shingle. Adults of both sexes are found from April to June and in September and October.

Status
This species has been abundant wherever it has been found, which makes the possibility of its being under-recorded less likely.

Threats
Disturbance of shingle and destruction of its vegetation by, for example, trampling, off-road vehicles or construction of sea defences. On shingle beds outside nature reserves, holiday developments are also a possible threat.

Conservation
Needs Ore Point lies within North Solent NNR. Colne Point is an Essex Trust reserve and SSSI, and part of Dunwich Marsh is an SSSI. Tideline litter should be left undisturbed.

Author
P. Merrett, using information from Locket, Millidge & Merrett (1974).

TRICHONCUS AFFINIS

VULNERABLE

Phylum CHELICERATA
Class ARACHNIDA

Order ARANEAE
Family LINYPHIIDAE

Trichoncus affinis Kulczynski, 1894.

Identification
Locket & Millidge (1953); Locket, Millidge & Merrett (1974); Roberts (1987).

Distribution
Recorded from Hayling Island, South Hampshire; Rye, East Sussex; Dungeness, East Kent; and Orford Beach and Havergate Island, East Suffolk, all records except one being since 1960. It has been

reported from France, the Netherlands, Germany, Switzerland, Austria, Hungary, Czechoslovakia and Poland, but the taxonomy of this genus is rather confused in Europe.

Habitat and ecology It has been found among the roots of sparse vegetation on shingle. Adults of both sexes have been recorded in June.

Status Numerous at Orford Beach and Dungeness, but the other records are based on few individuals.

Threats The habitat is susceptible to public pressure, shingle vegetation being very vulnerable to trampling. Dungeness is being damaged by gravel extraction, a problem which may get worse as gravel reserves are exhausted elsewhere in Kent. Irrevocable damage is being caused by motorcycles and other vehicles crossing the shingle, damaging the vegetation and soil. The plans for further nuclear power station construction on the site are unclear at present but pose a potential threat.

Conservation Occurs on Orfordness—Havergate NNR, part of which, Havergate Island, is an RSPB reserve, and on Dungeness SSSI. A small part of Hayling Island is a reserve of the Hampshire and Isle of Wight Trust.

Author P. Merrett, using information from Locket & Millidge (1953) and Locket, Millidge & Merrett (1974).

TAPINOCYBOIDES PYGMAEUS   RARE

Phylum CHELICERATA   Order ARANEAE
Class ARACHNIDA   Family LINYPHIIDAE

Tapinocyboides pygmaeus (Menge, 1869), formerly known as *T. pygmaea* (Menge) and *Tapinocyba antepenultima* (O. P.-Cambridge).

Identification Locket & Millidge (1953) (as *Tapinocyba antepenultima*); Locket, Millidge & Merrett (1974); Roberts (1987).

Distribution Recorded from the South Downs near Heyshott, West Sussex, in 1951; the Chilterns at Buttler's Hangings and Swain's Wood, Buckinghamshire, in 1982; Town Kelloe Banks, Co. Durham, in 1982 and 1986; a farm at East Lilburn, North Northumberland, in 1987; and near Duddingston, Midlothian. Elsewhere in Europe, known from Belgium, Germany, Switzerland, Austria, Czechoslovakia, Poland, Sweden and Finland.

Habitat and ecology This species has been found among grass roots on chalk and limestone grassland and, in Northumberland, in grass on boulder clay. During pitfall-trapping at Buttler's Hangings, the females of this species built their webs between the plastic cup and the tin sleeve of the pitfall-trap, and the main habitat is probably mouse tunnels and crevices created by soil creep (J. Hancock unpublished). Both sexes are found in September, April and May, and males also in March. The peak of activity is possibly in April.

Status Rarely recorded but, as the species is very small and pale and lives among grass roots, it could easily be overlooked. The wide geographical spread of the six known sites suggests that it may be commoner than the present records indicate. It was numerous at Heyshott and Buttler's Hangings.

Threats Conversion of calcareous grassland to arable agriculture or the scrubbing-over of sites if grazing lapses.

Conservation Town Kelloe Banks, Swain's Wood and Buttler's Hangings are SSSIs. The first includes part of a Durham County Trust reserve (in which portion the spider has been recorded) and the last two are BBONT reserves. Sheep-grazing at the third is being used to maintain a diversity of sward heights, and the soil and vegetation structure required by this spider are likely to be maintained. It is hoped that some monitoring can be implemented to define the needs of *T. pygmaeus* more closely.

Author P. Merrett, using information from Locket & Millidge (1953), Locket, Millidge & Merrett (1974), Rushton (1988) and R.B. Coleman, S.P. Rushton and R. Thomas (pers. comms).

GLYPHESIS SERVULUS   INSUFFICIENTLY KNOWN

Phylum CHELICERATA   Order ARANEAE
Class ARACHNIDA   Family LINYPHIIDAE

Glyphesis servulus (Simon, 1881).

Identification Locket, Millidge & Merrett (1974); Roberts (1985b, 1987).

Distribution In Britain, recorded from Wicken Fen and Chippenham Fen, Cambridgeshire; Bracketts Coppice, Dorset; and Esgyrn Bottom and Llangloffan Fen, near Fishguard, Pembrokeshire, all since 1955. Also known from France, Belgium, the Netherlands, Germany and Switzerland.

Habitat and ecology Found in wet litter under *Rhamnus* carr and in old sedge litter in fens, in *Deschampsia* and *Molinia* litter in a damp ungrazed pasture (Bracketts Coppice), and in dense *Molinia caerulea* litter on a raised bog (Esgyrn Bottom). The main period of activity is from April to June, but adults of both sexes have also been found in July,

October and December and a female in August.

Status   Abundant at the three English localities. Only one specimen was found at Esgyrn Bottom and two at Llangloffen Fen. This species was not known from Wales until an extensive peatland invertebrate survey was conducted in the late 1980s and it may exist undiscovered in other parts of Britain. See addendum.

Threats   In the absence of grazing or mowing, seral succession may destroy the habitat of this species. Grazing is not part of the management of Esgyrn Bottom or Bracketts Coppice at the time of writing (1987). At Chippenham Fen it is becoming increasingly difficult to maintain a high water table, probably owing to water abstraction in the vicinity reducing the output of the springs which feed the fen.

Conservation The three English localities have nature reserve and SSSI status, managed respectively by the National Trust, the Nature Conservancy Council (as an NNR) and the Dorset Trust. Esgyrn Bottom is an SSSI and Llangloffen Fen is an NNR. At Wicken Fen, scrub clearance is restoring the area of sedge-beds. There has been some scrub clearance in the field at Bracketts Coppice and the introduction of cattle-grazing is being considered. Grazing should be at an intensity sufficient to prevent scrub encroachment and maintain the species-rich turf but should also maintain some areas of the rougher tussocky grassland. Monitoring of the effects of grazing upon the *C. servulus* population would be useful and, until the effects of the grazing regime have been established, parts of the field should perhaps be left ungrazed as refugia.

Author   P. Merrett, using information from Locket, Millidge & Merrett (1974), Merrett & Snazell (1975), the NCC Welsh Peatland Invertebrate Survey and J.R. White (pers. comm.).

DIPLOCEPHALUS CONNATUS   VULNERABLE

Phylum CHELICERATA   Order ARANEAE
Class ARACHNIDA   Family LINYPHIIDAE

Diplocephalus connatus Bertkau, 1889, previously known as *D. adjacens* O. P.-Cambridge.

Identification Locket & Millidge (1953); Locket, Millidge & Merrett (1974); Roberts (1987). *D. jacksoni* O. P.-Cambridge was recorded as a species new to science from the north bank of the River South Tyne near Hexham, South Northumberland, in 1902. It was found among *D. connatus* and its status as a separate species from *D. connatus* is now in doubt. It is suspected that males of *D. connatus* are dimorphic (Roberts 1987) and that *D. jacksoni* is a form of *D. connatus*.

Distribution	In Britain, only recorded from South Northumberland, from the north bank of the River South Tyne near Hexham (1902 and subsequently) and the confluence of the Rivers West and East Allen (1965). Also known from France, Germany, Switzerland, the Balkans and Poland.
Habitat and ecology	Originally found among waterborne debris on the river bank, but all recent records have been from under stones and boulders on sandy shingle banks at the side of rivers. Adults of both sexes have been found in June, September and October.
Status	Numerous at both sites. Further survey work is needed to establish the limits of its range.
Threats	No immediate threats known, but vulnerable to river engineering work.
Conservation	The Allen Rivers confluence is within an SSSI.
Author	P. Merrett, using information from Locket & Millidge (1953), Locket, Millidge & Merrett (1974) and J.R. Parker (pers. comm.).

TYPHOCHRESTUS SIMONI VULNERABLE

Phylum CHELICERATA   Order ARANEAE
Class ARACHNIDA   Family LINYPHIIDAE

Typhochrestus simoni de Lessert, 1907.

Identification	Locket, Millidge & Merrett (1974); Parker & Coleman (1977); Roberts (1987).
Distribution	Recorded in Britain only from the south slope of Y Lliwedd, Snowdonia, Caernarvonshire; Porton Down, South Wiltshire; and the south slope of Bindon Hill, Lulworth, Dorset, all since 1966. Also known from Italy, France, Switzerland and Germany.
Habitat and ecology	The Welsh site is montane *Festuca-Nardus* grassland at 450-600 metres altitude. The other sites are at low altitudes on short rabbit-grazed or lichen-rich chalk grassland. The main period of activity is probably in March and April, but both sexes have also been found in January and February and a male in November. Most continental records have suggested *T. simoni* to be a montane species, but the records from Lulworth and Porton Down indicate that it also occurs at low altitudes on dry exposed downland.
Status	Numerous in one area of Porton Down. Rare in Europe.
Threats	Its chalk grassland habitat is the more severely threatened, by conversion to arable agriculture on shallow slopes and by scrub

encroachment where grazing ceases on steeper slopes.

Conservation   Occurs within Y Wyddfa—Snowdon NNR. Porton Down and Bindon Hill are SSSIs.

Author   P. Merrett, using information from Locket, Millidge & Merrett (1974), Parker & Coleman (1977) and R.B. Coleman (pers. comm.).

RHAEBOTHORAX PAETULUS   VULNERABLE

Phylum CHELICERATA   Order ARANEAE
Class ARACHNIDA   Family LINYPHIIDAE

Rhaebothorax paetulus (O. P.-Cambridge, 1875).

Identification   Locket, Millidge & Merrett (1974); Roberts (1987).

Distribution   Recorded from Ben Lawers, Mid Perthshire, first in 1965 and on several subsequent occasions; from the Braeriach and Cairngorm—Ben Macdui plateaux, Inverness-shire, in 1981; and from Creag Meagaidh, West Inverness-shire, in 1983. Also known from France, Germany, Austria, Switzerland, Czechoslovakia, Sweden and Finland.

Habitat and ecology   Found under stones above 850 metres and taken in *Nardus stricta* snow-bed grassland on Creag Meagaidh. May be associated with mat vegetation. Adults of both sexes have been found in May, June, August and September.

Status   Apparently well-established on Ben Lawers and in the Cairngorms, but very local. An arctic-alpine species.

Threats   Additional skiing developments, with plans to increase numbers of skiers in the existing skiing areas as well as open up new slopes, periodically threaten the fragile high-altitude vegetation of the Cairngorms region. Hill-walking could threaten this species, its habitat being on the top of the Cairngorm plateau where the effects of trampling are quite severe (N.P. Ashmole pers. comm.).

Conservation   Occurs within Ben Lawers, Cairngorms and Creag Meagaidh NNRs. Increased use of the Cairngorms northern corries area by skiers was opposed successfully at a public inquiry in 1981. The likelihood of future skiing developments in the area should now have receded as a result of the structure plan being amended to show a presumption in favour of conservation.

Author   P. Merrett, using information from Locket, Millidge & Merrett (1974) and N.P. Ashmole, D. Horsfield and M.J. Roberts (pers. comms).

203

CARORITA LIMNAEA   ENDANGERED

Phylum CHELICERATA   Order ARANEAE
Class ARACHNIDA   Family LINYPHIIDAE

Carorita limnaea (Crosby & Bishop, 1927).

Identification Locket, Millidge & Merrett (1974); Roberts (1987).

Distribution In Britain, only recorded from Wybunbury Moss, Cheshire, where it was first found in 1962. It was also recorded there in 1963, 1970 and 1982. It is also known from Germany, Sweden and Finland.

Habitat and ecology In *Sphagnum* bog, sometimes in association with *Erica tetralix*, *Eriophorum* and *Vaccinium oxycoccus*. Both sexes are found in June and July.

Status The spider fauna of the Cheshire Mosses is well-studied, but Wybunbury Moss is the only one at which this species has been recorded. It has been abundant at its one site, but a brief search in 1988 failed to find it.

Threats Wybunbury Moss suffered severe pollution from septic tank overflow and road drainage for many years up to 1986. This nutrient enrichment has had a marked effect on the vegetation and is causing the deep peat to degrade. Much of the former *Sphagnum* lawn has developed into fen. Eutrophication from agricultural run-off still threatens further damage. Further substantial areas of the nutrient-poor raft have developed into pine and birch woodland, aided by previous drainage attempts.

Conservation Wybunbury Moss is an NNR. In 1986 the major sources of eutrophic water were intercepted and diverted away from the reserve. As a result peat degradation and fen encroachment appear to be receding. Removal of the tree invasion also commenced in 1986 and is continuing, with encouraging results.

Author P. Merrett, based on personal observations, Duffey & Merrett (1963), Locket, Millidge & Merrett (1974) and M.P. Bailey, R.S. Key and R.A. Lindsay (pers. comms).

CARORITA PALUDOSA

VULNERABLE

Phylum CHELICERATA
Class ARACHNIDA

Order ARANEAE
Family LINYPHIIDAE

Carorita paludosa Duffey, 1971.

Identification Locket, Millidge & Merrett (1974); Roberts (1987).

Distribution Recorded in Great Britain only from Reedham Marsh and Hickling Broad in 1970 and Catfield Fen in 1989, all in East Norfolk; and Westhay Moor, North Somerset, in 1973. First discovered in Ireland in 1969. Also recorded from Belgium (Huble 1980; Decleer & Bosmans 1989) and Sweden (Granstrom 1978).

Habitat and ecology In *Sphagnum* and litter and among cut grass and sedge, in marshy areas with *Cladium*, *Phragmites*, and *Betula/Alnus* carr. Adults of both sexes have been found in September, October and February.

Status Clearly uncommon, and restricted to a vulnerable and much diminished habitat.

Threats Drainage of the marsh habitat. Conversion of grazing levels to arable agriculture with attendant drainage is lowering the water table over much of the Somerset Levels, to the detriment of those species requiring waterlogged conditions. Westhay Moor is also being severely damaged by peat extraction for horticultural use. Scrub development in the absence of regular mowing is a threat to the remaining sedge- and reed-beds of the Norfolk Broads.

Conservation Hickling Broad is an NNR and Norfolk Trust reserve within a larger SSSI; Reedham Marsh and Catfield Fen are parts of an SSSI; and Westhay Moor is an SSSI and a reserve of the Somerset Trust. The Somerset Trust has recently enlarged its holdings on Westhay Moor, having purchased an area of worked-out peat-diggings, and, though management of these will be largely for waterbirds (McGeoch 1987), there are plans also to re-establish the acid bog habitat (Hancock 1987).

Author P. Merrett, using information from Duffey (1971a), Locket, Millidge & Merrett (1974) and D.A. Procter and R.G. Snazell (pers. comms).

PSEUDOMARO AENIGMATICUS   INSUFFICIENTLY KNOWN

Phylum CHELICERATA   Order ARANEAE
Class ARACHNIDA   Family LINYPHIIDAE

Pseudomaro aenigmaticus Denis, 1966.

Identification   Snazell (1978); Roberts (1987).

Distribution   In Britain, recorded only from Lyscombe Hill, Dorset, between
1976 and 1979, and from a field near Redbourn, Hertfordshire, in
1988. Also known from Italy, Belgium and Germany.

Habitat and ecology   Found on a steep south-facing slope of chalk grassland in Dorset
and in an arable field growing winter wheat in Hertfordshire. It is
possible that this species lives underground in fissures in the soil
or in ants' nests. The reduced eyes and pale colour suggest a
subterranean habitat, as does the finding of females in a cellar and
caves in Europe. Adult females have been found in England from
November to February.

Status   Apparently very rare, but once the habitat is known it may be
discovered more frequently. Only four females have been found in
Britain and six on the Continent.

Threats   Too little is known of the habitat requirements of this spider for
threats to be identified. The loss of chalk grassland to arable
agriculture may be a threat, depending on whether arable land is
suitable habitat for the species. The finding of one specimen on
arable land does not clarify the matter. Possibly more detrimental
is the encroachment of scrub onto chalk grassland where grazing
lapses, as this alters the temperature regime of the soil. Mowing
would probably not be a satisfactory alternative to grazing for
several reasons, particularly the disruption of ants' nests likely to
occur during the mowing.

Conservation   Lyscombe Hill is a Dorset Trust reserve within an SSSI. The chalk
grassland is being maintained by grazing, the ideal management
for this habitat.

Author   P. Merrett, using information from Snazell (1978) and D. Powell and
R.G. Snazell (pers. comms).

PORRHOMMA ROSENHAUERI

VULNERABLE

Phylum CHELICERATA
Class ARACHNIDA

Order ARANEAE
Family LINYPHIIDAE

Porrhomma rosenhaueri (L. Koch, 1872).

Identification Locket & Millidge (1953); Roberts (1987).

Distribution In Great Britain, known only from Lesser Garth Cave near Cardiff and Ogof-y-Ci, Glamorgan. There are also records of this species from Ireland, Italy, Spain, France, Belgium and Germany, but the confusion over the taxonomy of this group of species casts some doubt over their validity. (There is no doubt about the determinations of the British specimens.)

Habitat and ecology Exclusively cave-dwelling. Females have been found only in July, but adults probably occur all year.

Status Until recently it was known in the British Isles only from Ireland. Few British cave systems support strictly cave-dwelling invertebrates, so there are only a very limited number of sites likely to support this species. At Ogof-y-Ci it has been found as recently as 1980.

Threats The hillside near Lesser Garth Cave is being quarried. Plans for expansion of the quarry will involve driving a tunnel within 50 metres of the cave and there are fears that blasting may affect the cave (Anon 1989). The cave itself may eventually be lost to the quarry. Whilst occasional human access to such caves is unlikely to be damaging, activities such as enlarging the cave entrance or illuminating the cave for long periods may pose a threat by altering the microclimate and allowing the cave to be colonised by surface-dwelling species (Fiers & Wouters 1985).

Conservation Cessation of quarrying near Lesser Garth Cave is desirable but unlikely. Thus a high priority for the conservation of this species is survey work to locate populations not under threat and to establish the area of occurrence. It may be necessary to set aside refuges within the caves where human access is closely controlled.

Author P. Merrett, using information from Locket & Millidge (1953), Chapman (1980) and C.M. Merrett and M.J. Roberts (pers. comms).

MARO LEPIDUS

RARE

Phylum CHELICERATA
Class ARACHNIDA

Order ARANEAE
Family LINYPHIIDAE

Maro lepidus Casemir, 1963.

Identification Locket, Millidge & Merrett (1974); Roberts (1987).

Distribution Recorded from Malham Tarn Moss and Pen-y-Ghent, Mid-west Yorkshire; Blelham Bog and Rusland Moss, Westmorland; Llyn Tyn-y-Mynydd, Caernarvonshire; and Mynydd Hiraethrog, Denbighshire, all since 1946. Also known from Germany and Finland.

Habitat and ecology Has been found among *Sphagnum* in raised bogs; among wet grass and *Juncus* by a stream; in a sedge marsh surrounded by *Sphagnum*; and in rank *Molinia* grassland. Adults of both sexes have been taken between September and December.

Threats Commercial peat-cutting has destroyed the majority and degraded the remainder of the major peat-mosses in northwest England. Rusland Moss is drying out, pine is invading, and there are further drainage proposals along one side of the surviving bog.

Conservation Blelham Bog and Malham Tarn are National Trust properties, the former an NNR and the latter an SSSI. Pen-y-Ghent also has SSSI status. Part of Rusland Moss is an NNR, but much of the former bog is outside the control of the NCC. Pine invasion on the NNR is being reversed.

Author P. Merrett, using information from Locket, Millidge & Merrett (1974) and D. Horsfield, R.A. Lindsay and J.R. Parker (pers. comms).

CENTROMERUS LEVITARSIS

VULNERABLE

Phylum CHELICERATA
Class ARACHNIDA

Order ARANEAE
Family LINYPHIIDAE

Centromerus levitarsis (Simon, 1884), referred to as *C. laevitarsis* (Simon) in some publications (see Roberts (1987) for explanation).

Identification Locket & Millidge (1953); Roberts (1987).

Distribution Known from Delamere Forest, Cheshire, since 1906, and recorded since 1970 also from Glasson Moss and Biglands Bog,

Cumberland, and Foxtor Mires, Dartmoor, South Devon. The European distribution includes Estonia, France, Italy, Germany, the Netherlands, Sweden, Finland, Czechoslovakia and Poland.

Habitat and ecology Found among *Sphagnum*, both in damp woodland (mainly birch) and on open moorland. Adults of both sexes have been found in March and April, females also in May and a male in October.

Status May be more widespread than its few records suggest, considering that its main period of maturity appears to be early in the year when not much spider-recording is carried out.

Threats Much of Glasson Moss has been commercially cut for peat, a practice which ceased in the 1950s. There have been a series of fires on this bog, the most recent and most serious being in 1976. There are signs that eutrophication of Biglands Bog is occurring. This may be due to run-off from the heavily fertilised pasture and arable land which surrounds it, or from Bampton Beck, or both. Bampton Beck crosses the site and carries the outflow of a sewage works. It occasionally floods the bog.

Conservation Part of Glasson Moss is an NNR. Raising of the water table and prevention of fires are being achieved by damming the drains on the bog. Biglands Bog is an SSSI and Cumbria Trust reserve. Parts of Delamere Forest are SSSIs.

Author P. Merrett, using information from Locket & Millidge (1953), [Parker] (1976) and R.A. Lindsay (pers. comm.).

CENTROMERUS INCULTUS   VULNERABLE

Phylum CHELICERATA   Order ARANEAE
Class ARACHNIDA   Family LINYPHIIDAE

Centromerus incultus Falconer, 1915.

Identification Locket, Millidge & Merrett (1974); Roberts (1987).

Distribution One female was found at Wicken Fen, Cambridgeshire, in 1913; six females and two males were found in open areas of Woodbastwick Fens, East Norfolk, in 1970; and two males and one female were found in Catfield Fen, East Norfolk, in 1989. Also reported from Estonia, Poland, Switzerland, Germany, Belgium, the Netherlands, Czechoslovakia, Sweden and Finland.

Habitat and ecology In Britain it has been found in the litter layer of *Calamagrostis canescens* and *Thelypteris palustris* growing by the edge of fen waterways; in heaps of cut saw-sedge *Cladium mariscus*; and in litter and moss on the wet floor of sedge-beds. Adults of both sexes

have been found in September and a female in July. Decleer &
Bosmans (1989) suggest that this species occurs mainly in open
wetlands, sometimes under carr, but not under closed-canopy
woodland.

Status

This species has never been rediscovered at Wicken Fen, despite
much recording, but seems to be well-established at
Woodbastwick Fens.

Threats

Loss of fen habitat through drainage and encroachment of alder
and willow carr.

Conservation

Woodbastwick Fens are included in Bure Marshes NNR. Catfield
Fen forms part of an SSSI. Wicken Fen is an SSSI and nature
reserve owned by the National Trust. The tendency to scrub
encroachment at Wicken Fen is being reversed by scrub
clearance followed by the introduction of mowing. The current
management regime at Woodbastwick Fens, which includes
regular mowing of the sedge-beds and cutting of *Phragmites*,
should maintain the site in a suitable condition for this spider.
Heaps of sedge litter left in the fens may be of additional benefit.

Author

P. Merrett, using information from Duffey (1971b), Locket, Millidge
& Merrett (1974), Decleer & Bosmans (1989) and D.A. Procter
(pers. comm.).

CENTROMERUS AEQUALIS   RARE

Phylum CHELICERATA   Order ARANEAE
Class ARACHNIDA   Family LINYPHIIDAE

Centromerus aequalis (Westring, 1851).

Identification

Locket, Millidge & Merrett (1974); Roberts (1987).

Distribution

Recorded from Iping Common, Blackdown and Marley Heights
near Kingsley Green, and east of Duncton, West Sussex; Hampden,
Buckinghamshire; Corehouse, Lanarkshire; and Insh Marshes, East
Inverness-shire. Elsewhere in Europe it is recorded from the
Balkans, Italy, Switzerland, Austria, France, Belgium, the
Netherlands, Germany, Poland, Czechoslovakia, Hungary, Russia,
Finland, Sweden and Denmark.

Habitat and ecology

Among deciduous litter, especially in deep beech litter, and among
tall heather. Males have been found in October and April, and
females from October to May.

Status

Never found in abundance. This species has a strangely scattered
distribution, with five records from the southeast of England and
two isolated records in Scotland.

Insh Marshes SSSI, East Inverness-shire. A mosaic of open water, marsh and carr on the floodplain of the River Spey, supporting a number of uncommon invertebrates including the spiders *Centromerus aequalis* and *Maro sublestus*. There remains the constant threat of piecemeal drainage and agricultural 'improvement'. (Photo by P. Wakely.)

Threats	Loss of heath through pine and bracken invasion is a problem at Blackdown. In 1976, large areas of heath at Iping Common were burnt, which may have reduced the amount of the preferred tall heather available to this spider for several years. Drainage for improved agriculture is a chronic threat to the Insh Marshes, and some areas have already been drained.
Conservation	Blackdown and Marley Heights are National Trust properties. Iping Common is an SSSI. The Insh Marshes are an SSSI and in part an RSPB reserve.
Author	P. Merrett, using information from Locket, Millidge & Merrett (1974) and N.P. Ashmole and R. Jones (pers. comms).

CENTROMERUS ALBIDUS — VULNERABLE

Phylum CHELICERATA
Class ARACHNIDA
Order ARANEAE
Family LINYPHIIDAE

Centromerus albidus Simon, 1929.

Identification	Locket, Millidge & Merrett (1974); Roberts (1987).
Distribution	Known from Box Hill and White Downs, Surrey, and Stockbridge, Hampshire, all since 1962. Also reported from France.
Habitat and ecology	In beech litter in beech woods. Adult males have been found between August and November and females between August and April.
Status	Numerous at its Surrey sites.
Threats	Loss of established beech woods. The National Trust's foresters have in past years clear-felled ancient beech woods on the North Downs and used a nurse crop of conifers in the replanting, a policy which could be detrimental to the ancient woodland fauna and flora, including this spider.
Conservation	Box Hill is National Trust property, as are some other beech woods on the North Downs. The felling policy of the National Trust has now changed to small group fellings with no conifer nurse crop (K.N.A. Alexander pers. comm.), a move which should ameliorate the effects of its management on the beechwood ecosystem. Box Hill also has the protection of lying within the Mole Gap to Reigate Escarpment SSSI, and part of White Downs lies within an SSSI.
Author	P. Merrett, using information from Locket, Millidge & Merrett (1974).

CENTROMERUS CAVERNARUM   RARE

Phylum CHELICERATA   Order ARANEAE
Class ARACHNIDA   Family LINYPHIIDAE

Centromerus cavernarum (L. Koch, 1872), formerly known as *C. jacksoni* Denis.

Identification   Locket & Millidge (1953) (as *C. jacksoni*); Locket, Millidge & Merrett (1974); Roberts (1987).

Distribution   Recorded from Hampden and Great Kimble, Buckinghamshire; Durford Heath, West Sussex; Matfield, West Kent; Blean Woods, East Kent; Maidstone, Kent; Whippendell Wood, Hertfordshire; and Nettlebed, Oxfordshire. There are old records from unknown localities in Surrey and Cornwall, the latter record being doubtful. Possibly most frequent in the Chilterns. It has also been found in Germany, Austria, Switzerland, Poland, Romania and northern Europe.

Habitat and ecology Most known sites are beech woods in southeast England, but the habitat of the Cornish specimen is not known. This species is usually found deep amongst beech litter, or sometimes on sheet webs inside empty beechnut husks. At Durford Heath it was found in oak litter (R. Jones pers. comm.) and once elsewhere it was in litter of coppiced sweet chestnut. Males have been found in October and females from September to March.

Status   Known from few sites. It is reported to be difficult to find and has never been found abundantly. However, enough beech woods have been searched unsuccessfully to establish that it is a truly rare species.

Threats   Loss of old beech woods, frequently through coniferisation.

Conservation   Occurs at Blean Woods NNR. Whippendell Wood is an SSSI and Durford Heath is a property of the National Trust.

Author   P. Merrett, using information from Locket & Millidge (1953), Locket, Millidge & Merrett (1974) and G.H. Locket and J.R. Parker (pers. comms).

CENTROMERUS PERSIMILIS

INSUFFICIENTLY KNOWN

Phylum CHELICERATA
Class ARACHNIDA

Order ARANEAE
Family LINYPHIIDAE

Centromerus persimilis (O. P.-Cambridge, 1912), formerly known as *Maro persimilis.*

Identification   Locket & Millidge (1953); Locket, Millidge & Merrett (1974); Roberts (1987).

Distribution   The first report of this species in Britain was from the bank of the River West Allen below Whitfield, at the junction with the River East Allen, South Northumberland, in 1916. However, this often-quoted record may have been a misidentification, and ideally the specimens should be re-examined if they still exist. The only definite British record of this species was from Malham Cove, Midwest Yorkshire, in 1961. A second record from Midwest Yorkshire, from Pen-y-Ghent, is now known to be false, referring to a misidentified specimen of *Maro lepidus* Casemir. Elsewhere in Europe, *C. persimilis* is known from Ireland, Germany, Austria, Belgium, the Netherlands, Sweden, Finland, Poland and Czechoslovakia.

Habitat and ecology   Two females attributed to this species were found under stones by the River West Allen in July. At Malham, a single male was found in a crevice of limestone pavement in September. The sites of the records and the small size and pale colour of this species suggest that it may live in a subterranean habitat, which would account for only stray individuals being found.

Status   Rarely found. Further searching at Malham Cove has failed to locate more specimens (C.J. Smith pers. comm.).

Conservation   Malham Cove and the confluence of the Allen Rivers lie within SSSIs.

Author   P. Merrett, using information from Hull (1916, 1931), Locket & Millidge (1953) and Locket, Millidge & Merrett (1974).

LEPTHYPHANTES ANTRONIENSIS   ENDANGERED

Phylum CHELICERATA   Order ARANEAE
Class ARACHNIDA   Family LINYPHIIDAE

_____

Lepthyphantes antroniensis Schenkel, 1933.

Identification   Ashmole & Merrett (1981); Roberts (1987).

Distribution   Recorded from two places in the Lairig Ghru in 1979 and 1980 and
                       from Sron a' Cha-no in 1980, both sites in the Cairngorms,
                       Inverness-shire. Also known from the Swiss and Austrian Alps, the
                       Carpathians and Fennoscandia between latitudes 61°N and 70°N.

Habitat and ecology In Scotland, found under rocks and among low vegetation
                       consisting mainly of *Empetrum*, *Vaccinium myrtillus*, grasses and
                       mosses, at about 900 to 980 metres elevation. Adults of both sexes
                       have been found from May to September. In the Alps this species
                       occurs in spruce *Picea* and pine *Pinus* woods, and in Fennoscandia
                       in spruce and birch *Betula* forests. The ground vegetation of the
                       Lairig Ghru site is similar to its Fennoscandian habitat in spite of the
                       absence of trees at the Scottish site. Subalpine birch woods may be
                       worth searching for this species in Scotland.

Status   A northern and subalpine species apparently established in the
                       Cairngorms. Only two males and six females have been found,
                       despite an extensive arachnological survey of the Cairngorms
                       which included over a hundred sites above 600 metres (Ashmole
                       & Merrett 1981).

Threats   There have been proposals for ski-development close to the sites
                       where this species was found. Lurcher's Gully was the subject of a
                       public inquiry in 1981 and the proposals for ski development were
                       rejected at that time. In the late 1980s there were further proposals
                       for another ski-tow, a cafe and other means of access, but these
                       may not be permitted now that the structure plan for the area
                       shows a presumption in favour of conservation. The compaction of
                       snow caused by heavy skiing can have severely damaging effects
                       on upland vegetation, which, owing to its slow growth, is unable to
                       recover during the summer months. Snow-fences increase the
                       duration of the snow cover, which causes the vegetation to change
                       from dwarf heath to a *Nardus stricta* sward. Such a change in the
                       vegetation structure is not likely to be within the tolerance limits of
                       this spider.

Conservation   Has been found just outside the boundary of Cairngorms NNR, but
                       may well occur within the reserve as well.

Author   P. Merrett, using information from Ashmole & Merrett (1981) and
                       N.P. Ashmole (pers. comm.).

LEPTHYPHANTES MIDAS   VULNERABLE

Phylum CHELICERATA   Order ARANEAE
Class ARACHNIDA   Family LINYPHIIDAE

Lepthyphantes midas Simon, 1884, formerly known as *L. carri* Jackson.

Identification   Locket & Millidge (1953) (as *L. carri*); Roberts (1987).

Distribution   Recorded from Sherwood Forest, Nottinghamshire; Donington Park, Leicestershire; Epping Forest, South Essex; and Windsor Forest, Berkshire. Also known from France.

Habitat and ecology Adults of both sexes have been found in August and September, and a male also in June. Epping Forest records are from woodpigeon nests, squirrel dreys, an old and weathered thrush nest and a nest, possibly of a stock dove, in a rot-hole of an old hornbeam. At Donington Park, an ancient hollow oak supports a population in the deep litter inside the tree and among the leaf litter, bark and root cavities around the base of the tree. An old jackdaw nest and leaf litter inside a hollow living beech tree are the recorded habitats at Windsor Forest, whilst at Sherwood Forest a wandering male was found on the trunk of an old oak tree and single females have been found in a jackdaw nest and in an artificial nest placed inside a hollow oak. Searches by the British Arachnological Society of a full range of micro-habitats at Sherwood Forest have failed to discover breeding colonies of *L. midas*.

Status   Few records, all from areas of ancient forest or parkland.

Threats   The loss of old woodlands and parks to other land-uses such as intensive forestry and agriculture. The removal of overmature trees from surviving woods and parks is also detrimental but is often carried out for reasons of safety and tidiness or from the belief that woodlands should be 'vigorous'. In Epping Forest, many of the ancient trees have been felled for firewood. The chronic loss of ancient trees at Windsor Forest is also a matter for great concern, large areas having been turned over to conifers in the 1940s and 1950s. Though new planting has now switched to using native broadleaved trees, this is no substitute for the ancient oaks and beeches. Much of the historical Sherwood Forest has been lost to other land-uses, including conifer forestry. There is concern that increasing use of the site for public recreation will lead to management decisions which are incompatible with maintaining the overmature trees in their present state, mainly through safety considerations. The single oak known to support *L. midas* at Donington Park is now no more than a stump after severe wind damage, and intensive searching in similar trees nearby has failed to locate further populations of the spider.

Conservation

All four sites listed are SSSIs. Sherwood Forest is a Country Park where the conservation value of overmature trees is now fully recognised. At Donington Park, planting of oak and lime saplings is being planned (P. Kirby pers. comm.) but may be too late to prevent there being a break in the continuity of overmature trees. Negotiations are still in progress at Windsor Forest aimed at safeguarding the habitat of the unique invertebrate assemblage associated with the ancient trees. It is of interest that *L. midas* has been found in an artificial nest placed inside a hollow oak. It is unclear whether provision of artificial habitat in this way has a role to play in the spider's conservation. It is more likely to be the shortage of the hollow tree habitat than of the old nest micro-habitat which limits the spider's abundance at a site.

Authors

P. Merrett and J.H. Bratton, using information from Locket & Millidge (1953) and J. Crocker, R.M. McGibbon and A. Russell-Smith (pers. comms).

Addendum

At a late stage in the production of this book there was a delay of several months caused by the reorganisation of the Nature Conservancy Council and partial merger with the Countryside Commission to form the Countryside Council for Wales, English Nature, Joint Nature Conservation Committee and Nature Conservancy Council for Scotland. During that period, new information has been gathered on some species, and is presented below. It has not been possible to amend the whole text to take into account the reorganisation of the NCC. In most cases where the text refers to a responsibility or activity of the NCC, this role will now be carried on by one of the successor bodies.

Licences
The reorganisation of the NCC will lead to a change in the issuing of licences involving species protected under Section 9 of the Wildlife and Countryside Act 1981 (see p. 11). Licences formerly issued by the NCC to cover England, Scotland and Wales will in future be issued by each country agency and will only cover work in the country issuing the licence, though the devolution of this responsibility to Scotland and Wales will not take effect immediately.

Vertigo moulinsiana (Dupuy, 1849) (Mollusca, Vertiginidae), p. 65.
This snail was found at East Walton Common SSSI, West Norfolk, by I. Killeen in February 1991.

Chirocephalus diaphanus Prevost, 1803 (Crustacea, Chirocephalidae), p. 104.
The data sheet mentions a colony whose pool on a County Trust reserve had been filled in (see p. 105). This occurred at Noar Hill, North Hampshire, where a tenant farmer filled wheel ruts with rubble. The ruts were re-excavated in February 1991 by volunteers removing the rubble but not the underlying mud. It was hoped that the mud contained viable eggs of *Chirocephalus*. By late March 1991 over 100 juvenile *Chirocephalus* were present. The estate which owns the land has constructed a short section of new trackway to provide an alternative route avoiding the rutted section.

Hyptiotes paradoxus (C.L. Koch, 1834) (Arachnida, Uloboridae), p. 133.
This spider was found on yew at two sites in the Wye valley in September 1990 during a field meeting of the Spider Recording Scheme (Farr-Cox 1990).

Heliophanus dampfi Schenkel, 1923 (Arachnida, Salticidae).
Two females of this jumping spider have recently been found at Cors Fochno, Cardiganshire, part of Dyfi NNR (Williams, in press). These were the first British records of this species. Cors Fochno is an actively-growing estuarine raised mire. In Europe the usual habitat of *H. dampfi* is *Molinia* and *Eriophorum* on raised bogs. As this undoubtedly native species escaped detection in Britain until very recently and was not found by the extensive sampling of the Welsh Peatland Invertebrate Survey, it would appear to be of some rarity. Its raised bog habitat suffers a number of conservation problems in Britain. However, it would seem from the work at Cors Fochno that *H. dampfi* is not easily found. Until its true status in Britain is clarified, it is graded RDB K, Insufficiently Known.

Sitticus floricola (C.L. Koch, 1837) (Arachnida, Salticidae), p. 156.
In May and June 1988 this spider was found in heads of *Eriophorum* spp. at Bettisfield Moss (SSSI and, in part, an NNR), Shropshire, and at Llay Bog SSSI and Vicarage Moss SSSI, both in Denbighshire (Wallace & Wallace 1991).

Dolomedes plantarius (Clerck, 1757) (Arachnida, Pisauridae), p. 167.
There are now further records of this spider in the Pevensey Levels. Specimens collected in 1983 by M.A. Palmer during an NCC survey and identified as *D. fimbriatus* (Clerck) have been re-examined and found to be *D. plantarius*. *D. plantarius* was also seen within the Pevensey Levels NNR in 1990 by the warden, A. Bowley. At Redgrave and Lopham Fens, the other British site supporting this species, negotiations are continuing with the aim of closing down the nearby water abstraction borehole. These fens have now been declared a Ramsar site. During the drought summer of 1990 very few *Dolomedes* were seen in Lopham Fens. For the second year in succession all the pools dried out. Redgrave Fen no longer contains suitable habitat. Extinction for *Dolomedes* and other fenland species at this site may be imminent if pools of high quality water are not maintained through the summer of 1991.

Glyphesis servulus (Simon, 1881) (Arachnida, Linyphiidae), p. 200.
Work by the Welsh Peatland Invertebrate Survey has recorded this spider in seven sites in five vice-counties in Wales. Full details will be published elsewhere. In view of this number of records of what is obviously an under-recorded species, *G. servulus* can no longer be regarded as having Red Data Book status.

The addition of *H. dampfi* and deletion of *G. servulus* from the Red Data Book lists leaves the summary table on p. 21 still correct.

Pseudomaro aenigmaticus Denis, 1916 (Arachnida, Linyphiidae), p. 206.
One more female of this spider was found by D.F. Powell on 13 November 1990. It was in another field of winter wheat adjoining the field in which this species was found in 1988, near Redbourn, Hertfordshire (Powell 1990).

References

FARR-COX, F. 1990. The SRS weekend in the Forest of Dean, September 14-16, 1990. *Spider Recording Scheme Newsletter*, No. 8: 5.
POWELL, D.F. 1990. The recording of *Pseudomaro aenigmaticus*. *Spider Recording Scheme Newsletter*, No. 8: 7.
WALLACE, B., & WALLACE, I. 1991. Some records and observations on *Sitticus floricola* (C.L. Koch). *Newsletter of the British Arachnological Society*, No. 60: 3-4.
WILLIAMS, S.A. In press. *Heliophanus dampfi* Schenkel (Salticidae) in mid Wales and new to Britain. *Newsletter of the British Arachnological Society*.

John H. Bratton, April 1991.

REFERENCES

ADAM, W. 1960. *Faune de Belgique. Mollusques I, Mollusques terrestres et dulcicoles.* Brussels, Institut Royal des Sciences Naturelles de Belgique.

ALLMAN, G.J. 1856. *A monograph of the freshwater Polyzoa, including all the known species, both British and foreign.* London, Ray Society.

ALMADA-VILLELA, P.C. 1988. *Checklist of fish and invertebrates listed in the CITES Appendices.* Peterborough, Nature Conservancy Council.

ALMQUIST, S. 1978. *Robertus insignis* O. P.-Cambr. described on material from Sweden (Araneae: Theridiidae). *Entomologica Scandinavica, 9:* 124-128.

ALTABA, C.R. 1990. The last known population of the freshwater mussel *Margaritifera auricularia* (Bivalvia, Unionoida): a conservation priority. *Biological Conservation, 52:* 271-286.

AMOROS, C. 1984. Introduction pratique a la systematique des organisms des eaux continentales francaises. 5. Crustaces Cladoceres. *Bulletin de la Societe Linneenne de Lyon, 53:* 72-145.

AMOUREUX, L. 1983. Annelides Polychetes du golfe d'Aqaba (Mer Rouge). Description d'un genre nouveau et de deux especes nouvelles. *Bulletin du Museum National d'Histoire Naturelle, Paris,* Serie 4, *5(A):* 723-742.

ANON 1937. The Bryozoa of Suffolk. *Transactions of the Suffolk Naturalists' Society, 3:* 254-256.

ANON 1979. *Explanatory report concerning the Convention on the Conservation of European Wildlife and Natural Habitats.* Strasbourg, Council of Europe.

ANON 1989. Lesser Garth surveyed. *Descent,* No. 88: 8.

ASHMOLE, N.P., & MERRETT, P. 1981. *Lepthyphantes antroniensis* Schenkel, a spider new to Britain (Araneae: Linyphiidae). *Bulletin of the British Arachnological Society, 5:* 234-236.

ATHERSUCH, J., HORNE, D.J., & WHITTAKER, J.E. 1989. *Marine and brackish water ostracods (superfamilies Cypridacea and Cytheracea). Keys and notes for the identification of the species.* Leiden, E.J. Brill, for Linnean Society of London and Estuarine and Brackish-water Sciences Association. (Synopses of the British Fauna, No. 43, ed. by D.M. Kermack and R.S.K. Barnes).

BAGNALL, R.S. 1913. Review of field work in 1911. *Entomologist's Record and Journal of Variation, 25:* 224-226.

BAIN, C. 1987. *Native pinewoods in Scotland. A review 1957-1987.* Edinburgh, Royal Society for the Protection of Birds.

BAIRD, W. 1850. *The natural history of the British Entomostraca.* London, Ray Society.

BALFOUR-BROWNE, F. 1962. *Water beetles and other things. Half a century's work.* Dumfries, Blacklock Farries.

BALL, I.R., & REYNOLDSON, T.B. 1981. *British planarians. Platyhelminthes: Tricladida. Keys and notes for the identification of the species.* Cambridge, Cambridge University Press, for Linnean Society of London and Estuarine and Brackish-water Sciences Association. (Synopses of the British Fauna, No. 19, n.s., ed. by D.M. Kermack and R.S.K. Barnes).

BARBER, A.D. 1987. *An investigation into the status of* Chalandea pinguis *(Broleman, 1898) (Chilopoda, Geophilomorpha) in north Devon.* Unpublished report to the Nature Conservancy Council.

BARBER, A.D. 1988. Dyfed centipedes. *Dyfed Invertebrate Group Newsletter*, No. 10: 1-9.

BARBER, A.D., & KEAY, A.N. 1988. *Provisional atlas of the centipedes of the British Isles.* Huntingdon, Biological Records Centre, for British Myriapod Group.

BARNES, R.S.K., DOREY, A.E., & LITTLE, C. 1971. An ecological study of a pool subject to varying salinity (Swanpool, Falmouth). An introductory account of the topography, fauna and flora. *Journal of Animal Ecology, 40*: 709-734.

BAUER, G. 1986. The status of the freshwater pearl mussel *Margaritifera margaritifera* L. in the south of its European range. *Biological Conservation, 38*: 1-9.

BAUER, G. 1988. Threats to the freshwater pearl mussel *Margaritifera margaritifera* L. in central Europe. *Biological Conservation, 45*: 239-253.

BEESTON, H. 1919. Field notes on *Helicodonta obvoluta* Muller. *Journal of Conchology, 16*: 31-36, 44-50.

BEIER, M. 1963. Ordnung Pseudoscorpionidea (Afterskorpione). *Bestimmungsbucher Bedenfauna Europas, 1*: 1-313.

BERRY, G. 1982. *A tale of two lakes: the fight to save Ennerdale Water and Wastwater.* Kendal, Friends of the Lake District.

BEVEN, G. 1988. Survey of Bookham Common. Forty-sixth year. Progress report for 1987. Hirudinea. *London Naturalist*, No. 67: 151.

BISHOP, M.J. 1976. *Hydrobia neglecta* Muus in the British Isles. *Journal of Molluscan Studies, 42*: 319-326.

BLOWER, J.G. 1958. *British millipedes (Diplopoda).* London, Linnean Society of London. (Synopses of the British Fauna, No. 11).

BLOWER, J.G. 1984. The British Chordeumatidae. *Bulletin of the British Myriapod Group, 2*: 8-23.

BLOWER, J.G. 1985. *Millipedes. Keys and notes for the identification of the species.* London, E.J. Brill and Dr W. Backhuys, for Linnean Society of London and Estuarine and Brackish-water Sciences Association. (Synopses of the British Fauna, No. 35, n.s., ed. by D.M. Kermack and R.S.K. Barnes).

BOYCOTT, A.E. 1921. Oecological notes. *Proceedings of the Malacological Society, 14*: 128-130.

BOYCOTT, A.E. 1929. The habitat of *Clausilia biplicata* Mont. *Journal of Conchology, 18*: 340-343.

BOYCOTT, A.E. 1934. The habitats of land Mollusca in Britain. *Journal of Ecology, 22*: 1-38.

BOYCOTT, A.E. 1936. The habitats of fresh-water Mollusca in Britain. *Journal of Animal Ecology, 5*: 116-186.

BOYCOTT, A.E. 1939. Distribution and habitats of *Ena montana* in England. *Journal of Conchology, 21*: 153-159.

BOYDEN, C.R., CROTHERS, J.H., LITTLE, C. & METTAM, C. 1977. The intertidal invertebrate fauna of the Severn Estuary. *Field Studies, 4*: 477-554.

BRADY, G.S. 1868. A monograph of the recent British Ostracoda. *Transactions of the Linnaean Society of London, 26*: 353-495.

BRADY, G.S. 1878. *A monograph of the free and semi-parasitic Copepoda of the British Islands. Vol. I. Calanidae, Misophriidae, Cyclopidae, Notodelphyidae, Buproridae.* London, Ray Society.

BRADY, G.S. 1880. *A monograph of the free and semi-parasitic Copepoda of the British Islands. Vol. II. Harpacticidae.* London, Ray Society.

BRADY, G.S., & NORMAN, A.M. 1889. A monograph of the marine and freshwater Ostracoda of the North Atlantic and of North-Western Europe. Section I: Podocopa. *Scientific Transactions of the Royal Dublin Society, 4*: 63-270.

BRADY, G.S., & NORMAN, A.M. 1896. A monograph of the marine and freshwater Ostracoda of the North Atlantic and of North-Western Europe. Part II, Sections II-IV: Myodocopa, Cladocopa and Platycopa. *Scientific Transactions of the Royal Dublin Society*, *5*: 621-746.

BRAEM, F. 1951. Uber *Victorella* und einiger ihrer nachsten Verwandten, sowie uber die Bryozoenfauna des Ryck bei Greifswald. *Zoologica Stuttgart*, *37* (Hft 102): 1-59.

BRATTON, J.H., & FRYER, G. 1990. The distribution and ecology of *Chirocephalus diaphanus* Prevost (Branchiopoda: Anostraca) in Britain. *Journal of Natural History*, *24*: 955-964.

BRIAN, M.V. 1977. *Ants*. London, Collins. (New Naturalist Series).

BRIND, R.A. 1978. *The distribution and density of* Catinella arenaria *at Braunton Burrows, Devon*. Unpublished report to the Nature Conservancy Council South-West Region.

BRINKHURST, R.O. 1971. A guide for the identification of British aquatic Oligochaeta. *Scientific Publications of the Freshwater Biological Association*, No. 22.

BRISTOWE, W.S. 1939. *The comity of spiders, volume 1*. London, Ray Society.

BRISTOWE, W.S. 1958. *The world of spiders*. London, Collins. (New Naturalist Series).

BRITISH MYRIAPOD GROUP 1988. *Preliminary atlas of the millipedes of the British Isles*. Huntingdon, Biological Records Centre.

BRITTEN, H. 1912. The arachnids, (spiders, etc.,) of Cumberland. *Transactions of the Carlisle Natural History Society*, *2*: 30-65.

BROLEMANN, H.W. 1930. *Myriapodes Chilopodes*. Paris, Lechevalier. (Faune de France, 25).

BUSHNELL, J.H. 1974. Bryozoans (Ectoprocta). *In*: *Pollution ecology of freshwater invertebrates*, ed. by C.W. Hart and S.L.H. Fuller, 157-194. London, Academic Press.

BUTTERFLIES UNDER THREAT TEAM (BUTT) 1986. *The management of chalk grassland for butterflies*. Peterborough, Nature Conservancy Council. (Focus on nature conservation, No. 17).

CAMATINI, M., ed. 1979. *Myriapod biology*. London, Academic Press.

CAMERON, R.A.D. 1972. The distribution of *Helicodonta obvoluta* (Mull.) in Britain. *Journal of Conchology*, *27*: 363-369.

CARTER, C.I. 1972. A note on the occurrence of *Clubiona juvenis* Simon in the fens of the Norfolk Broads. *Bulletin of the British Arachnological Society*, *2*: 68.

CASTELL, C.P. 1962. Some notes on London's molluscs. *Journal of Conchology*, *25*: 97-117.

CHAPMAN, P. 1980. A new record of *Porrhomma rosenhaueri* in Wales. *Newsletter of the British Arachnological Society*, No. 27: 12-13.

CHAPMAN, S.B., ROSE, R.J., & BASANTA, M. 1989. Phosphorus adsorption by soils from heathlands in southern England in relation to successional change. *Journal of Applied Ecology*, *26*: 673-680.

CHATER, A.O. 1985. *Vertigo lilljeborgi* living in Cardiganshire. *Journal of Conchology*, *32*: 147-148.

CHATER, A.O. 1986. Recent woodlouse records from Dyfed. *Newsletter of the Isopod Survey Scheme*, No. 21: 4-5.

CHATER, A.O. 1988a. *Armadillidium pictum* in Radnorshire. *Newsletter of the Isopod Survey Scheme*, No. 24: 2.

CHATER, A.O. 1988b. Woodlice in the cultural consciousness of modern Europe. *Isopoda*, *2*: 21-39.

CLAPHAM, A.R., ed. 1978. *Upper Teesdale. The area and its natural history*. London, Collins.

CLARK, D.J., & JERRARD, P.C. 1972. A note on *Cheiracanthium pennyi* O. P.-Cambridge. *Bulletin of the British Arachnological Society*, *2*: 110.

COLES, B., & COLVILLE, B. 1979. *Catinella arenaria* (Bouchard-Chantereaux) and *Vertigo geyeri* Lindholm, from a base-rich fen in north-west England. *Journal of Conchology*, *30*: 99-100.

COLES, B., & COLVILLE, B. 1980. A glacial relict mollusc. *Nature*, *286*: 761.

COLLINS, N.M., & WELLS, S.M. 1987. *Invertebrates in need of special protection in Europe*. Strasbourg, European Committee for the Conservation of Nature and Natural Resources.

COOKE, J.A.L. 1961. The spiders of Colne Point, Essex, with descriptions of two species new to Britain. *Entomologist's Monthly Magazine*, *97*: 245-253.

COOKE, J.A.L. 1967. New and rare British spiders. *Journal of Natural History*, *1*: 135-148.

COOPER, J.E. 1924. Note on *Planorbis stroemi*, Westerlund (= *acronicus*, Ferrussac), living in the Thames. *Proceedings of the Malacological Society*, *16*: 15.

CORBET, G.B. 1989. A second British site for *Pachymerium ferrugineum* (C L Koch). *Bulletin of the British Myriapod Group*, *6*: 34-35.

CRAWFORD, G.I. 1937a. A review of the amphipod genus *Corophium*, with notes on the British species. *Journal of the Marine Biological Association of the United Kingdom*, *21*: 589-630.

CRAWFORD, G.I. 1937b. The fauna of certain estuaries in west England and south Wales, with special reference to the *Tanaidacea*, *Isopoda* and *Amphipoda*. *Journal of the Marine Biological Association of the United Kingdom*, *21*: 647-662.

CROCKER, J. 1973. The habitat of *Tetrilus macrophthalmus* (Kulczynski) in Leicestershire and Nottinghamshire (Araneae: Agelenidae). *Bulletin of the British Arachnological Society*, *2*: 117-123.

DALE, C.W. 1878. *The history of Glanville's Wootton, in the county of Dorset, including its zoology and botany*. London, Hatchards.

DANCE, S.P. 1956. A new Sussex locality for *Pisidium pseudosphaerium* Favre. *Journal of Conchology*, *24*: 91-92.

DANCE, S.P. 1957. Notes on the *Pisidium* fauna of the Pevensey Levels district, with special reference to *P. pseudosphaerium* Favre. *Journal of Conchology*, *24*: 195-199.

DANCE, S.P. 1972. *Vertigo lilljeborgi* Westerlund in North Wales. *Journal of Conchology*, *27*: 387-389.

DANDY, J.E. 1969. *Watsonian vice-counties of Great Britain*. London, Ray Society.

DARBY, H.C. 1983. *The changing fenland*. Cambridge, Cambridge University Press.

DAVIS, A.G. 1952. *Trucatellina cylindrica* (Ferussac) in Norfolk. *Journal of Conchology*, *23*: 269-270.

DAVIS, A.G. 1955. *Truncatellina cylindrica britannica* in Dorset and Isle of Wight. *Journal of Conchology*, *24*: 61-62.

DE FOLIN, L. 1869. Un mot sur le golfe de Gascogne. *Les Fonds de la Mer*, *1*: 146-151.

DECLEER, K., & BOSMANS, R. 1989. Distribution and ecological aspects of four rare wetland spiders, recently reported from Belgium. *Bulletin of the British Arachnological Society*, *8*: 80-88.

DEMANGE, J.M. 1981. *Les mille-pattes*. Paris, Editions Boubee.

DOBSON, S. 1982. *Sitticus floricola* (C. L. Koch) in Scotland - a request for help. *Newsletter of the British Arachnological Society*, No. 34: 4-5.

DOBSON, S. 1987. A further note on *Sitticus floricola* (C. L. Koch) in Scotland. *Newsletter of the British Arachnological Society*, No. 48: 4.

DONISTHORPE, H. St J.K. 1927. *The guests of British ants. Their habits and life histories*. London, Routledge.

DOREY, A.E., LITTLE, C., & BARNES, R.S.K. 1973. An ecological study of the Swanpool, Falmouth. II. Hydrography and its relation to animal distributions. *Estuarine and Coastal Marine Science*, *1*: 153-176.

DOUBLEDAY, H.A., ed. 1900. *A history of Hampshire and the Isle of Wight. Volume 1.* Westminster, Archibald Constable.

DRISCOLL, R.J. 1980. *Distribution maps of aquatic vertebrates and invertebrates and aquatic plants recorded from Rivers Bure and Yare and from Strumpshaw, Surlingham, Rockland and Wheatfen Broads, 1976-1977.* Unpublished report to the Nature Conservancy Council, East Anglia Region.

DRISCOLL, R.J. 1982. *The aquatic vertebrate and invertebrate fauna and aquatic flora of the lower reaches of the Rivers Bure and Yare, Breydon Water, and Strumpshaw, Surlingham, Rockland and Wheatfen Broads.* Unpublished report to the Nature Conservancy Council, East Anglia Region.

DUFFEY, E. 1958. *Dolomedes plantarius* Clerck, a spider new to Britain, found in the upper Waveney valley. *Transactions of the Norfolk and Norwich Naturalists' Society, 18:* 1-5.

DUFFEY, E. 1960. A further note on *Dolomedes plantarius* Clerck in the Waveney Valley. *Transactions of the Norfolk and Norwich Naturalists' Society, 19:* 173-176.

DUFFEY, E. 1970. Habitat selection by spiders on a saltmarsh in Gower. *Nature in Wales, 12:* 15-23.

DUFFEY, E. 1971a. *Carorita paludosa* n. sp., a new linyphiid spider from Ireland and eastern England. *Bulletin of the British Arachnological Society, 2:* 14-15.

DUFFEY, E. 1971b. The rediscovery of *Centromerus incultus* Falc. (*C. alnicola* Schenkel) (Araneae: Linyphiidae), in Britain. *Bulletin of the British Arachnological Society, 2:* 48.

DUFFEY, E., & DENIS, J. 1967. *Wideria stylifrons* (O. P.-Cambridge), a southern European spider from the Norfolk Breckland. *Transactions of the Norfolk and Norwich Naturalists' Society, 21:* 25-31.

DUFFEY, E., & MERRETT, P. 1963. *Carorita limnaea* (Crosby & Bishop), a linyphiid spider new to Britain, from Wybunbury Moss, Cheshire. *Annals and Magazine of Natural History (Series 13), 6:* 573-576.

DUIGAN, C. 1988. *Eurycercus glacialis* Lilljeborg 1887 (Crustacea, Cladocera) in Scotland. *Bulletin of the British Ecological Society, 19:* 244-247.

DUIGAN, C., & FREY, D.G. 1987. *Eurycercus glacialis,* a chydorid cladoceran new to Ireland. *Irish Naturalists' Journal, 22:* 180-183.

EASON, E.H. 1964. *Centipedes of the British Isles.* London, Warne.

EASON, E.H. 1982. A review of the north-west European species of Lithobiomorpha with a revised key to their identification. *Zoological Journal of the Linnean Society, 74:* 9-33.

ELLIOTT, J.M., & MANN, K.H. 1979. A key to the British freshwater leeches with notes on their life cycles and ecology. *Scientific Publications of the Freshwater Biological Association,* No. 40.

ELLIOTT, J.M., MUGRIDGE, R.E.R., & STALLYBRASS, H.G. 1979. *Haementeria costata* (Hirudinea: Glossiphoniidae), a leech new to Britain. *Freshwater Biology, 9:* 461-465.

ELLIOTT, J.M., & TULLETT, P.A. 1982. Provisional atlas of the freshwater leeches of the British Isles. *Occasional Publications of the Freshwater Biological Association,* No. 14.

ELLIOTT, J.M., & TULLETT, P.A. 1984. The status of the medicinal leech *Hirudo medicinalis* in Europe and especially in the British Isles. *Biological Conservation, 29:* 15-26.

ELLIOTT, J.M., & TULLETT, P.A. 1986. The effects of temperature, atmospheric pressure and season on the swimming activity of the medicinal leech, *Hirudo medicinalis* (Hirudinea; Hirudinidae), in a Lake District tarn. *Freshwater Biology, 16:* 405-415.

ELLIS, A.E. 1928. *Planorbis vorticulus,* Troschel, in West Sussex. *Proceedings of the Malacological Society, 18:* 127.

ELLIS, A.E. 1931. Notes on some Norfolk Mollusca. *Journal of Conchology, 19:* 177-178.

ELLIS, A.E. 1932. Further localities for *Planorbis vorticulus* Troschel. *Journal of Conchology, 19:* 258-259.

ELLIS, A.E. 1969. *British snails*. Oxford, Clarendon Press. (Reissue of 1926 edition, with supplementary matter.)

ELLIS, A.E. 1978. *British freshwater bivalve Mollusca. Keys and notes for the identification of the species*. London, Academic Press, for Linnean Society of London. (Synopses of the British Fauna, No. 11, n.s., ed. by D.M. Kermack).

ELLIS, E.A. 1944. Flora and fauna of Norfolk, miscellaneous observations. *Transactions of the Norfolk and Norwich Naturalists' Society, 15*: 423-440.

ENGHOFF, H. 1971. *Geophilus insculptus* Attems, en hidtil upaaglet dansk skolopender, samt bemaerkninger om *G. proximus* (C.L. Koch) (Chilopoda). *Entomologiske Meddelelser, 39*: 119-121.

EVANS, J. 1841. Apus Cancriformis. *Entomologist, 1*: 226.

EVANS, J. 1842. Apus Cancriformis. *Entomologist, 1*: 341-342.

FAUVEL, P. 1923. *Polychetes errantes*. Paris, Lechevalier. (Faune de France, 5).

FAUVEL, P. 1927. *Polychetes sedentaires, addenda aux errantes, archiannelides, myzostomaires*. Paris, Lechevalier. (Faune de France, 16).

FIERS, F., & WOUTERS, K. 1985. Human impacts on the crustacean stygiofauna. *In: Conference - debat: invertebres menacants, invertebres menaces*, 36-37. Gembloux, Facultes des Sciences Agronomiques de l'Etat.

FITTER, R., & MANUEL, R. 1986. *Field guide to the freshwater life of Britain and North-West Europe*. London, Collins.

FLOSSNER, D. 1972. *Krebstiere, Crustacea (Branchiopoda, Branchiura)*. Jena, Fischer. (Tierwelt Deutschlands, 60 Teil).

FORBES, E., & HANLEY, S. 1849-1853. *A history of British Mollusca and their shells*. 4 vols. London, John van Voorst.

[FOSTER, G.N.] 1977. (Untitled note) *Balfour-Browne Club Newsletter*, No. 6: 2.

FOX, H.M. 1949. On Apus: its discovery in Britain, nomenclature and habits. *Proceedings of the Zoological Society of London, 119*: 693-702.

FOX, H.M. 1964. New and interesting cyprids (Crustacea, Ostracoda) in Britain. *Annals and Magazine of Natural History, 7*: 623-633.

FOX, H.M. 1967. More new and interesting cyprids (Crustacea, Ostracoda) in Britain. *Journal of Natural History, 4*: 549-559.

FRETTER, V., & GRAHAM, A. 1978a. The prosobranch molluscs of Britain and Denmark, part 3. *Journal of Molluscan Studies*, supplement 5.

FRETTER, V., & GRAHAM, A. 1978b. The prosobranch molluscs of Britain and Denmark, part 4 - marine Rissoacea. *Journal of Molluscan Studies*, supplement 6.

FRYER, G. 1981. The copepod *Salmincola edwardsii* as a parasite of *Salvelinus alpinus* in Britain, and a consideration of the so-called relict fauna of Ennerdale Water. *Journal of Zoology, 193*: 253-268.

FRYER, G. 1982. The parasitic Copepoda and Branchiura of British freshwater fishes. A handbook and key. *Scientific Publications of the Freshwater Biological Association*, No. 46.

FRYER, G. 1986. *The distribution and ecology of the fairy shrimp* Chirocephalus diaphanus *Prevost and its historical and present status in Britain*. Unpublished report to the Nature Conservancy Council.

FRYER, G. 1988. Studies on the functional morphology and biology of the Notostraca (Crustacea: Branchiopoda). *Philosophical Transactions of the Royal Society of London, Series B, 321*: 27-124.

GALLIFORD, A.L. 1967. On *Triops cancriformis*, a living fossil. *Country-side, 20* (n.s.): 480-485.

GEORGE, J.D., & HARTMANN-SCHRODER, G. 1985. *Polychaetes: British Amphinomida, Spintherida & Eunicida. Keys and notes for the identification of the species.* London, E.J. Brill and Dr W. Backhuys, for Linnean Society of London and Estuarine and Brackish-water Sciences Association. (Synopses of the British Fauna, No. 32, n.s., ed. by D.M. Kermack and R.S.K. Barnes).

GEORGE, R.S. 1961. More records of Gloucestershire falsescorpions. *North Gloucestershire Naturalists' Society Report, 1959-60:* 38.

GIBSON, R. 1982. *British nemerteans. Keys and notes for the identification of the species.* Cambridge, Cambridge University Press, for Linnean Society of London and Estuarine and Brackish-water Sciences Association. (Synopses of the British Fauna, No. 24, n.s., ed. by D.M. Kermack and R.S.K. Barnes).

GILBERT, O. 1951. Observations. New Suffolk Arachnida. *Transactions of the Suffolk Naturalists' Society, 7:* 127.

GLEDHILL, T., SUTCLIFFE, D.W., & WILLIAMS, W.D. 1976. Key to British freshwater Crustacea: Malacostraca. *Scientific Publications of the Freshwater Biological Association,* No. 32.

GLENNIE, E.A. 1967. The distribution of the hypogean Amphipoda in Britain. *Transactions of the Cave Research Group of Great Britain, 9:* 132-136.

GODDARD, J.S., & HOGGER, J.B. 1986. The current status and distribution of freshwater crayfish in Britain. *Field Studies, 6:* 383-396.

GODWIN, H. 1978. *Fenland: its ancient past and uncertain future.* Cambridge, Cambridge University Press.

GOODHART, C.B. 1941. The ecology of the Amphipoda in a small estuary in Hampshire. *Journal of Animal Ecology, 10:* 306-322.

GRANSTROM, U. 1978. The spider fauna of the province Vasterbotten. A species list with faunistic and phenological notes. *Fauna Norrlandica, 10:* 1-14.

GRAYSON, R.F. 1971. The freshwater Hydras of Europe. 1. A review of the European species. *Archiv fur Hydrobiologie, 68:* 436-449.

GRAYSON, R.F., & HAYES, D.A. 1968. The British freshwater hydras. *Country-side, 20* (n.s.): 539-546.

GREEN, J. 1961. *A biology of Crustacea.* London, H.F. & G. Witherby.

GURNEY, R. 1907. The Crustacea of the East Norfolk rivers. *Transactions of the Norfolk and Norwich Naturalists' Society, 8:* 411-438.

GURNEY, R. 1924. The rearing of Crustacea from dried mud. *Transactions of the Norfolk and Norwich Naturalists' Society, 12:* 25-29.

GURNEY, R. 1929. The fresh-water Crustacea of Norfolk. *Transactions of the Norfolk and Norwich Naturalists' Society, 12:* 550-581.

GURNEY, R. 1931. *British Fresh-water Copepoda. Vol. I.* London, Ray Society.

GURNEY, R. 1932. *British Fresh-water Copepoda. Vol. II.* London, Ray Society.

GURNEY, R. 1933. *British Fresh-water Copepoda. Vol. III.* London, Ray Society.

HAACKER, U. 1971. Die Funktion eines dorsalen Drusenkomplexes im Balzverhalten von *Chordeuma. Forma et Functio, 4:* 162-170.

HAMOND, R. 1972. The marine Mollusca of Norfolk. *Transactions of the Norfolk and Norwich Naturalists' Society, 22:* 271-306.

HANCOCK, C. 1987. Westhay Moor: creative conservation. *Nature in Somerset, 1987:* 10-11.

HANCOCK, E.G. 1983. Further record of *Craspedacusta sowerbyi* Lankester in Lancashire. *Naturalist, 108:* 119-120.

HARDING, J.P., & SMITH, W.A. 1974. A key to the British freshwater cyclopid and calanoid copepods. *Scientific Publications of the Freshwater Biological Association,* No. 18. 2nd ed.

HARDING, P.T. 1975. A preliminary list of the fauna of Staverton Park, Suffolk. Part 3. *Transactions of the Suffolk Naturalists' Society*, *16*: 399-419.

HARDING, P.T. 1977. A re-examination of the work of W.E. Collinge on woodlice (Crustacea, Isopoda, Oniscoidea) from the British Isles. *Journal of the Society for the Bibliography of Natural History*, *8*: 286-315.

HARDING, P.T., & GREENE, D.M. 1988. *Computerization of data on selected cave fauna in Britain.* Peterborough, Nature Conservancy Council. (CSD Report No. 886).

HARDING, P.T., & SUTTON, S.L. 1985. *Woodlice in Britain and Ireland: distribution and habitat.* Huntingdon, Institute of Terrestrial Ecology.

HARDING, W.A. 1910. A revision of the British leeches. *Parasitology*, *3*: 130-201.

HARRIS, G.J. 1985. *Pseudamnicola confusa* rediscovered in the Thames estuary. *Journal of Conchology*, *32*: 147.

HARVEY, P. 1990. News from Essex for 1990. *Spider Recording Scheme Newsletter*, No. 7: 4.

HASKINS, L. 1988. Still mourning Dorset heaths. *Ecos*, *9*(4): 26-32.

HAYWARD, P.J. 1985. *Ctenostome bryozoans. Keys and notes for the identification of the species.* London, E.J. Brill and Dr W. Backhuys, for Linnean Society of London and Estuarine and Brackish-water Sciences Association. (Synopses of the British Fauna, No. 33, n.s., ed. by D.M. Kermack and R.S.K. Barnes).

HAYWARD, P.J., & RYLAND, J.S. 1979. *British ascophoran bryozoans. Keys and notes for the identification of the species.* London, Academic Press, for Linnean Society of London and Estuarine and Brackish-water Sciences Association. (Synopses of the British Fauna, No. 14, n.s., ed. by D.M. Kermack and R.S.K. Barnes).

HAYWARD, P.J., & RYLAND, J.S. 1985. *Cyclostome bryozoans. Keys and notes for the identification of the species.* London, E.J. Brill and Dr W. Backhuys, for Linnean Society of London and Estuarine and Brackish-water Sciences Association. (Synopses of the British Fauna, No. 34, n.s., ed. by D.M. Kermack and R.S.K. Barnes).

HEATH, A.W. 1969. British Naturalists' Association green hydra survey: report of the survey from 1st January 1968 to 31st May 1969. *Country-side*, *21* (n.s.): 212-213.

HERBERT, R.J.H. 1988. Isle of Wight marine biological report for 1987. *Proceedings of the Isle of Wight Natural History and Archaeological Society*, *8*(3): 37-42.

HICKLIN, A.J. 1986. *An evaluation of the nature conservation status of the Lewes Brooks drainage system, East Sussex.* Unpublished report to the Nature Conservancy Council South-East Region.

HILLYARD, P.D. 1983. *Episinus maculipes* Cavanna (Araneae, Theridiidae): rediscovery in Britain. *Bulletin of the British Arachnological Society*, *6*: 88-92.

HINGLEY, M.R. 1979. The colonization of newly-dredged drainage channels on the Pevensey Levels (East Sussex), with special reference to gastropods. *Journal of Conchology*, *30*: 105-122.

HOLDICH, D.M., & REEVE, I.D. 1989. *Status of native crayfish with particular reference to crayfish plague, alien introductions and pollution. Update - September 1989.* Peterborough, Nature Conservancy Council. (CSD Report No. 999).

HOLLOWDAY, E.D. 1947. Concerning freshwater Polyzoa. *The Microscope, London*, *6*: 274-277.

[HOPKIN, S.P.] 1987. *Metatrichoniscoides celticus* and *Trichoniscoides albidus*. *British Isopod Study Group Newsletter*, No. 23: 2.

HORSFIELD, D., MURRAY, S., & GALBRAITH, H. 1989. Recent captures of the rare wolf-spider *Tricca alpigena* (Doleschall) on high-altitude plateaux in the Scottish Highlands. *Newsletter of the British Arachnological Society*, No. 54: 6-7.

HOWES, N.H. 1939. The ecology of a saline lagoon in south-east Essex. *Journal of the Linnean Society of London (Zoology)*, *40*: 383-445.

HUBLE, J. 1980. Captures remarquables d'araignees linyphiides dans la reserve naturelle "de Blankaart" (Flandre Occidentale). *Bulletin et Annales de la Societe Royale Entomologique de Belgique, 116*: 99-101.

HULL, J.E. 1916. Notes and records. *Vasculum, 2*: 90-91.

HULL, J.E. 1931. A note on *Diplocentria* and *Lophocarenum* (genera of spiders). *Vasculum, 17*: 7-10.

HULL, J.E. 1948. The spiders of Essex. Recent additional records. *Essex Naturalist, 28*: 58-64.

HURLEY, J. 1981. A history of the occurrence of *Lymnaea glabra* (Gastropoda: Pulmonata) in Ireland. *Irish Naturalists' Journal, 20*: 284-287.

HURRELL, H.E. 1904. Pond life notes of the Yarmouth district in 1903. *Transactions of the Norfolk and Norwich Naturalists' Society, 7*: 755-756.

HURRELL, H.E. 1911. Distribution of the Polyzoa in Norfolk waters. *Transactions of the Norfolk and Norwich Naturalists' Society, 9*: 197-205.

HURRELL, H.E. 1927. The ecology of the freshwater Polyzoa in East Anglia. *Journal of the Royal Microscopical Society, 47*: 135-142.

HURRELL, H.E. 1943. Pond life. *Transactions of the Norfolk and Norwich Naturalists' Society, 15*: 319-331.

ISMAY, E. 1982. *Conservation policy for the Widewater*. Shoreham, Adur District Council.

JACKSON, A.R. 1924. On new and rare British spiders. *Proceedings of the Dorset Natural History and Antiquarian Field Club, 45*: 101-120.

JERRARD, P.C. 1963. Notes on some rare British spiders. *Entomologist's Monthly Magazine, 99*: 184-186.

JOB, W. 1968. Das Rohrengeweb von *Aulonia albimana* (Walckenaer) (Araneida: Lycosidae) und seine systematische Bedeutung. *Zoologischer Anzeiger, 180*: 403-409.

JOCQUE, R. 1976. Contribution a la connaissance des araignees de Belgique. II. *Bulletin et Annales de la Societe Royale Entomologique de Belgique, 112*: 182-192.

JONES, N.S. 1948. The ecology of the Amphipoda of the south of the Isle of Man. *Journal of the Marine Biological Association of the United Kingdom, 27*: 400-439.

JONES, P.E. 1979. Pseudoscorpions from Little Wood, Eye, with some additional records from Northamptonshire. *Journal of the Northamptonshire Natural History Society and Field Club, 38*: 198-201.

JONES, P.E. 1980a. The ecology and distribution of the pseudoscorpion *Dendrochernes cyrneus* (L. Koch) in Great Britain. *Proceedings and Transactions of the British Entomological and Natural History Society, 13*: 33-37.

JONES, P.E. 1980b. *Provisional atlas of the Arachnida of the British Isles. Part 1. Pseudoscorpiones*. Huntingdon, Biological Records Centre.

JONES, R. 1982. The habitat site of *Pellenes tripunctatus* (Walckenaer). *Newsletter of the British Arachnological Society, 34*: 4.

JONES, R. 1983. *The Country Life guide to spiders of Britain and Northern Europe*. Feltham, Hamlyn.

JONES, R. 1984. *Tegenaria picta* Simon, a spider new to Britain (Araneae: Agelenidae). *Bulletin of the British Arachnological Society, 6*: 178-180.

JONES, R.E., & KEAY, A.N. 1986. *Trachysphaera lobata* (Ribaut), a millipede new to Britain, from the Isle of Wight. *Bulletin of the British Myriapod Group, 3*: 17-20.

KEAY, A.N. 1987. *Trachysphaera lobata* Ribaut, a millipede new to Britain from Bembridge, Isle of Wight. *Proceedings of the Isle of Wight Natural History and Archaeological Society, 8*: 43-44.

KEAY, A.N. 1988. The April weekend in Wales full of surprises. *British Myriapod Group Newsletter*, No. 9: 1.

KEAY, A.N. 1989a. *Lithobius tenebrosus* Meinert from Aberystwyth, Cardiganshire. *Bulletin of the British Myriapod Group, 6*: 3-5.

KEAY, A.N. 1989b. *Pachymerium ferrugineum* again. *Bulletin of the British Myriapod Group, 6*: 35.

KENNETT, J.A.B. 1985. *Report on the ecological status of* Dolomedes plantarius *on Redgrave and Lopham Fens*. Unpublished report to the Suffolk Trust for Nature Conservation.

KERNEY, M.P. 1966. Snails and man in Britain. *Journal of Conchology, 26*: 3-14.

KERNEY, M.P. 1970. *Pisidium tenuilineatum* Stelfox in Sussex. *Journal of Conchology, 27*: 115-116.

KERNEY, M.P., ed. 1976. *Atlas of the non-marine Mollusca of the British Isles*. Huntingdon, Conchological Society of Great Britain and Ireland and Biological Records Centre.

KERNEY, M.P., & CAMERON, R.A.D. 1979. *A field guide to the land snails of Britain and north-west Europe*. London, Collins.

KERNEY, M.P., & MAY, F. 1960. *Planorbis (Anisus) vorticulus* Troschel in the Thames valley. *Journal of Conchology, 24*: 403-404.

KERNEY, M.P., & NORRIS, A. 1972. *Lauria sempronii* (Charpentier) living in Britain. *Journal of Conchology, 27*: 517-518.

KERNEY, M.P., & STUBBS, A.E. 1980. *The conservation of snails, slugs and freshwater mussels*. Shrewsbury, Nature Conservancy Council.

KEVAN, D.K. 1931. The occurrence of a rare snail (*Succinea oblonga*) in East Lothian and Stirlingshire. *Scottish Naturalist, 1931*: 185-186.

KEVAN, D.K., & WATERSTON, A.R. 1933. *Vertigo lilljeborgi* (West.) in Great Britain (with additional Irish localities). *Journal of Conchology, 19*: 296-313.

KEW, H.W. 1929. Notes on some Coleoptera and a *Chelifer* observed on a Richmond Park oak after nightfall. *Entomologist's Monthly Magazine, 65*: 83-86.

KILLEEN, I.J. 1983. *Vertigo angustior* Jeffreys living in Suffolk. *Journal of Conchology, 31*: 257.

KIRBY, P. 1990. *Dolomedes plantarius* in East Sussex. *Newsletter of the British Arachnological Society*, No. 58: 8.

KITCHING, J.A. 1987. Ecological studies at Lough Hyne. *Advances in Ecological Research, 17*: 115-186.

KLIE, W. 1938. *Krebstiere oder Crustacea III: Ostracoda, Muschelkrebse*. Jena, Fischer. (Tierwelt Deutschlands und der Angrenzenden Meersteile, 34).

KNEIB, R.T. 1985. Predation and disturbance by grass shrimp, *Palaemonetes pugio* Holthuis, in soft-substratum benthic invertebrate assemblages. *Journal of Experimental Marine Biology and Ecology, 93*: 91-102.

KRONESTEDT, T. 1979. *Acanthophyma gowerense* (Locket) (Araneae, Linyphiidae), an erigonine spider new to Sweden. *Bulletin of the British Arachnological Society, 4*: 398-401.

KUIPER, J.G.J. 1949. *Pisidium pseudosphaerium* Favre in England. *Journal of Conchology, 23*: 27-32.

LANG, K. 1948. *Monographie der Harpacticiden*. Lund, Hakan Ohlssons Boktryckeri.

LEGG, G., & JONES, R.E. 1988. *Pseudoscorpions (Arthropoda; Arachnida). Keys and notes for the identification of the species*. Leiden, E.J. Brill and Dr W. Backhuys, for Linnean Society of London and Estuarine and Brackish-water Sciences Association. (Synopses of the British Fauna, No. 40, n.s., ed. by D.M. Kermack and R.S.K. Barnes).

LEWIS, J.G.E. 1981. *The biology of centipedes*. Cambridge, Cambridge University Press.

LIGHT, J. 1986. *Paludinella littorina* living along the Fleet, Dorset. *Journal of Conchology, 32*: 260.

LINCOLN, R.J. 1979. *British marine Amphipoda: Gammaridea*. London, British Museum (Natural History).

LITTLE, C. 1985. *Coastal saline lagoons in Cornwall*. Peterborough, Nature Conservancy Council. (CSD Report No. 601).

LITTLE, C. 1986. Fluctuations in the meiofauna of the Aufwuchs community in a brackish-water lagoon. *Estuarine, Coastal and Shelf Science, 23*: 263-276.

LITTLE, C., MORRITT, D., SEAWARD, D.R. & WILLIAMS, G.A. 1989. Distribution of intertidal molluscs in lagoonal shingle (The Fleet, Dorset, U.K.). *Journal of Conchology, 33*: 225-232.

LOCKET, G.H. 1965. A new British species of linyphiid spider. *Entomologist's Monthly Magazine, 101*: 48-50.

LOCKET, G.H., & MILLIDGE, A.F. 1951. *British spiders. Vol. I*. London, Ray Society.

LOCKET, G.H., & MILLIDGE, A.F. 1953. *British spiders. Vol. II*. London, Ray Society.

LOCKET, G.H., MILLIDGE, A.F., & LA TOUCHE, A.A.D. 1958. On new and rare British spiders. *Annals and Magazine of Natural History (Series 13), 1*: 137-146.

LOCKET, G.H., MILLIDGE, A.F., & MERRETT, P. 1974. *British spiders. Vol. III*. London, Ray Society/British Museum (Natural History).

LONG, D.C. 1968. *Planorbis vorticulus* Troschel in Suffolk East. *Conchologists' Newsletter*, No. 27: 71.

LONG, D.C. 1974. A *Vertigo lilljeborgi* site in Wigtownshire. *Conchologists' Newsletter*, No. 49: 375-376.

LONG, D.C. 1986. A second site for *Lauria sempronii* living in Britain. *Journal of Conchology, 32*: 201-202.

LONGHURST, A.R. 1955. A review of the Notostraca. *Bulletin of the British Museum (Natural History). Zoology, 3*: 1-57.

LOVESEY, E. 1988. Notes and comments. *Newsletter of the British Arachnological Society*, No. 53: 3.

MACAN, T.T. 1949. A key to the British fresh- and brackish-water gastropods. *Scientific Publications of the Freshwater Biological Association*, No. 13. (Several later issues, with minor revisions.)

McGEOCH, J. 1987. Westhay Moor: a future for birds? *Nature in Somerset, 1987*: 6-9.

MACKIE, D.W. 1970. Two interesting linyphiid spiders from County Kerry, Ireland. *Bulletin of the British Arachnological Society, 1*: 89.

MANN, K.H. 1954. A key to the British freshwater leeches. *Scientific Publications of the Freshwater Biological Association*, No. 14.

MANN, K.H. 1962. *Leeches (Hirudinea) - their structure, physiology, ecology and embryology*. Oxford, Pergamon.

MANUEL, R.L. 1975. A new sea-anemone from a brackish lagoon in Sussex, *Edwardsia ivelli*, sp. nov. *Journal of Natural History, 9*: 705-711.

MANUEL, R.L. 1981. *British Anthozoa. Keys and notes for the identification of the species*. London, Academic Press, for Linnean Society of London and Estuarine and Brackish-water Sciences Association. (Synopses of the British Fauna, No. 18, n.s., ed. by D.M. Kermack and R.S.K. Barnes).

MANUEL, R.L. 1983. *The Anthozoa of the British Isles - a colour guide*. Revised ed. Ross-on-Wye, Marine Conservation Society.

MARCUS, E. 1934. Uber *Lophopus crystallinus* (Pall.). *Zoologischer Jahrbucher. Abteilung fur Anatomie, 58*: 501-606.

MARGARITORA, F.G. 1985. *Cladocera*. Bologna, Calderini. (Fauna d'Italia, 23).

MARRIOTT, D.K., & MARRIOTT, R.W. 1982. The occurence of *Vertigo angustior* in North Lancashire. *Journal of Conchology, 31*: 72.

MARRIOTT, R.W., & MARRIOTT, D.K. 1988. *Vertigo modesta*, a snail new to the British Isles. *Journal of Conchology, 33*: 51-52.

MARTENS, J. 1988. Species boundary problems in Opiliones. *Newsletter of the British Arachnological Society*, No. 52: 2-4.

MATIC, Z., & DARABANTU, C. 1969. Contributo alla conoscenza del genere *Nesoporogaster* Verhoeff, 1924 (Geophilomorpha). *Memorie del Museo Civico di Storia Naturale di Verona, 16*: 447-454.

MAYES, B. 1987. Norfolk and Suffolk Broads Bill. *Ecos, 8*(2): 49-50.

MENDEL, H. 1981. A review of Suffolk pseudoscorpions. *Transactions of the Suffolk Naturalists' Society, 18*: 226-232.

MERRETT, P. 1980. *Tuberta maerens* rediscovered in Dorset. *Newsletter of the British Arachnological Society*, No. 29: 9-10.

MERRETT, P., LOCKET, G.H., & MILLIDGE, A.F. 1985. A check list of British spiders. *Bulletin of the British Arachnological Society, 6*: 381-403.

MERRETT, P., & SNAZELL, R.G. 1975. New and rare British spiders. *Bulletin of the British Arachnological Society, 3*: 106-112.

MITCHELL, B.D., & GEDDES, M.C. 1977. Distribution of the brine shrimps *Parartemia zietziana* Sayce and *Artemia salina* (L.) along a salinity and oxygen gradient in a South Australian saltfield. *Freshwater Biology, 7*: 161 167.

MOON, H.P., & HARDING, P.T. 1981. *A preliminary review of the occurrence of* Asellus *(Crustacea: Isopoda) in the British Isles*. Abbots Ripton, Institute of Terrestrial Ecology.

MORGAN, M.J. 1987. Field notes. Invertebrates. *Nature in Wales, 6* (n.s.): 72-75.

MUNDY, S.P. 1980. A key to the British and European freshwater bryozoans. *Scientific Publications of the Freshwater Biological Association*, No. 41.

MURPHY, F.M. 1971. *Callilepis nocturna* (Linnaeus) (Araneae, Gnaphosidae) newly found in Britain. *Entomologist's Gazette, 22*: 269-271.

MURPHY, J.A., & MURPHY, F.M. 1979. *Theridion pinastri* L. Koch, newly found in Britain. *Bulletin of the British Arachnological Society, 4*: 314-315.

NAGGS, F. 1983. *Perforatella*, a genus of Palaearctic snails newly recognised in Britain, is found in the London area. *London Naturalist*, No. 62: 59.

NATURE CONSERVANCY COUNCIL 1984. *Nature conservation in Great Britain*. Shrewsbury.

NEW FOREST REVIEW GROUP 1987. *New Forest Review. Consultation draft report 1987*. Lyndhurst.

NICOL, E.A.T. 1935. The ecology of a salt-marsh. *Journal of the Marine Biological Association of the United Kingdom, 20*: 203-261.

NORRIS, A. 1976. *Truncatellina cylindrica* (Ferussac) in Yorkshire. *Naturalist, 101*: 25-27.

NORRIS, A., & COLVILLE, B. 1974. Notes on the occurrence of *Vertigo angustior* Jeffreys in Great Britain. *Journal of Conchology, 28*: 141-154.

OLDHAM, C. 1922. *Paludestrina confusa* (Frauenfeld) in the Waveney valley. *Journal of Conchology, 16*: 324-325.

OLIVER, P.G., & TREW, A. 1981. A new species of *Metatrichoniscoides* (Isopoda: Oniscoidea) from the coast of South Wales, UK. *Journal of Natural History, 15*: 525-529.

PAGE, W., *ed.* 1908. *The Victoria History of the County of Kent. Vol. 1*. London, Archibald Constable.

[PARKER, J.R.] 1976. Local English and Welsh records of interest. *Newsletter of the British Arachnological Society*, No. 14: 7-8.

PARKER, J.R. 1977. Spiders. Rare species re-discovered and new records. *Birds in Cumbria, 1976-77*: 52-55.

PARKER, J.R., & COLEMAN, R.B. 1977. The female of *Typhochrestus simoni* de Lessert. *Bulletin of the British Arachnological Society, 4*: 129-131.

PERRING, F.H., & FARRELL, L. 1977. *British Red Data Books: 1. Vascular plants*. Lincoln, Society for the Promotion of Nature Conservation.

PERRING, F.H., & FARRELL, L. 1983. *British Red Data Books: 1. Vascular plants*. 2nd ed. Lincoln, Royal Society for Nature Conservation.

PHILP, E.G. 1987. *Tandonia rustica* (Millet), a slug new to Britain. *Journal of Conchology*, *32*: 302.

PICKARD-CAMBRIDGE, O. 1907. On new and rare British Arachnida. *Proceedings of the Dorset Natural History and Antiquarian Field Club*, *28*: 121-148.

PICKARD-CAMBRIDGE, O. 1914. On new and rare British arachnids noted and observed in 1913. *Proceedings of the Dorset Natural History and Antiquarian Field Club*, *35*: 119-142.

PREECE, R.C., & WILLING, M.J. 1984. *Vertigo angustior* living near its type locality in South Wales. *Journal of Conchology*, *31*: 340.

PREECE, R.C., & WILMOT, R.D. 1979. *Marstoniopsis scholtzi* (A. Schmidt) and *Ferrissia wautieri* (Mirolli) from Hilgay, Norfolk. *Journal of Conchology*, *30*: 135-139.

PRESTON, C.D. 1989. The ephemeral pools of south Cambridgeshire. *Nature in Cambridgeshire*, No. 31: 2-11.

PROCTER, D. 1990. *Robertus insignis* O.P.-Cambridge (Theridiidae) rediscovered in Britain at Catfield Fen in Norfolk. *Newsletter of the British Arachnological Society*, No. 57: 2.

QUICK, H.E. 1933. The anatomy of British *Succineae*. *Proceedings of the Malacological Society*, *20*: 295-318.

RASSI, P., & VAISANEN, R. 1987. *Threatened animals and plants in Finland. English summary of the report of the Committee for the Conservation of Threatened Animals and Plants in Finland*. Helsinki, Government Printing Centre.

RAWCLIFFE, C.P. 1987. Myriapods in the Lothians. *Bulletin of the British Myriapod Group*, *4*: 49, 51.

REDSHAW, E.J., & NORRIS, A. 1974. *Sphaerium solidum* (Normand) in the British Isles. *Journal of Conchology*, *28*: 209-212.

REYNOLDSON, T.B. 1978. A key to the British species of freshwater triclads (Turbellaria, Paludicola). *Scientific Publications of the Freshwater Biological Association*, No. 23. 2nd ed.

RIBAUT, J. 1954. Nouvelle Espece Francaise du Genre *Gervaisia*. *Bulletin de la Societe d'Histoire Naturelle de Toulouse*, *89*: 239-240.

RICHARDSON, D.T. 1989. *Armadillidium pictum* Brandt in Yorkshire. *Isopoda*, *3*: 13-14.

ROBERTS, D.J., & ROBERTS, M.J. 1985. *Aulonia albimana* (Walckenaer) (Araneae: Lycosidae) found again in Britain. *Newsletter of the British Arachnological Society*, No. 44: 7.

ROBERTS, M.J. 1985a. *The spiders of Great Britain and Ireland. Vol. 1. Atypidae to Theridiosomatidae*. Colchester, Harley Books.

ROBERTS, M.J. 1985b. *The spiders of Great Britain and Ireland. Vol. 3. Colour plates - Atypidae to Linyphiidae*. Colchester, Harley Books.

ROBERTS, M.J. 1987. *The spiders of Great Britain and Ireland. Vol. 2. Linyphiidae and check list*. Colchester, Harley Books.

ROEBUCK, W.D. 1921. Census of the distribution of British land and freshwater Mollusca. *Journal of Conchology*, *16*: 165-212.

ROSE, F. 1987. Letters to the editor. National Trust. *Ecos*, *8*(1): 45-46.

ROWELL, T.A. 1986. The history of drainage at Wicken Fen, Cambridgeshire, England, and its relevance to conservation. *Biological Conservation*, *35*: 111-142.

ROWELL, T.A. 1988. *The peatland management handbook*. Peterborough, Nature Conservancy Council. (Research & survey in nature conservation, No. 14).

RUSHTON, S.P. 1988. *Tapinocyboides pygmaeus* (Menge): new records for Northumberland and Durham. *Newsletter of the British Arachnological Society*, No. 53: 4.

RYLAND, J.S., & HAYWARD, P.J. 1977. *British anascan bryozoans. Cheilostomata: Anasca. Keys and notes for the identification of the species.* London, Academic Press, for Linnean Society of London. (Synopses of the British Fauna, No. 10, n.s., ed. by D.M. Kermack).

SANKEY, J.H.P. 1988. *Provisional atlas of the harvest-spiders (Arachnida : Opiliones) of the British Isles.* Huntingdon, Biological Records Centre.

SARS, G.O. 1903-1911. *Copepoda Harpacticoida. An account of the Crustacea of Norway. 5.* Bergen, Bergen Museum.

SARS, G.O. 1922-1928. *Ostracoda. An account of the Crustacea of Norway. 9.* Bergen, Bergen Museum.

SAWYER, R.T. 1981. Why we need to save the medicinal leech. *Oryx, 16*: 165-168.

SAWYER, R.T. 1986. *Leech biology and behaviour.* 3 vols. Oxford, Clarendon Press.

SAWYER, R.T. 1988. The medicinal leech in Dyfed. *Dyfed Wildlife Trust Bulletin*, No. 48: 8.

SCHERREN, H. 1896. Nest-building amphipod in the Broads. *Nature, 54*: 367.

SCHMITT, W.L. 1973. *Crustaceans.* Newton Abbot, David and Charles.

SCOURFIELD, D.J. 1941. Discovery of *Mysis relicta* in Ennerdale. *Nature, 148*: 228.

SCOURFIELD, D.J., & HARDING, J.P. 1966. A key to the British species of freshwater Cladocera with notes on their ecology. *Scientific Publications of the Freshwater Biological Association*, No. 5. 3rd ed., with addendum.

SEAWARD, D.R. 1980. The marine molluscs of the Fleet, Dorset. *Proceedings of the Dorset Natural History and Archaeological Society, 100*: 100-108.

SEAWARD, D.R., ed. 1982. *Sea area atlas of the marine molluscs of Britain and Ireland.* Shrewsbury, Nature Conservancy Council, for Conchological Society.

SEAWARD, D.R. 1986. The Fleet, Dorset a saline lagoon with special reference to its molluscs. *Porcupine Newsletter, 3*: 140-146, 173.

SEAWARD, D.R. 1989. *Caecum armoricum* (Prosobranchia: Rissoacea) new to the British marine fauna. *Journal of Conchology, 33*: 268.

SHEADER, M., & SHEADER, A.L. Undated. *Survey of brackish coastal lagoons. Sussex to Dorset 1984-5. Field report.* Peterborough, Nature Conservancy Council. (CSD Report No. 739).

SHEADER, M., & SHEADER, A.L. 1984. New records for lagoonal species in Britain. *Porcupine Newsletter, 2*: 296-298.

SHEADER, M., & SHEADER, A.L. 1985. New distribution records for *Gammarus insensibilis* Stock, 1966, in Britain. *Crustaceana, 49*: 101-105.

SHEADER, M., & SHEADER, A.L. 1987a. *A lagoon survey of the Isle of Wight: field report.* Peterborough, Nature Conservancy Council. (CSD Report No. 820).

SHEADER, M., & SHEADER, A.L. 1987b. The distribution of the lagoonal amphipod, *Gammarus insensibilis* Stock, in England. *Porcupine Newsletter, 3*: 220-223.

SHIRT, D.B., ed. 1987. *British Red Data Books: 2. Insects.* Peterborough, Nature Conservancy Council.

SIMON, E. 1932. *Les Arachnides de France, 6*(4): 773-978. Paris, Encyclopedie Roret.

SIMON, E. 1937. *Les Arachnides de France, 6*(5): 979-1298. Paris, Encyclopedie Roret.

SIMS, R.W., & GERARD, B.M. 1985. *Earthworms. Keys and notes for the identification and study of the species.* London, E.J. Brill and Dr W. Backhuys, for Linnean Society of London and Estuarine and Brackish-water Sciences Association. (Synopses of the British Fauna, No. 31, n.s., ed. by D.M. Kermack and R.S.K. Barnes).

SLACK, H.J. 1863. Crystals in the intestines of *Artemia salina. Intellectual Observer, 4*: 94-98.

SNAZELL, R. 1978. *Pseudomaro aenigmaticus* Denis, a spider new to Britain (Araneae: Linyphiidae). *Bulletin of the British Arachnological Society, 4*: 251-253.

SNAZELL, R., & DUFFEY, E. 1980. A new species of *Hahnia* (Araneae, Hahniidae) from Britain. *Bulletin of the British Arachnological Society, 5*: 50-52.

SPOONER, G.M. 1947. The distribution of *Gammarus* species in estuaries. Part 1. *Journal of the Marine Biological Association of the United Kingdom, 27*: 1-52.

SPOONER, G.M., & SPOONER, M.F. 1988. The fairy shrimp *Cheirocephalus diaphanus* in Devon. Unpublished typescript. (Submitted to *Nature in Devon* but not published.)

STELFOX, A.W. 1918. The *Pisidium* fauna of the Grand Junction Canal in Herts. and Bucks. *Journal of Conchology, 15*: 289-304.

STEVEN, H.M., & CARLISLE, A. 1959. *The native pinewoods of Scotland.* Edinburgh, Oliver and Boyd.

STOCK, J.H. 1967. A revision of the European species of the *Gammarus locusta*-group (Crustacea, Amphipoda). *Zoologische Verhandelingen, Leiden,* No. 90: 1-56.

STOCK, J.H. 1984. Observations morphologiques et ecologiques sur une population intertidale de "*Melita*" *pellucida* Sars (Amphipoda) a Etretat (Seine-Maritime, France). *Cahiers de Biologie Marine, 25*: 93-106.

STUBBS, A.E. 1972. Wildlife conservation and dead wood. *Journal of the Devon Trust for Nature Conservation, 4*: 169-182.

STUBBS, A.E. 1983. The management of heathland for invertebrates. *In: Heathland management,* ed. by L. Farrell, 21-35. Peterborough, Nature Conservancy Council. (Focus on nature conservation No. 2).

SUTTON, S.L. 1972. *Invertebrate types. Woodlice.* London, Ginn.

SWANN, P.H. 1971. *Wideria mitrata* (Menge). A spider new to Britain (Araneae: Linyphiidae). *Bulletin of the British Arachnological Society, 2*: 11-12.

SYKES, E.R. 1890. *Assiminea littorina* at Weymouth. *Journal of Conchology, 6*: 166.

TATTERSALL, W.M., & TATTERSALL, O.S. 1951. *The British Mysidacea.* London, Ray Society.

THOMPSON, T.E., & BROWN, G.H. 1984. *Biology of opisthobranch molluscs.* London, Ray Society.

THORNHILL, W.A. 1985. The distribution of the Great Raft Spider, *Dolomedes plantarius,* on Redgrave and Lopham Fens. *Transactions of the Suffolk Naturalists' Society, 21*: 18-22.

TURK, F.A. 1945. Myriapodological notes, I. *North Western Naturalist, 20*: 137-144.

TURNER, A.H. 1950. *Laciniaria biplicata* (Montagu) in Somerset. *Journal of Conchology, 23*: 116.

TURNER, R.K., & BROOKE, J. 1988. Management and valuation of an Environmentally Sensitive Area: Norfolk Broadland, England, case study. *Environmental Management, 12*: 193-207.

VAINOLA, R. 1986. Sibling species and phylogenetic relationships of *Mysis relicta* (Crustacea: Mysidacea). *Annales Zoologici Fennici, 23*: 207-221.

VAN AARTSEN, J.J., & HOENSELAAR, H.J. 1984. European marine mollusca: notes on less well-known species VIII. *Caecum armoricum* De Folin, 1869. *Basteria, 48*: 23-26.

VAN HELSDINGEN, P.J. 1980. *Novus catalogus aranearum hucusque in Hollandia inventarum.* Leiden, Rijksmuseum van Natuurlijke Historie.

VERDCOURT, B. 1982. The occurrence of *Perforatella (Monachoides) rubiginosa* (Schmidt) in the British Isles. *Conchologists' Newsletter,* No. 83: 46-48.

WADDINGTON, H.J. 1913. Notes on *Chirocephalus diaphanus* and *Artemia salina. Journal of the Royal Microscopical Society, 1913*: 250-254.

WALTERS, M.G. 1972. The fairy shrimp at Fowlmere. *Nature in Cambridgeshire,* No. 15: 35-39.

WALTERS, M.G. 1978. The fairy shrimp at Fowlmere. *Nature in Cambridgeshire,* No. 21: 18-23.

WATERSTON, A.R. 1934. Occurrence of *Amnicola taylori* (E.A. Smith) and *Bithynia leachii* (Sheppard) in Scotland. *Journal of Conchology*, *20*: 55-56.

WEBB, N.R. 1986. *Heathlands*. London, Collins. (New Naturalist Series).

WEBB, N.R., & HASKINS, L.E. 1980. An ecological survey of heathlands in the Poole Basin, Dorset, England, in 1978. *Biological Conservation*, *17*: 281-296.

WEBSTER, S.D. 1987. The fairy shrimp *Chirocephalus diaphanus* at Weston in Devon. *Nature in Devon*, No. 8: 13-18.

WELCH, J.M., & POLLARD, E. 1975. The exploitation of *Helix pomatia* L. *Biological Conservation*, *8*: 155-160.

WELLS, S.M., ELLIOTT, J.M., & TULLETT, P.A. 1984. Status of the medicinal leech *Hirudo medicinalis*. *Biological Conservation*, *30*: 379-380.

WELLS, S.M., PYLE, R.M., & COLLINS, N.M. 1983. *The IUCN Invertebrate Red Data Book* Gland, International Union for Conservation of Nature and Natural Resources.

WHITING, P. 1978. The fairy shrimp in Gwent. *Gwent Trust for Nature Conservation Newsletter*, Spring 1978: 2.

WIEHLE, H. 1960. Beitrage zur Kenntnis der deutschen Spinnenfauna. II. Theridiidae. *Zoologische Jahrbucher. Abteilung fur Systematik, Okologie und Geographie der Tiere*, *88*: 229-254.

WILDISH, D.J. 1987. Estuarine species of *Orchestia* (Crustacea: Amphipoda: Talitroidea) from Britain. *Journal of the Marine Biological Association of the United Kindom*, *67*: 571-583.

WILKIALIS, J. 1970. Investigations on the biology of leeches of the Glossiphoniidae family. *Zoologica Poloniae*, *20*: 29-54.

WILKIALIS, J. 1973. The biology of nutrition in *Haementeria costata* (Fr. Muller, 1846). *Zoologica Poloniac*, *23*: 213-225.

WILKIN, P.J. 1987. *A study of the medicinal leech,* Hirudo medicinalis *(L), with a strategy for its conservation.* Ph.D. thesis, Wye College, University of London.

WILKIN, P.J. 1988. *An update of the status of the medicinal leech,* Hirudo medicinalis *(L), at Lade gravel pit and other sites within the Dungeness SSSI, Kent.* Unpublished report to the Nature Conservancy Council.

WILKIN, P.J., & SCOFIELD, A.M. 1990. The use of a serological technique to examine host selection in a natural population of the medicinal leech, *Hirudo medicinalis*. *Freshwater Biology*, *23*: 165-169.

WILLIAMS, R.B. 1972. Notes on the history and invertebrate fauna of a poikilohaline lagoon in Norfolk. *Journal of the Marine Biological Association of the United Kingdom*, *52*: 945-963.

WILLIAMS, R.B. 1975. A redescription of the brackish-water sea anemone *Nematostella vectensis* Stephenson, with an appraisal of congeneric species. *Journal of Natural History*, *9*: 51-64.

WILLIAMS, R.B. 1976. Conservation of the sea anemone *Nematostella vectensis* in Norfolk, England and its world distribution. *Transactions of the Norfolk and Norwich Naturalists' Society*, *23*: 257-266.

WILLIAMS, R.B. 1987. The current status of the sea anemone *Nematostella vectensis* in England. *Transactions of the Norfolk and Norwich Naturalists' Society*, *27*: 371-374.

WILLIAMS, R.B. 1988. The current status of the sea anemone *Nematostella vectensis* in England - a correction. *Transactions of the Norfolk and Norwich Naturalists' Society*, *28*: 50.

WILLIAMS, S.A., & LOCKET, G.H. 1982. The occurrence of *Apostenus fuscus* Westring (Clubionidae) in Britain. *Bulletin of the British Arachnological Society*, *5*: 408-409.

WOOD, P., & PEARCE, T. 1988. Musseling in. *Scottish Wildlife*, No. 6: 21-22.

YOUNG, M.R., & WILLIAMS, J.C. 1983a. Redistribution and local recolonisation by the freshwater pearl mussel *Margaritifera margaritifera* (L.). *Journal of Conchology*, *31*: 225-234.

YOUNG, M.R., & WILLIAMS, J.C. 1983b. The status and conservation of the freshwater pearl mussel (*Margaritifera margaritifera* Linn.) in Great Britain. *Biological Conservation*, *25*: 35-52.

Index to invertebrate species

Numbers in **bold** typeface indicate a data sheet for that species or genus.

Index to place names

Includes site names, vice-counties and counties within the British Isles. Place names are qualified with a vice-county where possible but in some cases modern counties have had to be used instead.

244